THE NATURAL HISTORY OF

CONNEMARA

TONY WHILDE

Production coordinator: Paula Casey Vine
Editor for Natural History of Ireland Series: Peter Vine
Design and illustration: Jane Stark, Connemara Graphics, Ireland.
Maps: Johan Hofsteenge, Galway, Ireland
Typesetting: Connemara Graphics and Johan Hofsteenge
Additional typesetting: Marianne ten Cate

All photographs are by the author, Tony Whilde, except the following:
Euan Clarkson - black and white photographs on page 34
Connemara National Park, Office of Public Works - pages 6, 48, 70, 99, 101, 115 main picture, 155, 174, 187
Don Cotton - page 77, royal fern on page 89, sundew on page 102 and on dust jacket, golden plover's nest on page 135, 181, 183, 191, 192, turf-cutting machine on page 272
Shay Fennelly - otter on dust jacket and page 171
John Hayward - pages 142, 146, 158, 167
Ian Herbert - golden plover on its nest on page 135
Dennis Kendrick - pages 59, 65, 97, 205
Graham Lowe - all photographs on pages 16 and 17
Pat McMahon - page 58
Richard Mills - pages 129, 130, 133, cormorant on page 150 and on dust jacket, 160
Pádraic Reaney - cover painting "Landscape near Roundstone, Connemara" and photograph of author
Peter Vine - pages 43, 47, 178, 222, hermit crab on page 236, 242, 243 and 245

ISBN 0 907151 91 4

IMMEL Publishing Limited
20 Berkeley Street
London W1X 5AE
Tel: 071 491 1799 & Fax: 071 493 5524

For
Marianne,
Jenny and Ronan
With Love

Ancient stone alignment revealed by bog cutting.

CONTENTS

Connemara in relation to the island of Ireland.

pREꝬACE

Connemara is a region of County Galway on the west coast of Ireland. It is a land of mountains, bogs, lakes, intricate coastal bays and offshore islands and occupies an area of about 2,000 square kilometres (800 square miles). Many of the inhabitants speak Irish, the language from which most of the area's placenames are derived. The name comes from *Conmaicne Mara*, a branch of the Conmaicne tribe who 'lived by the sea' more than a thousand years ago.

Connemara has no official borders, so I have felt free to define it according to its natural features. The eastern boundary follows the road north-westwards from Galway City to Oughterard along the junction between the limestone lowlands to the east and the granite hills to the west. From Oughterard it follows the western shore of Lough Corrib towards the oak-mantled Hill of Doon and then veers northwards to meet the Galway-Mayo border near Lough Nafooey. It follows the county boundary westwards to Killary Harbour and ends in the sea north of Inishbofin. The area's western and southern limits are defined by the sea.

In this book I trace the origin and development of Connemara's rock framework and the history of its landscape. I then describe the present-day flora and fauna of the region's many and varied habitats, ranging from the mountain summits to the seashore. Rather than spread my effort thinly over such a broad canvas, I take specific examples of plant and animal communities and look in some detail at the lives of their members. I do this, firstly, because I believe there is more to natural history than the mere cataloguing of species distributions. Secondly, I want to answer some of the many questions I receive from the students and visitors I meet during courses and field excursions in Connemara. Thirdly, I hope the descriptions of a representative sample of communities will encourage investigations in similar habitats elsewhere in the region. To those who prefer the more general approach, my apologies.

I use common plant and animal names where possible, but with some lower plants and invertebrates, where no common names exist, I have used the scientific names in the text. The English names of species are listed alphabetically in Appendix I along with their scientific and Irish names. Where there is a choice of Irish names, the one used in Connemara has been selected. I give the most recent names for all the plants and animals mentioned in the book. This means there may be surprises for some naturalists. But as the English and scientific names of any particular species are generally not changed at the same time, it should be possible to find a familiar name in the list. The names of the vascular plants, for example, are taken from the *English Names of Wild Flowers* by J.G. Dony, S.L. Jury and F.H. Perring, published in 1986 by The Botanical Society of the British Isles.

A number of books have been invaluable sources of information and amongst these I must highlight *Flora of Connemara and the Burren* by D.A. Webb and Mary J.P. Scannell. I have consulted many other works during the preparation of the book and these are listed in the Bibliography, along with several hundred other references culled from a wide range of sources. The Bibliography has over 900 titles which I hope will be of interest and value to students of Connemara's natural history. Compiling it has made me very conscious of the many naturalists and scientists who have studied Connemara's natural history. They deserve a book to themselves. Most of the early reports are expansive and evocative and echo the thrills of field research and discovery; the authors make you want to get out and join them.

I present several maps to guide visitors to locations mentioned in the text. More detailed information can be found on the Ordnance Survey 1/2inch to 1mile maps 10, 11 and 14 and on Tim Robinson's maps which are referred to in the Bibliography. For consistency I use the Ordnance Survey spellings of placenames. However, I must warn that these spellings may differ from those on Tim Robinson's maps, on general touring maps and on some roadsigns.

In the final chapter I introduce the subject of conservation. I discuss what is required to make conservation effective - knowledge, education and legislation - and briefly examine the current status and role of each of these factors in relation to Connemara. In taking this approach I focus on a framework of principles and tools which I hope will be of value in addressing the serious conservation issues which face the region - overgrazing in the mountains, bog destruction by turf cutting and afforestation, acidification of some streams and lakes, the impact of intensive fish farming, the effects of increasing tourism, traffic and general development. The issues will be immediately evident to Connemara visitors; some of the conservation tools, such as European Community legislation and financial aid, may not be.

Connemara is linked to many parts of the world both by migratory birds, fish and insects and also by people who visit the region to enjoy aspects of nature which have been destroyed in their own countries. So, it is right that conservation should function internationally as well as locally. Whether or not we get support for our conservation efforts from abroad, *we* must accept our duty to conserve Connemara's natural heritage on behalf of the international community .

This book is about nature, so I have avoided straying into the realms of archaeology and human history, except where people have had a significant impact on the landscape. Yet, the unfolding story of Connemara's human heritage is enthralling and deserves to be told. I hope my friends and colleagues in archaeology will take heed. Likewise, those of a geological persuasion. To say the geological history of Connemara is fascinating is greatly to understate the case. Unfortunately, much of it is available only in technical journals. But I am hopeful the detailed story of the rocks will be made accessible to a wider audience in the not too distant future.

I am fully aware, in this age of popularisation and mass nature consumption, of the dangers of writing about a wonderful area like Connemara. I am also under no illusion about the immense pressures being brought to bear on nature there and the enormous task facing conservationists in stemming the tide of destruction. My hope is that the sharing of knowledge about the region's natural history will lead to more sensitive land use, development and tourism during the coming years.

I have been very fortunate in the many friends and colleagues whose company in Connemara and knowledge of the region I have shared over the past twenty years. To all those I express my sincere appreciation. In the more immediate past I have received much kindness and support in preparing this book. I am particularly grateful to those who read and commented on drafts of the text and supplied valuable information - the improvements are theirs, the mistakes, inaccuracies, inconsistencies and incomprehensible bits are mine: David Harper (geology), Michael O'Connell (landscape history), Denis Fitzgerald and Tom Keane (climate and weather), Cilian Roden (flora), Liam Lysaght (birds), James Fairley (mammals), Don Cotton (terrestrial invertebrates), Ken Whelan and Brian Ottway (freshwater life), David McGrath (seashore life), Emer Colleran (conservation), Pádraic de Bhaldraithe (species list), Tim Collins (bibliography) and Noel Kirby (full text). I am especially indebted to Kevin Fitzpatrick who read the full text and improved my grammar and style with sensitivity and great tact.

For supplying information and support in many forms I thank Kevin Blehein, Bord Failte, Jim Bowman, John Bracken, John Breen, Reitze ten Cate, Euan Clarkson, Kevin Collins, Peter Coxon, Tom Curtis, Michael Davoren, Department of Environment Vehicle Registration Unit, David Drew, Eamon Doyle, Jimmy Dunne, Ian Enlander, Martin Feely, Denis Fitzgerald, Frank Gaffney, Seamus Hassett, Paul Haworth, Niall Herriott, David Hickie, Jim Higgins, John Higgins, David Hogan, the Irish Wildbird Conservancy, Michael Isaac and the staff and students of the Zoology Department, University College, Swansea, Brendan Kavanagh, Tom Keane, Ray Keary, John Kelly, John Kelly, Tim Kelly, Dennis Kendrick, Michael Kennedy, Barry Lamb, Peter Lennon, Joss Lynam, Graham Lowe,

Peter Mantle, Kate McAney, Declan McGrath, Claire McHugh, Pat McMahon, Brendan McWilliams, Michael Miller, Michael Mitchell, Steve Morgan, R. Murphy, Aidan Murray, Declan Murray, Brian Nelson, David Norriss, Kevin O'Connor, Michael O'Connell, Tim O'Connell, Colmán O'Criodain, Gerard O'Donnell, Niall O'Maoileidigh, Paddy O'Sullivan, Michael O'Toole, Karl Partridge, Pat Quigley, Pádraic Reaney, Julian Reynolds, Tim Robinson, Maura Scannell, Neil Sharkey, Ralph Sheppard, Micheline Sheehy Skeffington, Chris Smal, Michael Sweeney and Michael Viney, Richard Weyl, Clare and Gordon Young.

I would also like to thank Rolf and Gay Christ, Ann Fleming and Deirdre Joyce, who helped in various ways with the compilation of the Bibliography. Trish Fitzpatrick made valiant, but not always successful attempts to obtain, on my behalf, information from government agencies.

The book would not have been complete without the works of several photographers. Their contributions do great justice to nature in Connemara. It was a pleasure to work with Peter and Paula Vine and Jane Stark on the preparation of the book. I am especially grateful to Peter for providing me with the opportunity to write the sort of book I had been thinking about for some time.

My greatest debt is to Marianne. Without her enormous help and constant support I could not have undertaken, let alone completed, *The Natural History of Connemara*.

August 1993
Tony Whilde,
Oughterard.

DEFINITIONS OF COMMONLY USED TERMS

Some terms used in natural history are taken from general usage and given more specific meanings. The following definitions of such words used in the text may, therefore, be useful.

HABITAT	the place in which a plant or animal lives, sometimes likened to its 'address', e.g. a freshwater lake.
POPULATION	a group of plants or animals of one species living in a particular place, e.g. a population of arctic charr living in a lake.
COMMUNITY	several populations of plants and/or animals living together in a particular place, e.g. several species of fish, snails, insects and water plants living in a lake.

SHAPING THE LANDSCAPE

Mountains, bogs, lakes, rivers, seashores and islands are the basic fabric of the Connemara landscape. Add to these the climate, the hand of man and time and we have the ingredients of a fascinating, sometimes dramatic, often complex, unending story.

The rocks, the water, the wind and the waves all play their part in the lives of Connemara's plants and animals and are as much part of its natural history as the flowers, birds, fish and insects. This is why, in the next few pages, we will look in some detail at the geology of Connemara, together with the factors which have shaped its landscape since the end of the Ice Age and the effects of climate and weather on its wildlife, past and present.

What follows is only a brief summary of the story so far. Since the middle of the last century nearly 200 scientific reports have been written about, or have in some way been concerned with, the geology of Connemara. And, even as this book is being written, the theories about the area's distant (in both space and time) origins are changing, as new geological evidence comes to light. In such circumstances it would be presumptuous even to attempt to provide a comprehensive description of Connemara's geology. Instead, we will look first at the general sequence of events spanning the past 700 million years. Then, by means of a whistle-stop tour, we will visit several sites in the region where we can see some of the surface features which reflect past geological activity.

Our understanding of landscape development since the Ice Age is also being revolutionised as botanists and archaeologists make new discoveries in Connemara's bogs and lake sediments. So these are exciting times for all who wish to forge new links with the past, to move just a little closer to our natural history through scientific research and understanding and to develop a more rational view of human life in the context of an immensely complex, ever changing world.

OUT OF ANCIENT SEAS

The story of Connemara, as far as can be told from existing evidence, started over 700 million years ago during the Precambrian Era. At that time a great ocean covered much of the Earth's surface and the pattern of land masses was very different from the one we know today. The land which was to become Ireland was split by a widening ocean, the Iapetus Ocean, sometimes called the Proto-Atlantic because, in a sense, it was the forerunner of the modern Atlantic Ocean. To the north-west of the Iapetus Ocean, Connemara, north-west Ireland and Scotland were attached or adjacent to the continent of Laurentia, later to become North America. To the south-east, southern Ireland, England and Wales were associated with the Europe-to-be.

In just the same way as eroded rocks and soils are carried down to the sea today, sands and clays were washed from the neighbouring continents into the Iapetus Ocean. They accumulated on the sea floor to form marine sediments thousands of metres thick and their enormous weight compacted the sands into sandstones and the clays into shales. Incorporated into these newly formed sedimentary rocks were the remains of seashore and shallow water animals which became fossils, ancient markers which have proved vital to geologists in their understanding of how the Earth's crust has moved since the time of the Iapetus Ocean. Later, Laurentia and Europe started to

Figure 1: Distribution of the world's continents and oceans about 460 million years ago. The Iapetus Ocean separated the northern and southern parts of Ireland (after McKerrow, W.S. and Scotese, C.R. [Eds.], 1990 in Palaeozoic Palaeogeography and Biogeography, *Geological Society of London, Memoir 12).*

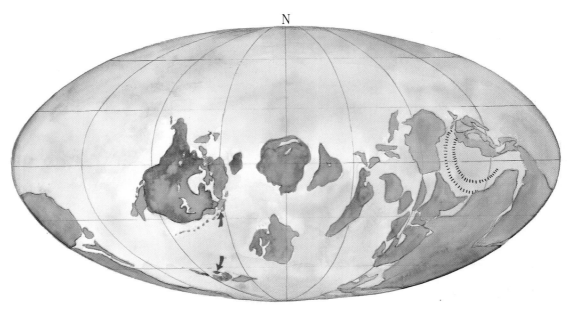

move together, closing the Iapetus Ocean. As the two shorelines approached one another, several micro-continents moved northwards between them and eventually became trapped between their jaws as they collided - slowly but with enormous force. The collision caused a lot of the sedimentary rocks to fold and break (fault) so that the positions of many of the formations we see on the geological map today are very different from those they held originally. The sedimentary rocks which had formed at the edges of the continents became the mountains of Joyce's Country and south Mayo while the insurgent micro-continents became the Twelve Bens, the Maumturks and the associated Dalradian structures. The fossils in the sedimentary rocks of Joyce's Country have been used to correlate and date rock strata in Connemara which have been broken and displaced by earth movements. Furthermore, sedimentary strata in Connemara have been correlated in this way with rocks on the other side of the Atlantic Ocean, where identical fossils have been found in Newfoundland. This startling evidence confirms that western Ireland and Newfoundland were once connected.

Just as we do when we rub our hands together to warm them, the movement and eventual collision of the continents generated great heat and pressure, and it was at this time that the Dalradian sandstones were turned into quartzites, limestone into marble and shales into schists. This process of change, brought about by intense heat and great pressure, is known as metamorphism and this produces metamorphic rocks of the type we see today in the Twelve Bens and Maumturk Mountains. Intense metamorphism like this destroys the original layering or stratification of the rocks and any fossils which may have been present in the original sediments, so it is very difficult to date and correlate metamorphic rocks.

Heat and pressure were also generated at great depth during this Caledonian Upheaval and rocks deep in the Earth's crust were melted to form a liquid magma. This flowed upwards through vents to the surface, where several batches coalesced and crystallized beneath a Dalradian cap to form the 1,000 square kilometre (386 square mile) Galway Granite batholith which occupies most of south Connemara. Rocks formed in this way are called igneous and, with the sedimentary and metamorphic rocks, complete the trio of rock types found in Connemara.

For all practical purposes, the formation of Connemara's rock framework as we see it today finished at the end of the Silurian Period, some 400 million years ago. The few younger rocks present in the area are neither extensive in distribution nor prominent in stature. That is not to say that later deposits have not had an influence on the landscape. It is suggested, for example, that the hills of Connemara and south Mayo were covered by Carboniferous deposits, laid down about 300 million years ago during that great coal-forming period. When these hills were subsequently uplifted, all but a few small patches of the Carboniferous rocks were eroded away to create the extraordinarily flat summits of the Maumtrasna and Partry Mountains and the patterns of rivers and streams in the hills which we see today. It has generally been considered that the Bens, Maumturks and granite uplands were high ground during the Carboniferous Period and therefore

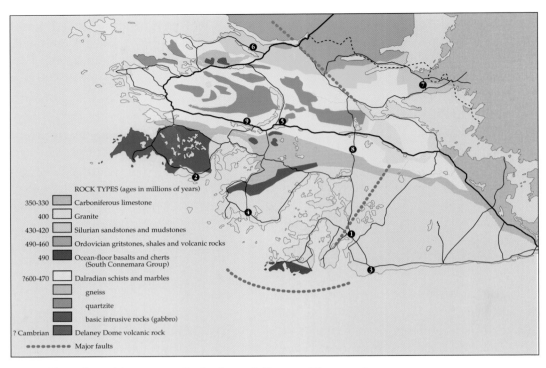

ROCK TYPES (ages in millions of years)

350-330	Carboniferous limestone
400	Granite
430-420	Silurian sandstones and mudstones
490-460	Ordovician gritstones, shales and volcanic rocks
490	Ocean-floor basalts and cherts (South Connemara Group)
?600-470	Dalradian schists and marbles
	gneiss
	quartzite
	basic intrusive rocks (gabbro)
? Cambrian	Delaney Dome volcanic rock
●●●●●	Major faults

Map 2: The geology of Connemara. (Scale of maps 2-12 ⌊___10km___⌋ *)*

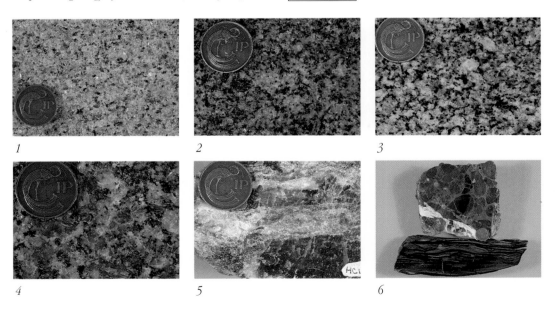

1

2

3

4

5

6

ERA	PERIOD	EPOCH	AGES (Millions of years before present)	EVENTS IN CONNEMARA
CENOZOIC	QUARTERNARY	Holocene	0.01	Bog formation
		Pleistocene	2	Glaciation
	TERTIARY	Pliocene	13	
		Miocene	25	
		Oligocene	36	
		Eocene	58	
		Palaeocene	70	Doon Hill, Benchoona vulcanicity
MESOZOIC	CRETACEOUS		135	
	JURASSIC		180	
	TRIASSIC		225	
PALAEOZOIC	PERMIAN		270	
	CARBONIFEROUS		350	
	DEVONIAN	Caledonian	400	Caledonian upheaval Galway Granite
	SILURIAN		430	Joyce's Country deposited
	ORDOVICIAN		500	Oughterard Granite
	CAMBRIAN	Dalradian	600	Connemara submerged
PRECAMBRIAN				Twelve Bens and Maumturks laid down as clays and sands

Figure 2: Geological timescale

1. *Galway Granite from the Casla area (alkali-Feldspar Granite).*
2. *Galway Granite from the Roundstone area (Errisbeg Townland Granite).*
3. *Galway Granite from the Inveran area (Biotite granodiorite).*
4. *Galway Granite from the Carna area (Biotite granodiorite).*
5. *Connemara Marble from Lissoughter (green Serpentine bands / white calcite).*
6. *Laminated siltstone from Lough Fee. Conglomerate from shore of Killary Harbour.*
7. *Quartz Breccia from Clonbur area.*
8. *Metamorphic rock from south of Maam Cross (Potash-Feldspar Gneiss).*
9. *Metamorphic rock from Glencoaghan (biotite / Sillimanite Schist).*

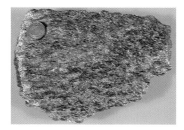

7   8   9

The distinctive flat top of Maumtrasna.

dry and free from deposition. However, it is also argued that the absence of Carboniferous sediments on these hills is no guarantee that they were not present at one time. There are differing opinions, too, about whether these hills were covered with sediment during the great chalk-forming, Cretaceous, period. Had the chalk existed on the hills it might have been expected that some remnants would have been found in Connemara or in the nearby sea, even if only as fragments broken off during later erosion. No such fragments have yet been found on the land. However, chalk and flint of the right age have been dredged from the seabed west of Connemara, where they may have been dumped by glaciers during the Pleistocene Epoch. While this evidence does not prove that Connemara was once covered with chalk, it does indicate that at least there must have been Cretaceous deposits not too far away.

About 150 million years ago Laurasia, the continent formed by the collision and welding of Laurentia and the Europe-to-be, started to break up and the present-day Atlantic Ocean began to form, more or less in the same position, relative to the two continents, as the earlier Iapetus Ocean. The break was to the north-west of the junction between the two earlier continents and this time Connemara remained in Ireland, though fossil evidence from Newfoundland, mentioned earlier, indicates that at least part of its western fringe went west. There is thus more than a cultural affinity between western Ireland and north-eastern North America.

During the Tertiary Period, between 65 and 25 million years ago, volcanic activity created various dykes, and a volcano was also active on what is now the Slyne Head peninsula. But now, all that remains to remind us of those violent times is a quiet, brooding volcanic plug in the form of Doon Hill, just to the west of Bunowen Castle.

After these final acts of 'construction' the geological story is one of denudation - a gradual wearing down of the landscape by glaciers and, of late, rain, wind and human activity.

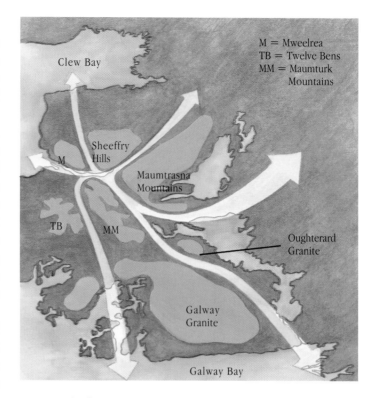

Figure 3: The flow of early Connemara glaciers.

The Pleistocene Epoch, known popularly as the Ice Age, started about 2 million years ago. At one time it was thought that great masses of ice were the main features of these times, but evidence is now indicating that, although there were intense periods of cold during the early stages, ice did not start forming in Europe until about 600,000 years ago. Ice probably developed in Ireland for the first time about 200,000 years ago. Since then, there have been cold periods during which all or part of Connemara was glaciated, separated by warmer periods called interglacials. The last ice disappeared from the region about 13,000 years ago, although there was a brief, intensely cold period between 10,500 and 10,000 years ago. Today we live in what is probably an interglacial period.

During the last glaciation Connemara was covered by a 1,000 metre (3,300 feet) thick dome of ice centered to the east of the Twelve Bens. And it is this ice which has left its imprint on the Connemara landscape, having apparently scoured away all evidence of previous glaciations in the region. Its glaciers flowed north, south, east and west, excavating the wide U-shaped valleys of north Connemara and grinding down the lowlands of the south. With their retreat, a new landscape appeared, one rich in glacial features such as corries, drumlins, eskers and moraines, which we will discuss in more detail in the next section. With relatively little modification by vegetation or man, this is the physical landscape of Connemara today.

A CLOSER LOOK

The geology of Connemara is complex and difficult to understand. For the most part, the evidence for the momentous transformations which have just been described are hidden from view under soil, peat, solid rock or water. And the clues which are visible on the surface are often so subtle that only a geologist with very specialised training can identify and interpret them. However, the large-scale surface features of the landscape, such as cliffs and moraines, reflect the nature of the underlying rocks and the geological processes which have produced them. Unlike details of the chemical composition, physical structure and past behaviour of particular rocks, they are visible and can be identified by the general naturalist. And, apart from being interesting in their own right, they can, to the ecological eye, also provide clues to the distribution, behaviour and history of the plants and animals which inhabit them.

In this section, therefore, we will take a swift tour of Connemara to see some of these easily recognisable features. We cannot follow the chronological sequence which was presented in the

Map 3: A geological tour of Connemara.

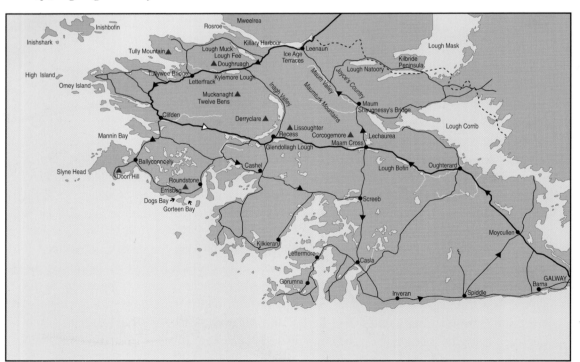

previous section because the rocks are now too jumbled up to do that. So it will be useful to consult the Geological Timescale (see p. 17) to confirm the ages of the rocks mentioned at each site.

We will start our tour in Oughterard and follow a route through Maam Cross, Maum, Leenaun, Letterfrack, Clifden, Ballyconneely, Roundstone, Screeb and Spiddle (see Map 3 on p. 20).

As we leave the sheltered, tree-lined confines of Oughterard on the road to Maam Cross we are greeted by a new world, an open landscape of hills, bogs, rock and water. This is Connemara, a landscape so different that it has excited the senses of artists, writers, scientists and travellers for centuries. It is a landscape which is hostile and uncompromising yet appealing and intriguing. It is a challenge to our senses and to our intellect.

We leave behind the simple grey Carboniferous limestones that make up so much of Ireland and enter a patchwork of older rocks - granites, quartzites, schists, sandstones and many more. The lush green lime-rich pastures give way to rolling hills of purple moor-grass. To the north of the road the hills are composed mainly of Oughterard Granite, one of the oldest granites in the region, which were intruded 470 million years ago. The extensive Galway granites, which make up all the high ground to the south, were intruded about 400 million years ago, as the Silurian was merging into the Devonian Period. The shallow hill-slopes to the south and the valley floor are underlain by Dalradian grey marble and other metamorphic rocks. Where the marble comes to the surface, as on the south shore of Lough Bofin, it has enriched the soils, hence the green pastures on an otherwise infertile hillside. The low mounds beside the road are moraines deposited by a glacier which had flowed south-eastwards from the Connemara highlands. Several have been opened up by quarrying and close examination will show that they are composed of sand and smoothed, angular boulders.

Dalradian marble at Cur.

21

Main photograph: A cross-section of the moraine at Shaughnessy's Bridge. Inset: Glacial till - a variety of rock types embedded in a hard matrix of fine glacial debris.

Beyond Lough Bofin the landscape opens out ahead of us and we see for the first time the stark quartzite summits of the Maumturk Mountains and, in the distance, the Twelve Bens. The ridges of the quartzite mountains are sharp and ragged, in marked contrast to the smooth profile of the granite hills. It may seem surprising that these younger hills have been lowered and smoothed to a greater extent than their older quartzite neighbours. However, quartzite is tougher than granite and it withstood the ravages of the Ice Age better. In addition, it is possible that the Twelve Bens and the Maumturks may have been raised above the granites by more recent earth movements.

Turning northwards at Maam Cross, the winding pass takes us between steep, craggy slopes of glistening quartzite with Leckavrea rising to 398 metres (1,307 feet) to the east and the more massive Corcogemore to 613 metres (2,012 feet) to the west. Beyond the summit of the pass the slope eases as we move on to schists and other Dalradian metamorphic rocks.

The work of ice and water

At Shaughnessy's Bridge, about 1.5 kilometres (1 mile) before Maum, we can see a variety of features ranging in age from the Precambrian to the Pleistocene. Rising high above us to the south-west is Corcogemore, its steep, quartzite outcrops representing the oldest rocks in the region. There is a deep, circular hollow 600-700 metres (660-770 yards) across, scooped out of its north-east face, about half way to the summit. We cannot see the floor of the hollow, which is obscured by a horizontal band of rock with easily distinguished low cliffs on its outer face. This hollow, known as a corrie, was the seat of a glacier during the last glaciation. It originated as a valley head or similar depression which, during the Ice Age, filled with snow. The accumulating snow became compacted to ice as weight and pressure forced the air out of it. And by the time it had grown in thickness to about 33 metres (110 feet) it was sufficiently heavy to slide out of the corrie and downhill to meet similar glaciers flowing along the main valley from other corries which we can see in the mountains to the west

The glacier expanded the corrie by plucking rocks out of the back wall and gouging out the floor. It carried its load of shattered rocks down to the low ground, grinding some of it to powder on the way. When it eventually melted, the material it had carried from the mountains was deposited as moraines - ridges of material called glacial till, like the one perched beside Shaughnessy's Bridge. The peat-covered moraine has been quarried and we can clearly see the ice-smoothed boulders and pebbles which are embedded in the hard matrix of fine glacial debris. Most of the rocks in this moraine are likely to be of local origin. But farther south glaciers have dumped Connemara boulders onto different rock types. For example, Connemara Granite boulders are

A change from hard to soft rock is marked by the waterfall downstream of Shaughnessy's Bridge.

conspicuous on the grey limestones of the Burren, to the south in County Clare. These 'out of place' boulders are called erratics and can often be distinguished from the local rocks by their different shape and colour, the different lichens which grow on them and their mineral content.

At Shaughnessy's Bridge, to the south of the moraine, a stream flows across the bog and under the road. To the east, the water is less than a metre below the bridge and flowing over a band of hard gritty quartzite. But on the other side of the bridge, the river bed is 6-9 metres (20-30 feet) below the bridge and water cascades over a near-vertical waterfall. This signals a very sharp change in rock type, from the hard quartzite upstream to softer rocks below the bridge, which

SIGNS OF LIFE

The Silurian sediments were laid down in a shallow sea which gradually flooded the late Ordovician landscape. The succession of events is best illustrated in the rocks of the Kilbride peninsula, to the north-east of Joyce's Country (see Figure 4). The first (oldest) Silurian rocks were deposited mainly by rivers and are red conglomerates (rounded boulders, perhaps from ancient beaches, cemented together in a matrix of finer material), sandstones and siltstones. The redness is due to the presence of an iron oxide and indicates that these sediments must have been derived from dry land sources. In wet conditions the iron oxide would have changed chemically and lost its red colour. Later, as the sea advanced, sandy beaches were formed and the shelly remains of brachiopods and snails were washed up onto the beaches, much as happens with clam and periwinkle shells today. The beached brachiopod shells had strong, coarse ribs, suggesting that they had lived in shallow, turbulent water where they would have required robust shells to survive.

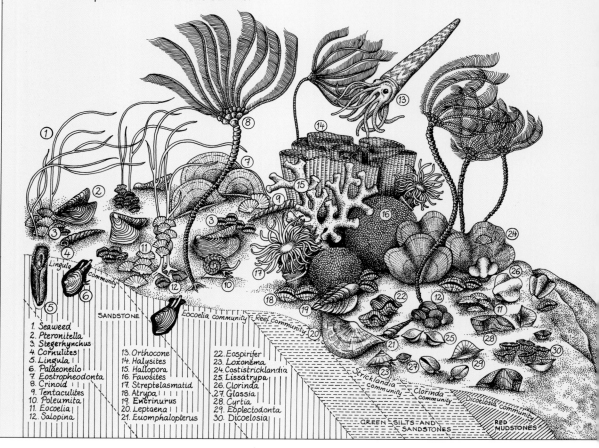

1. Seaweed		
2. Pteronitella		
3. Stegerhynchus		
4. Cornulites	13. Orthocone	22. Eospirifer
5. Lingula	14. Halysites	23. Loxonema
6. Palaeoneilo	15. Hallopora	24. Costistricklandia
7. Eostropheodonta	16. Favosites	25. Lissatrypa
8. Crinoid	17. Streptelasmatid	26. Clorinda
9. Tentaculites	18. Atrypa	27. Glassia
10. Poleumita	19. Encrinurus	28. Cyrtia
11. Eocoelia	20. Leptaena	29. Eoplectodonta
12. Salopina	21. Euomphalopterus	30. Dicoelosia

The next layer of sediment, a whitish sandstone, contains vertical burrows which are very similar to those made by lugworms today. The vertical burrows allowed the worms to retreat quickly from predators or turbulent conditions in the shallow water. In later sediments laid down in deeper waters, where the dangers were not so great, the worm burrows are horizontal and just under the surface of the sediment. The younger sediments contain a variety of animals and calcareous algae which must have occupied a wide range of habitats. Animals such as colonial corals, trilobites and tiny brachiopods were amongst the inhabitats of the deeper inshore waters of this Silurian sea. These brachiopods, in contrast to those which lived in shallower water, characteristically had many fine ribs in their shells. This suggests that they lived in calmer conditions where less robust shells would suffice.

There are several localities in the region where fossils appear in the surface rocks. These relics of ancient life should be treated with the respect that the 400 million year dead deserve and *must not be damaged or removed.*

Above: Eocoelia brachiopods in Silurian beach sediments.
Facing page: A schematic compression of Silurian seabed from the shore to the edge of the continental shelf. The main representatives are to be found in the Kilbride Formation (based on McKerrow, W.S. 1978 The Ecology of Fossils, *Duckworth).*

Skolithos worm burrows in shallow water Silurian sediments.

have been worn away much faster by the stream. Farther downstream, it is evident that the stream has also cut through the moraine and exposed its contents to the erosive effects of the elements.

In this one location we see clearly how ice and water have helped to shape the Connemara landscape, with the final touches being added by man with his quarries, roads and bridges.

The low ridge, rising westwards from Teernakill Bridge, is formed of Dalradian grey marble and other metamorphic rocks, which have produced fertile soils, green pastures and conditions suitable for one of the small areas of deciduous woodland in the region. The ridge is cut abruptly about 1.5 kilometres (1 mile) to the west by one of the major Maum Valley faults but appears again at Knocknagur. The low ground between the ridges, which is best viewed from the Maum Valley, is underlain by less resistant rocks which were forced into place by earth movements during late Silurian times.

To the north of the ridge we enter the Maum Valley and Joyce's Country - named after a Welsh-Norman family which settled in the area in the Middle Ages. The mountains here are lower, greener and generally smoother than the Maumturks and, for the most part, composed of younger rocks which have not been changed substantially by high temperatures and pressure. The ribbed and craggy slopes above and to the east of Keane's Pub at Maum are upper Dalradian metamorphic rocks, including schists, and these extend eastwards to the flat-topped summit of Benlevy. The smoother hills running westwards to Bunnacunneen are made of sedimentary materials deposited during the Silurian Period (see p. 24-25). And, further westwards, towards Leenaun, older, Ordovician sediments form the high ground.

Turning left at Maum, it is worth noting the stones used to build Keane's Pub - they are Carboniferous limestone. The original house was built by the well-known engineer Alexander Nimmo

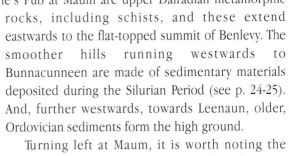

Folding in metamorphosed marble on Knocknagur near Maum.

in the early 1800s for his personal use while he supervised the building of bridges and roads in the area. Many of the bridges built at that time were also faced with limestone because it was easily quarried and dressed. Limestone is, of course, alien to the Connemara landscape and, like the Connemara erratics which occur in the Burren, it can be recognised at a distance by the plants which grow on it. This is particularly true of blocks which have fallen from bridges into streams; very soon they become covered with a bright algal growth which does not develop on the local rocks.

Great earth movements

As we travel north-westwards along the Maum Valley, the contrasts between the mountains to the north and to the south diminish as the metamorphic rocks of the Maumturks are replaced by Silurian sediments in the vicinity of Tonalee.

Down in the valley, below Tonalee and near the plantation at Culliaghbeg, is the headwater stream of Joyce's River which flows south-eastwards towards Lough Corrib. It is unusual to find the source of a river at such a low level in such a mountainous area. The explanation appears to lie in the great earth movements which occurred in late Silurian times. Huge blocks moved horizontally in opposite directions about 10 kilometres (6 miles) along the Maum Fault which runs north-west - south-east, breaking the stream which originally had its source on the eastern

OCHRE

In the river flowing between the terraces below the road to Leenaun, the boulders are covered with brown ochre, an iron compound which is common in streams and wet places in Connemara. The ochre is a form of ferric oxide which has been converted (oxidised) from ferrous iron by bacteria called *Thiobacillus ferrooxidans* (*ferroxydans*). Sometimes we will see an irridescent, oily film on lakeshores, in drains and on the bogs. This is *not* oil but ferric hydroxide, another natural product of bacterial activity which is prevalent in the acid conditions such as we find in many Connemara waters and in the bogs.

slopes of Mweelrea, where the Owennaglogh River flows today. On a clear day, these upper slopes of Mweelrea can be seen from the road near the present source of Joyce's River.

Ice Age terraces

As the road begins to descend into Leenaun, grassy terraces rise to flat summits. These terraces, which, it is suggested, have been moulded by generations of sheep, are etched into sandy sediments which were laid down under water during glacial times. It may be that they were deposited in the sea or in a lake held back by an ice dam in the vicinity of Leenaun during the final stages of the dissolution of the Connemara ice sheets. There are two distinct flat summits here at about 80 metres (260 feet) and 60 metres (200 feet) and a third at 12-15 metres (40-50 feet) in Leenaun. These features can be seen most clearly from the road on the north side of Killary Harbour.

Ireland's only fjord

The features described below can best be viewed from the parking area on the south shore near Dernasliggaun at the 'elbow' of Killary Harbour.

Killary Harbour is a fjord-like inlet, 15 kilometres (9 miles) long and about 700 metres (770 yards) wide for much of its length. Its average depth is about 20 metres (66 feet) but just inside the mouth the seabed descends to nearly 42 metres (140 feet). On the north shore Mweelrea rises steeply from the edge of the water to 817 metres (2,688 feet), making it the highest mountain in Connacht. It is composed of thick beds of Ordovician sediments, derived from mountains which existed in Connemara during the Precambrian. On the south shore there are Ordovician sediments between Leenaun and Dernasliggaun and on the Rosroe peninsula, and younger Silurian sediments between these two areas. Faulting along the line of Killary Harbour in late Silurian and early Devonian times provided a ready-made zone of weak, shattered rock for a glacier to excavate. For a number of years there were disputes among geologists and geomorphologists about the origin of Killary Harbour, and whether it is correct to call it a fjord. It was suggested by some that it was no more than an ice-moulded valley, lacking the classical threshold (lip of rock) that denotes a fjord. However, a survey in the mid-1970s showed a total absence of rock outcrops on the bottom from the bay head to Rusheen Point near the mouth and then a well-developed rock outcrop from there to the bay mouth. This is considered to be the threshold and so it now seems reasonable to suggest that Killary Harbour is a fjord and not just fjord-like.

Continuing south-westwards we pass Lough Fee to the west. It is interesting to note that the small wooded peninsula on the north shore is composed entirely of igneous rocks which have been intruded into the surrounding Silurian sediments. The presence of this isolated piece of woodland raises the question of whether its existence is due to the greater fertility of the soils on the peninsula or merely to protection and management.

Among the Twelve Bens and the Maumturks

A detour to the south at the next road junction, signposted to Recess, takes us into the heart of the Dalradian mountains - the Inagh Valley. All the major peaks are bare quartzite, except Muckanaght where more fertile schists support vegetation to the summit at 656 metres (2,153 feet). The Bens radiate from the highest peak, Benbaun (730 metres, 2,395 feet), like spokes of a wheel, while the Maumturks, to quote the nineteenth-century botanist H.C. Hart, look like 'the tangled cluster of the Twelve Bens stretched out in a curved line with their tops rubbed off'. Robert Lloyd Praeger, undoubtedly the best-known Irish naturalist of this century, also made a classic comment about the Maumturks in his delightful book *The Way that I Went* : 'A traverse of the whole ridge from Maam Cross to Leenaun provides a glorious day's walking.' This is true, but when it is considered that the trek covered over 24 kilometres (15 miles) and 2,286 metres (7,500 feet) of ascent on very rough ground and that Praeger was also scrambling up and down slopes to see flowers, we must applaud the extraordinary fitness and stamina of this brilliant naturalist. His like would be hard to find today.

The bare quartzite ridge between Derryclare and Bencorr in the Twelve Bens.

It is easy to pick out several glacial features on the Bens and the Maumturks. Corries are evident on the higher slopes and on Bencorr and Derryclare, in particular we can see hanging valleys and truncated spurs - valleys and ridges, the lower sections of which were cut off by a major glacier flowing through the main valley, leaving steep cliffs at the ends of the valleys and blunt-ended spurs.

A more recent feature, and one we might not expect to find in the area, is a pothole in the grey Dalradian marble high up on the western slopes of the Maumturks at Ilion West. It is only 9 metres (30 feet) deep and about 14 metres (45 feet) long, but it is a cave nonetheless.

Oakwoods and eskers

Returning to the Leenaun-Letterfrack road we head west into the deep, glaciated, U-shaped Kylemore valley, with Kylemore Lough beside us. To the north, the gentle slopes on the Dalradian grits and other metamorphosed sedimentary rocks, which are well exposed in roadside cuttings, soon steepen abruptly into a spectacular intermingling of vertical crags and

Eskers to the east of the Connemara National Park. Here, as elsewhere, eskers are being destroyed by quarrying or obliterated by afforestation.

rock-hugging oak trees. Here, on Doughruagh, we see exposures of what are called ultrabasic rocks. These were intruded into the surrounding landscape during the Dalradian Period. Ultrabasic rocks are igneous in origin and contain iron and magnesium and very little silica - in contrast to many of the other quartz-rich rock types in the region. (The term ultrabasic is not used in geology in the same sense as in chemistry, where it means alkaline.) Ultrabasics also occur in the neighbouring hill, Currywongaun, and in the lowlands of south-west Connemara.

Kylemore Abbey, its stature somewhat diminished by the towering cliffs of Doughruagh, is a granite-built castle faced with limestone which now serves as a girls' school.

About 1.5 kilometres (1 mile) to the west of Kylemore Abbey, near Tullywee Bridge, the road curves to the left beneath a smooth, brown cliff of glacial debris. This is a head-on view of the inside of an esker, first cut through by the Dawros River and later pared back by excavations for road improvements. An esker (from the Irish *eiscir*, glacial ridge) is a long, winding ridge of sand and gravel deposited by an ice sheet. This particular example may represent part of a marine delta which was deposited in still water at the edge of a glacier. Glacial sands are in great demand for building and much of this esker, like so many others around the country, has now been virtually quarried to extinction. There are, however, remnants intact between the plantation and the northern base of Diamond Hill, and these can best be appreciated from the slopes of the hill in the Connemara National Park.

Continuing towards Clifden, our road cuts through broad expanses of cut-over blanket bog, areas where turf has been cut for domestic and commercial purposes. There are splendid views of the Bens to the east as they stretch to their full height above the low, undulating bogland.

Bogs, lakes and Connemara marble - a detour

From Clifden, the road to Galway would take us past the vast lake-studded Roundstone bogs, Errisbeg standing in isolation at their southern edge. To the north we would skirt the slopes of the Twelve Bens, deeply dissected by the moraine-filled valleys of the Owenglin and Glencoaghan Rivers. The road follows an almost continuous band of Dalradian metamorphic rocks, occasionally straying onto the grey Lakes Marble which we have met on several occasions before. To the south, beneath the blanket bog, there are some highly metamorphised igneous rocks called migmatites. More ultrabasic intrusions are evident in the isolated peaks of Cashel Hill, a lower, unnamed hill to the east and the rocky protruberance to the south of Glendollagh Lough.

Lissoughter, which stands at the southern entrance to the Inagh Valley, is, geologically speaking, a small-scale version of the Bens and the Maumturks. But it has the distinction of having green Connemara Marble deposits on its western flanks. Commercially, these have now been exhausted, but this popular marble is still quarried on the shores of Derryclare Lough, some 3 kilometres (2 miles) to the west and, until recently, at the head of Streamstown Bay about 3 kilometres (2 miles) north of Clifden.

The seaward face of the drumlin at Silver Strand, Barna.

Connemara Marble developed through several stages of metamorphism from an ancient dolomitic limestone (one that contained a relatively large proportion of magnesium carbonate as well as the usual calcium carbonate) which was subjected to intense heat and pressure during the intrusion of the Galway Granite. The magnesium-rich mineral serpentine gives Connemara Marble its characteristic green hue.

South from Clifden
Taking the road southwards from Clifden, towards Ballyconneely, we exchange rugged hill and mountain scenery for a landscape of low-lying, undulating blanket bog, ice-scoured rock, lakes, coastal beaches, bays and islands.

To the east, beneath the blanket bog, there are metamorphic rocks about which little is known. They form the remains of a structure which geologists call the Delaney Dome. Its age is uncertain but it may be part of the base upon which the earliest Connemara rocks were laid.

Drumlin in the sea
At the other end of the geological scale, just offshore beyond the northern inlet of Mannin Bay, there is a drumlin (another geological term derived from Irish, *droimnín*, meaning small ridge) - a small whale-backed hill which was formed under the ice during the last glaciation of Connemara.

Its landward slope is broad and fairly steep whereas the seaward side, before waves washed it away, would have been shallow and tapering and pointing in the direction in which the ice was moving. Thousands of years of erosion have removed a substantial part of the drumlin, leaving an exposed, vertical cliff which can be examined by geologists at low tide. The body of the drumlin is formed of a matrix of fine, rock-hard material in which ice-smoothed boulders are embedded. These boulders are of local origin, but when glaciers travel farther afield they pick up samples of all the rock types over which they flow. As a consequence, we can then sometimes find, for example, granite, limestone and sandstone boulders plucked from widely separated localities, perched side by side in the exposed face of a drumlin such as that beside Silver Strand, just west of Galway City.

The term 'drumlin' refers primarily to the shape of the hills formed under glaciers and not to their composition, which ranges from solid rock to the glacial till (or boulder clay) as we see here in the Mannin Bay example. Drumlins are common in glaciated country and are sometimes so abundant as to be described as occurring in swarms, such as can be found south of Cleggan Bay and north-east of Tully Mountain. In parts of Northern Ireland, where they occur densely and in large numbers, they give rise to 'basket of eggs' scenery, a reference to their appearance from above.

'Coral' strand

Farther south, between low, rocky promontories, our eye is attracted by sparkling, white, sandy beaches, hardly the stuff of geology, it might be thought. But, of course, if we recall the Silurian deposits in Joyce's Country and on the Kilbride peninsula we will remember that some of the sedimentary strata in these areas were made up of beach deposits, including the remains of shells washed up by the tide. It is an intriguing thought that one day, millions of years hence, this beach will be solid rock, located who knows where on the Earth's surface. But will it be an 'ordinary' beach deposit, made up mainly of quartz grains? A handful will soon show that it will not. This beach is composed of countless fragments of broken, often branched, remains of the 'skeletons' of red seaweeds which lived on the seabed of Mannin Bay. The seaweeds do not have common names so must be accorded their scientific epithets, *Lithothamnion corallioides* and *Phymatolithon calcareum*. The fragments are quite coral-like in their appearance and so this, and similar beaches around the Connemara coast, are often called 'coral strands'. However, corals are actually animals which live in much warmer seas than we have around Ireland at the moment, so we will have to accept that these are but the remains of marine plants.

Volcanic activity

As we follow the road through Ballyconneely and then south-eastwards along the coast we cannot fail to notice Doon Hill in its isolated splendour, commanding the westward approach to Slyne Head. This impessive eminence, with Bunowen Castle on its sheltered, eastern flank, is described by geologists as a volcanic plug. It is the nearly circular feed channel of a volcano which

33

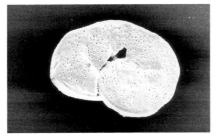

has been filled with solidified lava and subsequently exposed by erosion of the volcanic cone. It is estimated that the plug was formed at 900-1070°C. It is early Tertiary in age and confirmation that there was volcanic activity here as recently as 65 million years ago. It is also one of the most southerly examples of Tertiary volcanism in Europe.

A very unusual 'sand'

As the road meanders past the south-western slopes of Errisbeg, we get our first view of Dog's Bay, its white crescent beach set between a turquoise sea and green undulating turf. The bay is bordered to the south by a low granite island which is linked to the mainland by a sandy spit. This is known technically as a tombolo, and it separates Dog's Bay from Gorteen Bay, its 'mirror image'.

When we go down to the beach we will be in for another surprise. If we scoop up the fine sand it will be immediately obvious that this beach is not built up of quartz grains either. It will take a hand lens (x10 will be sufficient) to bring its constituents into focus and it will be found that they are mainly the shells and shell fragments of tiny marine animals called Foraminifera. These microscopic, single-celled creatures are related to the *Amoeba* of our school biology textbooks. They secrete calcium carbonate shells which can be incredibly intricate and beautiful. In many common species chambers are added in a spiral fashion, resulting in shells which resemble those of miniature snails. The forams, as they are commonly called, live mainly in the surface waters of the sea. When they die their shells generally sink to the seabed. However, for reasons which are not entirely clear, the currents around this part of the coast have swept the forams from the deeper water into the channel between the island and the mainland where they have accumulated to form the

Some of the microscopic components of the Dog's Bay sand. From top to bottom: Foraminiferan, Cibicides; Foraminiferan, Elphidium; spine of a sea urchin; sponge spicule; microscopic bivalve shell.

tombolo, which is 90 per cent calcium carbonate as a result. They also make up the South Bay beach on the seaward side of the island. Beaches like this are very uncommon and the only other reported example in Ireland is at Naran in Donegal.

At the turn of the century the naturalist J. Wright recorded 116 species and eight additional varieties of forams at Dog's Bay. Since then, however, there have been considerable advances in the identification and classification of forams so it would be very interesting to have a reassessment of the species composition and age of these fascinating 'sands'.

Bays, inlets and islands

Turning landwards we are faced by the distinctive, rock-ribbed Errisbeg - 'little western mountain'. The light granite of its shallow lower slopes is topped by distinctively dark, steeper outcrops of gabbro, a basic igneous rock which was intruded into the landscape some 500 million years ago, several tens of millions of years before the granite upon which it rests.

For the energetic, a climb to the summit of Errisbeg will be most rewarding for it will provide

The patchwork of lakes and bog between Errisbeg and Clifden.

superb all-round views of Connemara - the Bens and the Maumturks, the bogs, the coast and the islands in the Atlantic Ocean.

The coast road takes us eastwards around the shore and inlets of Bertraghboy Bay. The almost circular plan of this bay corresponds to the drowned portion of a granite intrusion. In fact, the whole crenulated coastal zone from Roundstone to Casla (Costelloe), has been substantially lowered by glacial erosion and then invaded by the sea.

Continuing through Cashel and across the bog road towards Derryrush we can experience a rare feeling of isolation (except for the ubiquitous electricity cables and poles) as we bump along the margins of one of the largest areas of blanket bog in the region.

At Screeb the road to the south leads to Casla. From here, a detour to Lettermore and Gorumna Islands takes us into a unique and intricate landscape of rock and water. On Gorumna Island ice-scoured granite dominates the landscape south to Lough Hibbert. It is hard to believe that this barren land was once covered by deep peat, all of which has been cut away to fuel the hearths of distant communities. Beyond Lough Hibbert we meet a line of low, sometimes cliff-girt, hills clad with bracken on their lower slopes and generally better vegetated than the land to the north. These are 'country rocks', of Ordovician age, into which the younger granite was intruded some 400 million years ago. Still and silent now, this boundary zone was the scene of immense geological upheaval all those millions of years ago.

From Casla the road soon turns eastwards and straightens out where the southern margin of the Spiddle Granite meets the sea. The landscape to the north is of blanket bog punctuated frequently by rounded granite outcrops. The shore is rocky and exposed, with just a few small beaches at river-mouths and other shallow inlets. These beach sands, unlike those of Mannin Bay and Dog's Bay, are composed mainly of quartz, although they do contain some foram remains as well as other pieces of calcite of organic origin and the well-preserved spines of sea-urchins.

The presence of peat along the shore below the high tide mark just west of Spiddle Pier, for example, indicates that this coastline was only recently submerged by the sea, perhaps 2,000-3,000 years ago. The presence of pine stumps dating back 3,730 years on the shore also serves to emphasise the fluctuation of sea-levels since the end of the Ice Age.

Back to where we started

The final stage of our tour takes us north-eastwards across the moorlands between Spiddle and Moycullen. Here the wet, inhospitable blanket bog is broken only by a swarm of drumlins. These are green islands of drier ground which border the road midway between the two villages.

As we approach Moycullen, the road descends steeply towards the limestone plain which stretches eastwards as far as the eye can see. For our geological purposes we have reached the landward edge of Connemara and can now return along the junction between the granite and the limestone by the main road from Moycullen to our starting point in Oughterard.

A GLOSSARY OF GEOLOGICAL TERMS NOT EXPLAINED IN THE TEXT
(see also Geological Time Scale on page 17)

BATHOLITH	A large dome-shaped mass of rock, often granite, formed by the intrusion of molten material.
BRACHIOPOD	Marine twin-valved shellfish with shells which are unequal in size. Commonly called lampshells. Some forms attach to the seabed by means of a stalk (pedicle). Most species of brachiopod are now extinct.
CALEDONIAN UPHEAVAL	A mountain-building period dating from Ordovician to Middle Devonian times. From Caledonia, the Roman name for Scotland.
CARBONIFEROUS	The great coal-forming age.
CRETACEOUS PERIOD	The major chalk-forming period. From *creta*, 'chalk'.
DALRADIAN	A series of mainly sedimentary rocks, now largely metamorphic, formed between 800 and 500 million years ago in the Scottish Highlands (the ancient territory of Dal Riada), northern and western Ireland.
DEVONIAN PERIOD	The period of deposition of most of the Old Red Sandstone in Ireland. Named after Devon, a county in south-west England where rocks of this age were first described.
DOLOMITE	A form of limestone containing calcium carbonate and more than 15 per cent magnesium carbonate.
FOSSIL	The remains or form of a plant or animal which has been buried and preserved for a long period in the rocks of the Earth's crust, or evidence of its activity.
HANGING VALLEY	The valley of a tributary which enters a main river valley from a considerable height above the bed of the latter, and so forms rapids or waterfalls down the slope. Created by a glacier which deepens the main valley and leaves the tributary valley 'hanging'.
MAGMA	A molten fluid generated at great depth below and sometimes within the crust of the Earth. If it reaches the surface and solidifies it becomes an igneous rock.
ORDOVICIAN PERIOD	A period named after the Ordovices, an ancient Celtic tribe in Central Wales where Ordovician rocks were first described.
PRECAMBRIAN	The first of the five great eras of geological time, extending back from about 570 million years ago to the consolidation of the Earth's crust. From Cambria, the Roman name for Wales.
SILURIAN PERIOD	A period named after the Silures, an ancient Celtic tribe of the Welsh borderlands where Silurian rocks were first described.
TRUNCATED SPUR	A blunted ridge between hanging valleys.

AFTER THE ICE

The retreat of the ice, some 13,000 years ago, opened the way for the return of plants and animals to Connemara. Although conditions remained relatively cold and harsh for many hundreds of years, some of our hardiest plants soon began to take a foothold on the fresh debris left behind by the glaciers. These were probably plants which had managed to survive at the edge of the ice-sheets, cold-tolerant species which could track the glaciers as they receded to their mountain corries and, finally, into oblivion.

What were these plants which colonised the tundra-like environment of the freshly exposed Connemara landscape? And how have scientists been able to piece together the story of the post-glacial re-greening of Connemara?

There was a welcome improvement in the climate about 10,200 years ago and juniper and crowberry returned to the scene, although only briefly as they were soon replaced by birch and willow scrub. Subsequently, this vegetation succumbed to the warming conditions but the water-plant communities flourished. It appears that the temperatures rose rapidly at this time. Although trees could not advance to the north and west as rapidly as the temperatures would have allowed them, the herbs, and especially the water plants, could and did spread quickly across the region. Scots pine was the first tall species to invade the area, about 9,200 years ago. The tundra-like landscape finally disappeared.

The climate continued to improve over the next 500 years and soon conditions were nearly as warm as they are today. Forests developed gradually, their growth being limited by the speed at which trees could advance from their Ice Age refuges. At first, birches were the most common species, with some willows, poplars and mountain ashes interspersed. High grasses, docks and meadowsweet grew in what must have been ungrazed grassland. Heather became more widespread and bell heather started to appear, too. Peat mosses (*Sphagnum*) settled locally, although they did not expand for a number of millennia. In the ponds and lakes alternate water-milfoil was being crowded out by other water plants.

Hazel started to appear towards the end of this period and spread rapidly to form dense scrub. It came to dominate the landscape, although its dense woods were gradually infiltrated, first by Scots pine and then by elm and oak. Ivy made its entrance in these woods and the infamous bracken started to settle along the margins and in the openings. Holly and honeysuckle were also noteworthy additions to the flora, being indicators of climatic improvement. During this time, too, many lakes and ponds filled up with organic material and changed into reed and sedge swamps and occasionally *Sphagnum* bogs.

The period from 7,000 to nearly 5,000 years ago brought warm and moist weather to Connemara. The composition of the deciduous forests became more varied, with wych elm, pedunculate and sessile oak, hazel, birch, alder, ash and some Scots pine. The alder arrived between 7,000 and 6,500 years ago. This tree spread rapidly as the environment became wetter and

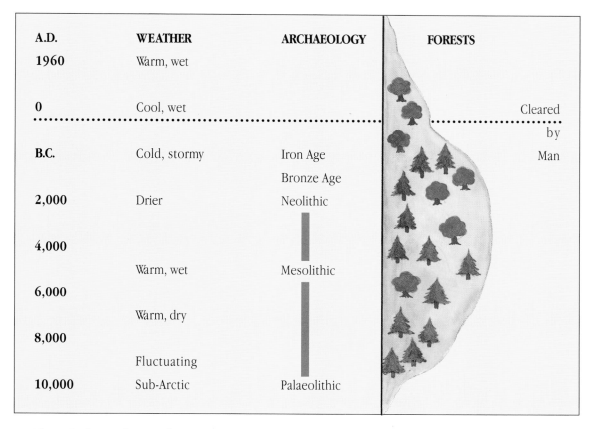

A.D.	WEATHER	ARCHAEOLOGY	FORESTS
1960	Warm, wet		
0	Cool, wet		Cleared
			by
B.C.	Cold, stormy	Iron Age	Man
		Bronze Age	
2,000	Drier	Neolithic	
4,000			
	Warm, wet	Mesolithic	
6,000			
	Warm, dry		
8,000			
	Fluctuating		
10,000	Sub-Arctic	Palaeolithic	

Figure 5: Climatic history of recent times.

more to its liking. In contrast, the Scots pine declined, except in areas with very poor soils such as the granites around Spiddle and Letterfrack.

The moist conditions favoured the establishment of bog asphodel, cross-leaved heath and many other species of flowering plants and mosses which thrive in damp habitats. Their appearance and spread signalled the onset of blanket bog formation, a topic we will look at in more detail later. Today, bog asphodel still brightens up the Connemara bogs with its delicate yellow flowers.

The arrival of people

By about 5,000 years ago it was becoming evident that some of the vegetation changes in Connemara were not entirely the result of climatic factors. Other forces were abroad, which, in the long run, were to have an enormous impact on the landscape and ecology of Connemara. These forces of course, were created by people.

Early attempts at farming had almost immediate effects on the vegetation, although presumably these were not widespread. Cereals and domesticated herbs began to appear in the pollen record, as did species like plantains. The latter have generally been associated with trampling by people and cattle and taken to be indicators of human interference with nature, especially the creation of pastures. However, they are also indicators of past natural fires. These were common in Connemara during the post-glacial period, as is evident from the occurrence of charcoal in the lake sediments.

During the period from 5,000 to 4,000 years ago the climate is considered to have been somewhat cooler and, at times, drier. These conditions probably suited Scots pine, which made a modest come-back, growing on the relatively dry surface of the blanket bogs. These pinewoods on peat represent the last occasion when pine was to play a major role in the landscape of Connemara.

The decline of the elm

There has been a long and vigorous debate among scientists about the causes of the elm decline, some ascribing it solely to the depredations of man, some suggesting climatic change, others invoking Dutch elm disease as the instigator of its demise. There is no doubt that Neolithic and Bronze Age people cut and burned elm and used its twigs as fodder for their livestock, although it is unlikely that any significant use was made of elm in Connemara because it was never plentiful there. It also seems unlikely that the relatively small human population of the time could have had such a direct and catastrophic effect over such a wide area (the decline occurred throughout northern Europe).

All this suggests that some sort of epidemic may have swept through Europe, perhaps aided by human movements. Climatic change can be ruled out as an immediate cause because other species would have been affected too and there is no evidence of this. Dutch elm disease, which has killed off many elms in Europe in recent decades, was suggested as a possible cause, but no evidence was found to support the suggestion until very recently. Now the fossil remains of a beetle (*Scolytus scolytus*) have been found in pre-elm decline deposits at Hampstead Heath in London. This beetle is the present-day carrier of the fungus (*Ceratocystis ulmi*) which causes Dutch elm disease and so it becomes all the more plausible that it also brought about the Europe-wide decline around 5,000 years ago. This possibility, however, may not absolve our ancestors from blame entirely because the pollarding of elms which leads to the vigorous growth of shoots, predisposes the trees to infection and to the rapid spread of the fungus.

From 4,000 years ago onwards the forests of Connemara diminished gradually, partly as a result of clearance by late Neolithic and Bronze Age people, but also in response to the expansion of the bogs. It is now thought that these people played an unconscious role in the enlargement of the bogs through land clearance and over-grazing, but the degree to which they altered the course of vegetation history is open to debate. Elm had almost disappeared and oak lost ground as well.

There was a resurgence of heather and a vigorous expansion of many other moorland plants as the blanket bogs continued to grow. White beak-sedge, oblong-leaved and round-leaved sundew, black bog-rush and purple moor-grass, familiar Connemara bog plants today, were also members of the bog community 4,000 years ago.

The disappearance of pine

After Scots pine died out on peat surfaces shortly after 4,000 years ago, it also continued to decline in the woodlands on mineral soils during the period from 3,700 years ago onwards and finally disappeared from Connemara about 2,000 years ago, destined never to occur naturally again here - or anywhere else in Ireland after about 1,400 years ago. We must go to the Highlands of Scotland now if we want to see natural pine forests with a lineage which stretches back to 9,000 years ago. The fondly held belief of naturalists that the pine trees which currently grace many Connemara lake islands are the descendants of those ancient pines has been firmly contradicted by recent research.

First, it has been shown by pollen studies that the present woodlands on two Connemara lake islands are only about 300 years old, having developed after previous clearance. Secondly, it has been argued, from studies of certain insects that are associated with native pine trees, that the current absence of most such species from Ireland indicates that native pines almost certainly became extinct and that the present 'wild' pines are the progeny of trees introduced about 300 years ago.

The climate of the period from 3,500 to 2,000 years ago was cooler, wetter and probably windier than it was in earlier periods. Bogs continued to expand, forests retreated and human influence on the vegetation increased. Many of the open-water communities seem to have disappeared by that time. With the onset of the historical period about 1,500 years ago, the great land clearance of Connemara began. Forests disappeared entirely as agricultural activities expanded and intensified into the Early Christian Period, 1,500 to 900 years ago. The pollen of cultivated grasses and members of the cabbage family, along with those of the plantains and other weeds associated with human activity, became dominant in the uppermost layer of peat in south Connemara, indicating the presence of cultivation nearby.

A treeless landscape

By 1600 AD the landscape of Connemara is thought by scientists to have been virtually treeless. However, according to tradition, one could walk on the tops of the trees from Letterfrack on the west coast to Galway City at about this time. Certainly, there were still pockets of woodland between Galway and Oughterard in the mid-seventeenth century. And, along the southern coast, there must have been some wood left to feed the iron works of Screeb, Lough Furnace and Doonmore. In the early nineteenth century it was noted that there was extensive shrubby timber, of oak, birch and hazel, on almost every dry knoll and cliff. Whatever the truth of these assertions, it is certain that nowhere in the region was there the sort of extensive natural deciduous forest which had existed 5,000 years previously, nor would there ever be again.

Undoubtedly, the burgeoning population from the seventeenth century onward took a heavy toll of any remaining woodland and scrub and by the time of the Famine, in the 1840s, it is hard to image anything but desolation in Connemara. After the Famine, tree planting was resumed, particularly on private estates. Unfortunately, this effort was not sustained and most of those trees, mainly beeches, are now coming to the end of their lives. This leaves us with the dismal prospect, as we approach the twenty-first century, of many more years without large, deciduous trees to enhance the landscape.

The state forestry service was established in the early years of this century and has planted large areas of upland and bog with alien conifers such as Sitka spruce and lodgepole pine. And now private enterprise is being encouraged to do the same. Can this be considered in any way as compensation for natural forests lost, or as a benefit to the natural history of Connemara? These are questions we will tackle later in the book.

Lettercraffroe Lough from the east.

In summary, we can now see that the Connemara landscape has changed profoundly since the Ice Age. Plant communities have ebbed and flowed as various combinations of warm and cold, dry and moist conditions have prevailed. Ultimately, however, the natural vegetation has been replaced by one almost totally generated and regulated by human activities. The generally bare countryside which we see around us today, and accept as the 'Connemara of all time', is really a man-made landscape which was established about 2,000 years ago. It is, in fact, a ravaged landscape which has been used and abused, not just recently - we cannot take all the blame - but also by our ancestors, dating back to Neolithic and possibly Mesolithic times. For although nature, in the form of earth movements and glaciation (as discussed earlier in this chapter) and climatic shifts can transform the surface of the Earth beyond recognition over very long periods of time, it must now be clear that the human species is a potent force for rapid landscape change, even with the primitive tools and methods employed by our ancestors. Consideration of the impact, actual and potential, of modern man on the face of Connemara awaits us in another chapter.

EARLY PEOPLE IN CONNEMARA

It was long believed that few people could ever have lived in Connemara in the distant past. The rough terrain, poor soils, difficult climate and remoteness would surely have discouraged the colonisation of this western outpost of Europe. But discoveries during the past two decades have turned that belief on its head. They have not only shown that Neolithic and Bronze Age communities lived in the region but also that some of Ireland's earliest Mesolithic settlers ventured at least as far as Connemara's eastern fringe, and possibly as far as the south coast.

Small but important finds of Later Mesolithic '*Bann flakes*' (flakes of flint from the vicinity of the River Bann in the north of Ireland where some of the earliest settlers lived) were made on the banks of the Owenriff River, near Oughterard, indicating a human presence in the area over 6,000 years ago. Limestone chipping floors of possible bivouac sites on Finish Island near Carna and the twenty or more coastal middens of

Stone wall and megalithic tomb near Cleggan.

THE POLLEN STORY

The key to the history of the Connemara landscape and its vegetation has been the study of pollen grains which were trapped in lake sediments and peat while these were being formed. This type of study, which is quite recent in origin, is known as palynology and is a specialised branch of botany.

The pollen grains of flowering plants and coniferous trees and the spores of ferns, clubmosses, horse-tails, mosses, liverworts and fungi have been preserved in the sediments and peat for two main reasons. First, the pollens and spores are coated in a decay-resistant substance called sporopollenin, and secondly, no organisms which might destroy them can live in the strongly acidic sediments and peat. In many cases the pollen or spore walls are distinctively textured and sculptured so that individual species can be identified with the aid of powerful microscopes.

The sediments and peat were formed slowly over long periods of time, the sediments by sands, silt and clay washed into lakes and the peat by the accumulation of dead plant material. So, by

taking a vertical core of material which has been deposited over a known time span, and identifying and counting the pollens and spores in small cross-samples cut off at regular intervals along the core, it is possible to construct a pollen diagram. The procedure is simple in principle but difficult in practice and the results are often hard to interpret, for many reasons. For example, some plants produce more pollen than others and could be over-represented in a core. Others produce light pollen which might have been carried many kilometres from its source, thereby wrongly suggesting the presence of species in a particular area. Ageing a core can be fraught with problems, too. This is usually done by means of the radiocarbon or ^{14}C technique. But even this tried and tested technique is subject to inaccuracies which must be corrected before a true date can be established. The dates used in the section 'Early People in Connemara' are based on corrected or calibrated dates as they are technically known.

The first Connemara pollen studies were carried out near Roundstone in the late 1940s by Professor Knud Jessen, the Danish pioneer of pollen analysis. He undertook the work at the invitation of the Royal Irish

Removing a peat core from the bog for pollen analysis.

Academy. This invitation was instigated by Robert Lloyd Praeger, who at that time found progress in his studies of plant distribution 'held up owing to absence of knowledge of the history of our flora'. It was a further thirty years before two Dutch scientists performed similar studies at another site near Roundstone. But then, in the 1980s, Dr Michael O'Connell and his colleagues in the Botany Department at University College Galway (U.C.G.) took up the challenge of interpreting the vegetation and early human history over a wider area of Connemara, partly in response to the new and exciting findings which archaeologists were making in the area. The U.C.G. scientists have worked at widely separated sites near Cleggan, Carna, Spiddle, Cornamona and in the Connemara National Park at Letterfrack. Their results, some of which have already been mentioned, on the one hand show overall similarities between the sites, but on the other hand, some interesting local differences in both the vegetation behaviour and human activity.

Clearly, there is a lot more research to be done if we are to fill in the gaps in our knowledge of post-glacial Connemara. But, with the growing co-operation between palynologists, archaeologists, geologists and ecologists, we can be assured that many new and exciting insights into the history of the landscape will surface in the coming years.

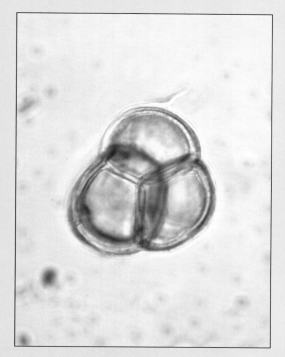 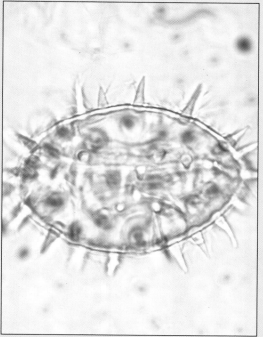

Examples of microscopic pollen grains found in peat and lake sediments. Left: crowberry; right: yellow water-lily.

south Connemara may also be relics of Mesolithic groups who exploited the rich fish and shellfish resources of the area. These groups may have overlapped with early Neolithic settlers, the Mesolithic people perhaps gradually adopting the life-style of the new inhabitants over a period of several hundred years.

Neolithic occupation seems to have been at a peak in the 200 years around 6,000 years ago, particularly in the area around Cleggan. Here, pollen studies of sediments in nearby Lough Sheeauns detected slight changes in the local species composition of around that period which suggested an opening up of the dense woodland canopy, possibly by newly arrived Neolithic farmers. While this evidence alone was not conclusive, the discovery of wheat pollen strengthened

Figure 6: Part of the pollen diagram for Lough Sheeauns showing the main trends in selected pollen curves before and during the earlier Neolithic (based on Molloy and O'Connell, 1988 Archaeology Ireland [2]).

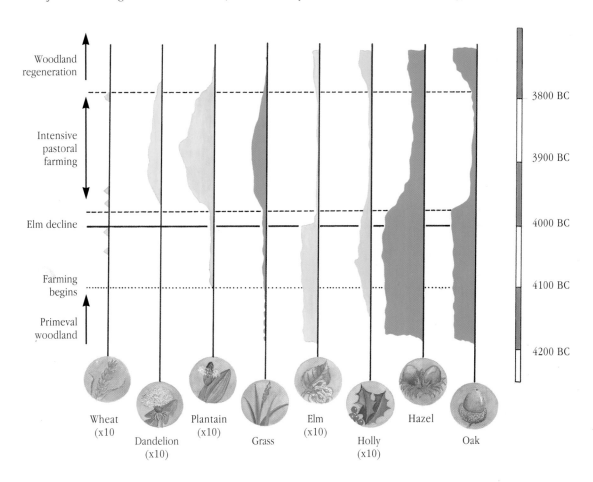

the likelihood that people were living in the area. Following on from that era, however, the landscape started to change quite rapidly and it became apparent from the pollen record that oak and hazel woodland was being cleared and replaced by open ground with ribwort plantain, dandelion, daisy, clover, dock, chickweed and meadowsweet. The large-scale clearance off the woodland would have been accomplished with stone axes. But to clear such a large area in this way would have required quite a substantial human population, the existence of which is borne out by the many megaliths in the Cleggan area.

After about 200 years, the grass and herb pollens declined and were replaced again by tree pollens, indicating a complete woodland recovery. This apparent abandonment of the area by the Neolithic farmers may have been due to declining soil fertility. Settlement appears to have returned in the early to mid-Bronze Age, about 4,000 years ago - during the period of bog formation - and continued, though at reduced levels, throughout that period.

Many Neolithic and Bronze Age field walls, built before and during the formation of the blanket bogs, are now coming to light as archaeologists learn to recognise telltale signs on the present bog surface and systematically probe the bogs with rods. These ancient field systems often occur in remote moorland areas where nobody could live today and testify, again, to the very different landscape which must have existed 4,000-5,000 years ago.

Megalithic tomb near Cleggan.

THE FIRST ANIMALS

The discerning reader will have noticed that throughout the account of Connemara's changing post-glacial landscape there has been little mention of animals. Surely, there must have been birds and insects inhabiting the forests, fish in the lakes and carnivorous mammals stalking the livestock of the Neolithic farmers? The answer, of course, must be yes. But unfortunately, there appears to be little evidence remaining of the animals which populated Connemara during the millennia which followed the retreat of the glaciers.

Irish place-names can give us some clues to the wild animals inhabiting Connemara in the recent past. For instance, *Mám Tuirc* (Maumturk), meaning 'boar's pass', suggests to us that wild boars lived in the forests of the mountains, a possibility confirmed by the discovery of boars' bones in caves elsewhere in Ireland. *Oileán Geabhróg*, 'tern island', is another plausible historical

A young red deer stag - a species which once roamed free in Connemara. Now it can be seen only within the fenced confines of the Connemara National Park.

reference because terns still nest on islands of that name. But, beyond a handful of place-names, which must be relatively recent in origin, there is virtually no material available by which we can build up even the slimmest impression of Connemara's ancient animal life.

Undoubtedly, the lakes and ponds were populated by snails and other tiny creatures which would have been preserved in the accumulating sediments. And it is just as likely that the hard parts of insects would have been preserved in the bogs. But, until some industrious scientist takes on the task of looking for these relics, we must turn to evidence from elsewhere in Ireland to discover which animals might have lived in Connemara.

We can start by excluding that most famous of Irish animals, the giant Irish deer (or Irish elk as it is often mistakenly called), which appears to have become extinct about 11,000 years ago. No remains have been found in Connemara. This is, perhaps, not surprising as this large animal needed rich, open grasslands to graze and a plentiful supply of calcium in its food to facilitate the annual growth of its enormous antlers. Connemara is unlikely to have met any of these requirements, but the animal was very common elsewhere in Ireland.

The wild boar would have felt at home in Connemara, particularly during the warmer phases when oak woods with grassy clearings were widespread and small lakes and marshes were easily accessible. Early Neolithic colonisers were, no doubt, familiar with its characteristic snorting. It is not clear when it became extinct in Ireland, though it is likely to have been well before the seventeenth century, when it became extinct in England.

Among the larger predators, the fox, wolf and possibly lynx were present in the region. The fox and the wolf were both animals which liked the cover of forests but could operate on open ground as well, be it on the low ground or in the mountains. The lynx today prefers primeval forests on rocky ground and is mainly restricted to mountains. Connemara could have favoured it during phases when forests extended high up the mountain sides. The lynx became extinct early on in Ireland, the last wolf is said to have been destroyed in the mountains of Joyce's Country in 1700 but the fox, of course, is still with us.

Present-day mammals which are likely to have lived in Connemara from fairly early post-glacial times are the pygmy shrew, the red squirrel, the pine marten, the stoat, the badger, the otter, the red deer, the Irish hare and all the present representatives of the bat family. To this list can now be added the wood (field) mouse, teeth of which were recently discovered in Dublin in deposits dating back to about 7,600 years ago. All these species are thought to have reached Ireland by natural dispersion and are described as being indigenous. All our remaining mammals, including the rabbit and the two rats, were either deliberately or accidentally introduced by people.

We find even less evidence in the fossil and archaeological records to reconstruct any impression of Connemara's early avifauna. But, because birds are so much more mobile than mammals, it seems safe to suggest that the bird communities of post-glacial times would have been akin to those we find in similar habitats today. Populations of particular species would have ebbed

SOIL

Soil is the growth medium for plants, which in turn sustain our animal life. Together with climate, it is the key to the natural history of Connemara. Fertile soil in a good climate will produce a rich and varied flora and fauna. Poor soils in a harsh climate will support only a modest complement of plants and animals. The soils of Connemara fall into the second category. But, that having been said, it should be stressed that in many ways the quality of Connemara's flora and fauna belies the poor quality of its soils, as we shall see later.

A glance at the soil map of Ireland shows us immediately that there are only four main types of soil in Connemara, blanket peat on the Galway Granite hills and the lowlands to the north, very shallow, stony soils with rock outcrops on the Twelve Bens, the Maumturks and the hills of Joyce's Country, peaty podsols on some of the lower hills and lowland shallow stony soils along the coast. A soil drainage map tells us that all are very wet. And finally, a land-capability map tells us what should already be fairly clear - that the soils of Connemara are generally unsuitable for anything other than very extensive grazing and coniferous forestry.

This may seem surprising if we recall the apparent richness of the region during the first 4,000 or 5,000 years after the Ice Age. To see why the situation has changed over the intervening period it is worth having a brief look at how the soils developed - and deteriorated - over time.

The glaciers of the last Ice Age scoured Connemara bare but, as they retreated, they dumped some of their load of ground-up rock and boulders as eskers, moraines and drumlins, some of which we saw on our geological tour of the region. So nature was left with a mosaic of bare rock, till and sand to work on. First, freezing conditions helped to break down the rocks further, then running water redistributed the finer materials over the surface and carried easily dissolved substances down to lower levels within the developing soil. Gradually, the bare surfaces were colonised by lichens and mosses and, eventually, hardy flowering plants. These also helped to break down the soils, by chemical and physical means, and when they died their remains - humus - combined with the mineral particles to form a richer soil in which bigger and more luxuriant plants could grow. Animals, too, played their part, burrowing in the soil and contributing their waste and, ultimately, their bodies to the growing reserve of organic matter.

Some rocks were richer in minerals than others and yielded more fertile soils. However, in those early times it is likely that most soils were reasonably well endowed with organic matter and minerals, including a wide range of trace elements, which plants and animals require to remain fit and healthy. So as the climate improved, ideal conditions awaited at least some of the plants and animals moving northwards from their Ice Age refuges.

In the natural scheme of things the fertility of a soil can be maintained over a long period by the recycling of chemicals through the system. Leaves die, fall to the ground, are dragged into the soil by worms, then broken down by micro-organisms, eventually to end up as nitrates, phosphates and other nutrients which the trees can use to grow and produce leaves again. But if this cycle is broken, by natural events or human over-cropping, the fertility of the soil can decline quickly. If, for example, the ground is bared by over-grazing, rain quickly washes away the nutrients, the fine mineral particles and the organic matter, leaving an impoverished soil that is of little value for farming or for wildlife. And as this process advances the soil becomes more acid and even less hospitable for plant life. A soil which has reached this stage of impoverishment is called a podsol (or podzol) and is the soil type which is often found on the lower Connemara hills.

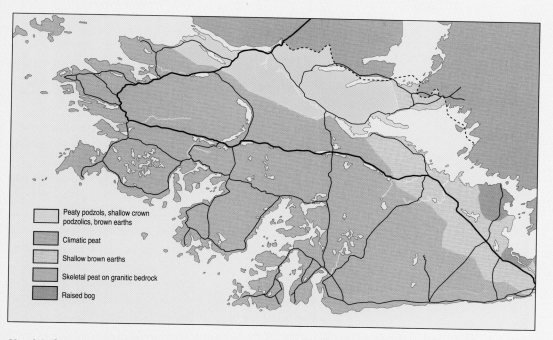

Legend:
- Peaty podzols, shallow crown podzolics, brown earths
- Climatic peat
- Shallow brown earths
- Skeletal peat on granitic bedrock
- Raised bog

Map 4: Soil types in Connemara

In the cool, moist conditions, which started about 2,700 years ago, rain carried dissolved iron downwards from the surface layer of these poor, acid soils to a level where it accumulated and cemented together the mineral particles into a distinctive brown iron pan which became so thick and hard that neither water nor roots could pass through it. The soil above the iron pan became waterlogged and the trees rooted in it were soon unable to obtain the minerals they needed and died. Only shallow-rooted sedges and rushes could tolerate these very wet conditions and they thrived. But when they died their remains did not decay because the tiny animals and micro-organisms which usually break down dead material had foresaken this inhospitably wet and acidic habitat. Their remains just lay where they had fallen and gradually built up over several thousands of years to form the most widespread soil type of Connemara - blanket peat, so named because it literally blankets the countryside.

On a positive note, we should recall that it was the acidity of the peat which helped to preserve the pollen which carried with it the fascinating story of Connemara's vegetation history. It is the acid peat, too, which saved the ancient pine and birch stumps which emerge from the cut-over bog. They can tell a story, too, and help to heat a Connemara kitchen.

The depth of the peat varies from place to place, from a few centimetres to several metres. It is usually shallower on hill slopes and deeper on the flatter ground where it overlies hollows. In some places the bog may have developed by the infilling of a lake with dead plant material, in the manner of the raised bogs of the Irish Midlands, but most such bogs have merged with the blanket peat and are no longer distinguishable on the surface.

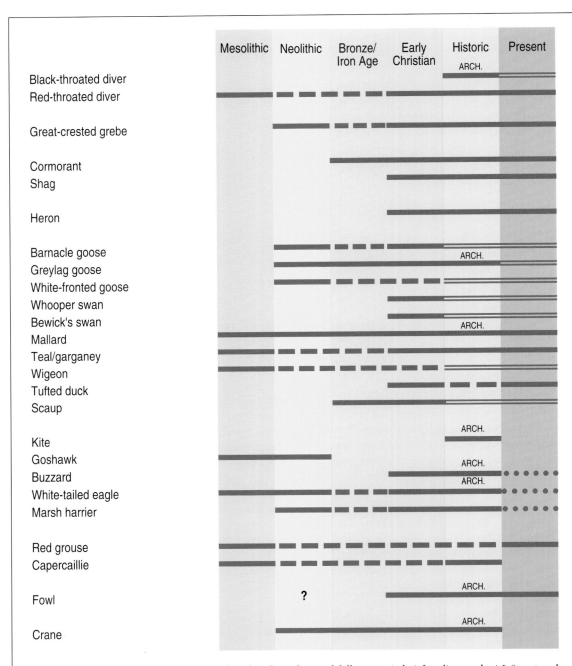

Figure 7: The presence of bird species in Irish archaeological sites of different periods (after diagram by A.J. Stuart and van Wijngaarden Bakker in Quarternary History of Ireland *by K.J. Edwards and W.P. Warren, Academic Press, 1985).*

	Mesolithic	Neolithic	Bronze/ Iron Age	Early Christian	Historic	Present
Water rail						
Corncrake						
Moorhen						
Coot						
Snipe/woodcock						
Black-headed gull						
Common gull						
Herring gull						
Great auk						
Razorbill/guillemot						
Puffin						
Wood pigeon				ARCH.		
Rock dove						
Barn owl						
Blackbird						
Song thrush						
Starling						
Jay						
Chough						
Jackdaw						
Rook						
Hooded crow						
Raven						

Present breeding   Supposedly present   Winter migrant

Rare vagrant   ARCH.   Historic and excavated evidence for presence and flowed with the changing climate and shifts in plant communities, just as we see happening at present. We can speculate that the bird community of the ancient pine forests might have been similar in many ways to that which we can now see in the Caledonian pine forests of Scotland, perhaps with species like the crested tit, which no longer occurs in Ireland. The mixed deciduous forests would have had communities like those found, say, in the Killarney woods today. The wetland bird-life might have been richer, too, perhaps with breeding red-throated and black-throated divers during the colder periods.

Bird remains have been found in association with ancient human settlements in other parts of the country, but the species list is short and biased towards those species which were presumably palatable and easily caught. The variety of birds in the wild must have been very much greater than these records suggest. The accompanying list, taken from the published work of Dr A.J. Stuart and Dr Louise van Wijngaarden-Bakker, includes many familiar species but also some which have become extinct as breeding birds or scarce as visitors in Ireland in more recent centuries. The capercaillie is a bird of Scots pine forests and would certainly have been a candidate for early Connemara pine forests. Of the birds of prey it is known that the white-tailed sea eagle nested in Connemara well into the last century (as did the golden eagle) and that persecution, which clearly started in Neolithic times, brought about its extinction here.

With fish we can, again, do no more than speculate on the composition of early river and lake communities. We do know, however, that Ireland has a very small number of native freshwater species. This is because the advance of fish from their Ice Age refuges in southern Europe was halted by the opening of the Irish Sea some 8,500 years ago. Thus, we find in Connemara only those species which could arrive from the sea, like Atlantic salmon, sea trout and European eels, and cold-tolerant species such as arctic charr. Elsewhere in the world the latter are sea-going, like Atlantic salmon, but in Ireland they have remained in freshwater lakes, presumably since early post-glacial times. Remains of Atlantic salmon, sea trout and European eels have been found in Mesolithic settlements elsewhere in Ireland, and it is suggested that they could have been part of the diet of Mesolithic people in Connemara, too.

The smaller freshwater animals of Connemara, such as snails, insects and crustaceans, which are presumably present in lake sediments and peat, have not been studied. However, elsewhere in Ireland the shells of arctic snails and tiny, hard-shelled mussel shrimps (ostracods) have been found in post-glacial deposits. The mussel shrimps, like pollen grains, have proved to be useful in reconstructing past environments.

On the coast, kitchen middens containing oyster, common mussel, common limpet and edible periwinkle shells tell us that seashore life from Mesolithic and Neolithic times well into the Christian era was similar to the kind we find today, providing a comforting link with the past and the feeling that perhaps not everything has changed for the worse since people arrived in Connemara over 6,000 years ago.

WEATHER AND CLIMATE

The weather is a regular topic of conversation in Connemara and rarely can it be far from the minds of the farmers, fishermen, foresters and visitors whose livelihoods and enjoyment depend so much on it. Weather and climate must also be a prime consideration for the naturalist because the distribution and behaviour of plants and animals are so closely governed by them.

But, before we go into details, let us be clear what we mean by these two terms. Weather refers to the local and short-term atmospheric events and conditions in a particular area. The shower of rain at noon in Letterfrack is a weather event, the high humidity can be described as a weather condition. The climate, however, is the long-term average condition of the weather in a given area. It rains a lot in Connemara so its climate can be described as moist. And, because the Connemara climate is affected by conditions over the sea, we can go a step further and say it has a moist, maritime or oceanic climate.

Climate sets the general limits of distribution and activity of flora and fauna while the weather affects them on a moment-to-moment, day-to-day basis. Thus we can say that the plants and animals of Connemara are adapted to a moist, maritime climate and, if we were to look for a similar flora and fauna elsewhere, we would first try to find areas with a similar climate. We would not, however, say that they are adapted to specific weather events, such as rain in the morning on Thursdays, though such weather could have an immediate effect on the behaviour or well-being of individual plants or animals.

The term moist maritime climate, because it refers to the average weather conditions in the region, covers a multitude of details about rainfall, temperature, humidity and wind, some of which we will turn to now.

Rainfall

Connemara has a well-deserved reputation for its high rainfall, up to 3,000 millimetres (120 inches) annually in some areas in the mountains. But not everywhere in Connemara is equally wet, nor is the rainfall distributed evenly throughout the year as Tables 1 and 2 (p. 56) show. The driest area is the narrow coastal fringe which stretches westwards from Inveran, through Gorumna Island and Lettermore to the lowlands around Carna where the rainfall is about 1,225 millimetres (48 inches) each year. Inland, towards the foot of the Twelve Bens and the Maumturks, eastwards over the Galway Granite and northwards around the coast to Letterfrack, there can be 1,200-1,600 millimetres (47-63 inches) per year. At Moyard, near the southern shore of Ballynakill Harbour, the annual average is about 1,300 millimetres (51 inches) whilst a little further north, and closer to the mountains, Letterfrack has 1,638 millimetres (66 inches), which is typical of a narrow band encircling the higher mountain ranges. In the valleys which dissect the Twelve Bens, the Maumturks and the Joyce's Country mountains the rainfall generally exceeds 2,000 millimetres (80

Table 1
Weather statistics for Galway City (University College).
Averages for period 1966-91 (25 years).

	Jan	Feb	Mar	Apr	May	Jun	Jul	Aug	Sept	Oct	Nov	Dec	Yearly
Total/average Rainfall (mm)	120.0	86.7	91.3	67.5	69.8	73.2	63.6	101.1	107.0	132.4	115.8	123.9	1151.4
Number of wet days (≥0.2mm)	21	18	21	15	17	17	16	18	19	21	21	22	226
Number of rain days (≥1.0mm)	18	14	16	11	13	12	12	14	15	17	16	18	175
Daily mean airtemp (°C)	5.5	5.4	7.0	8.7	11.1	13.7	15.5	15.4	13.7	11.0	7.5	6.5	10.1
Daily max air temp (°C)	8.0	8.2	10.0	12.3	14.6	17.2	18.8	18.7	16.7	13.8	10.2	8.9	13.1
Daily min air temp (°C)	3.0	2.7	4.0	5.1	7.5	10.2	12.2	12.1	10.4	8.2	4.6	4.0	7.0
Sunshine hours	53	66	106	148	179	156	142	143	113	85	61	38	1290

Table 2
Average, maximum and minimum rainfall (mm) 1970-91.*

	Elevation (metres)	Number of years recorded	Average	Maximum	Year	Minimum	Year
Carna	6	14	1224.8	1496.0	1986	941.7	1975
Moyard (from 1980)	13	9	1301.2	144.2	1986	1111.3	1991
Letterfrack (Connemara National Park) (since 1982)	58	9	1637.5	1850.2	1986	1404.2	1987
Delphi	32	21	2530.7	2838.2	1985 **	1956.8	1978
Maum Valley	58	13	2712.2	3143.3	1986	2209.5	1987
Cornamona	30	21	1926.4	2446.6	1986	1380.2	1972
Cloosh Valley`	101	22	1474.9	1797.5	1986	1074.4	1971
Galway City	14	22	1146.3	1366.1	1986	830.0	1971

*Measurements started in 1970 unless stated otherwise; **1986 not available

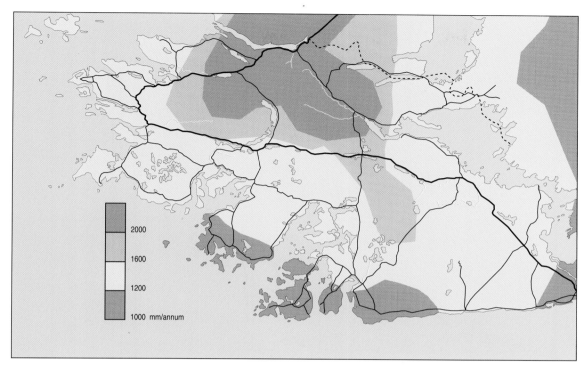

Map 5: Rainfall in Connemara.

inches) and can top 3,000 millimetres (120 inches) in a wet year. Maum holds the record with an annual average since 1970 of 2,712 millimetres (107 inches), a maximum of 3,143 millimetres (124 inches) in 1986 and a minimum of a mere 2,210 millimetres (87 inches) in 1987.

However, it should be remembered that most of these measurements are made at a height of no more than 60 metres (200 feet) above sea level. Higher up the mountains the rainfall is likely to be appreciably greater and more frequent, with noticeable consequences for the wildlife - and the naturalists who study it. Unfortunately, there are no mountain-top weather stations in Connemara so it is not possible to say exactly how extreme the weather is on these lofty and exposed summits.

The rainfall totals may seem grim, but there can be a respite from the rain, even in the mountains. April and May can be relatively dry and in some years there can even appear to be drought conditions when the streams dry out and the hillsides become dry and parched. The monthly totals in Galway City, presented in Table 1, usefully indicate the variation in rainfall over the year, but of course they are considerably lower than we find at most places in Connemara.

The frequency of rainfall, like the amount of rain, increases as we move westwards and into the mountains. In Galway City there are about 226 rain days (when 0.2 millimetres or more is recorded) and 175 wet days (when 1.0 millimetres or more is recorded) each year. In the mountain valleys there are likely to be upwards of 300 rain days and over 230 wet days every year and on the summits the figures will be higher still.

Heavy rainfall is a serious cause of soil erosion, particularly on the steep mountain slopes where the vegetation has been over-grazed by sheep. Gushing white torrents carry soil downslope into lakes, streams and rivers where it can do considerable damage to the invertebrate and fish life.

Snow and frost

Snow is an infrequent sight in Connemara and when it does arrive, it rarely lies for more than a few days, except perhaps in some of the north-facing corries on the higher mountains. Inland, ground frost occurs frequently during the winter and spring, less frequently in autumn and occasionally even in the summer months. Some areas, described as frost hollows, are more prone to ground frost than others and it is likely that their wildlife is affected to some degree by this more regular chilling, though there is no information from Connemara to substantiate this contention. Air frost occurs much less frequently, perhaps on 20-30 days each year at sea level. Like the ground frost, air frosts rarely persist through a whole day.

Snow on the Twelve Bens - Bengower and Benbreen.

In recent decades, only the winter of 1962-3 will be remembered for being prolonged, exceptionally cold and damaging to wildlife, though shorter cold snaps in 1978-9, 1985 and 1986, for example, badly affected the Connemara heron population, as we will see later.

Humidity and evaporation

Humidity is a measure of the amount of moisture in the air and is usually expressed as a percentage known as the relative humidity. There is a maximum amount of moisture which air can hold at any particular temperature. If this level is reached the relative humidity is 100 per cent. If the

Clouds over the mountains.

air temperature increases without any change in moisture content the relative humidity decreases; if the air cools, the moisture will condense to form dew or rain.

Because much of the air reaching the west coast of Ireland has spent a considerable time travelling over the ocean, it is not surprising that the humidity in Connemara is quite high, on average between 80 and 90 per cent. Furthermore, when this relatively warm, moist air meets the mountains it is forced to rise and, as it does so, its temperature drops, causing its moisture load to condense to form clouds and possibly rain. In these circumstances the humidity of the mountain air is likely to be high most of the time.

If the air is warm and its moisture content is low (i.e. it has a low relative humidity), it will have the capacity to draw water in from the surface of the soil and from the leaves of plants - the surface water will evaporate. The amount of water which evaporates into the Connemara air each year is 400-500 millimetres (16-20 inches), the highest rate of evaporation occurring on the coast. Over 75 per cent of this loss occurs during the drier April-August period. This means that there is always an overall excess of rainfall (1,100-1,200 millimetres, 43-47 inches), which keeps the soils wet and the streams flowing for all but short periods during the year. The considerable excess of annual rainfall over evaporation in Connemara is one of the most important factors, first in the formation of bogs and now their maintenance as 'living' features of the landscape. The blanket bogs could not exist on the low ground in the Midlands and east of Ireland because there, the balance between the lower rainfall and greater evaporation could not keep them sufficiently wet throughout the year.

Temperature

Air temperature

The annual average air temperature at sea-level in Connemara is about 10°C. By itself this figure tells us little about the temperature regime. In fact, it is really quite unhelpful, particularly when we consider that places such as Santa Fé in New Mexico (at an altitude of 2,164 metres, 7,100 feet) and Odessa in the Ukraine (at 64 metres, 211 feet), in very different parts of the world and with very different temperature regimes, have the same annual average temperature. So, we must look in more detail at how air temperature changes over the year, how it decreases as we climb the mountains and how the wind affects it, if we want to explain, for example, why some plants and animals live in one place rather than in another.

The monthly average air temperatures in Galway City (see Table 1) show us that January and February are the coldest months while July and August are the warmest. They also show us that the difference between the coldest and warmest months is quite small, only about 10°C. Connemara does not suffer any extremes of heat or cold, as do areas with continental climates. Its summer temperatures are like those of Helsinki, whilst in winter they are similar to those in Rome.

The average maxima and minima give us an idea of the range of temperatures plants and animals can be exposed to each month and are useful for drawing broad ecological conclusions about the distribution of our fauna and flora. However, it will be plain, particularly to anyone who has walked in the mountains, that the temperature can vary enormously over very short distances, depending on height, aspect (the direction in which the place in question is facing), wind speed, shelter, cloudiness and so on. It is important to be aware of these factors when trying to explain the distribution or behaviour of certain species. And, from a very practical point of view, it is essential that the naturalist who takes to the mountains should be aware of them for his or her own comfort and safety, for reasons which will soon become evident.

The air temperature drops by 1°C for every 150 metres (490 feet) of ascent, so a bird, or a walker for that matter, will experience a cooling of nearly 5°C between the floor of the Inagh Valley (which is not far above sea-level) and the summit of Benbaun (730 metres, 2,395 feet) at the heart of the Twelve Bens. In calm weather in the middle of a January day this means moving from a moderately comfortable temperature to almost freezing conditions if the sea-level temperature is 'average'. But the weather is never 'average' and rarely calm. A moderate breeze, say Force 4 on the Beaufort Scale, will have a further cooling effect (the wind chill factor) and reduce the temperature felt by the bird or walker to -10°C on the summit. A strong breeze, Force 6, will bring the temperature down to a very chilly -16°C. Beyond this, however, any increase in windspeed will have relatively little effect on the temperature. These are the figures for winter, but it is well to remember that, even on the warmest day in summer, a sea-level temperature of 20°C can be effectively halved by a moderate breeze on the top of Benbaun.

Clearly, the plants and animals which live on and around the high summits of Connemara experience a very different climate from those in the lowlands. In fact, their world is more akin to that of the subarctic than to the mild, maritime world which we take to be the 'real' Connemara.

Water temperature

Water temperature can be a critical factor in the lives of many of Connemara animals. If stream temperatures get too high in the summer, trout may die for lack of oxygen. If rivers and loughs freeze over in the winter, herons will die because they cannot reach their food. Even on the coast, herons may suffer during very cold winters because the fish species which they usually eat move offshore into deeper, warmer water. If sea temperatures are cool during the late spring and summer oysters will not produce as many offspring as they would in warmer conditions.

The sea temperature around the Connemara coast averages about 10°C in winter and 14-15°C in summer. However, temperatures can vary locally and in summer they may occasionally reach 18°C and more in some shallow, enclosed bays. In winter, the inflow of cold freshwater might reduce some shallow, inshore waters to 5 or 6°C.

The temperatures of loughs, rivers and streams are more variable and are influenced by altitude, aspect, depth and the source of the water. As there are so many bodies of water in Connemara, all differing in these characteristics, to write of averages would be misleading. However, it can be stated fairly confidently that the range of temperatures falls between extremes of about 3 and 20°C with an annual average of perhaps 8-10°C, depending on the location and type of water body.

Ice very rarely forms on the coastal waters and infrequently on most lowland lakes and rivers. It is more common on mountain lochans and, in severe conditions, small mountain streams and waterfalls can freeze solid.

Sunshine

The amounts of sunshine received in Connemara differ considerably between the coastal fringe and the mountains where cloud cover is always much greater. The monthly average values for Galway City probably reflect reasonably closely the sunshine levels for the coastal lowlands. However, these will, presumably, be quite a bit higher than those in the Maum Valley and substantially more than would be expected on the mountain summits. May is generally the sunniest month by far and December the dullest, with only just over one fifth of the May total.

Cloud

Cloud and sunshine levels are, of course, related. The greater the cover and duration of cloud the less direct sunshine reaches the ground. Cloud cover is measured in eighths (oktas) and for most of the country the annual average is between 5.5 and 6.0 oktas. This is a high and rather constant value and is due to Ireland's position on the western seaboard of Europe, close to the path of the humid and cloudy airflows which approach it from the Atlantic for much of the year. In Connemara, and particularly to the north-east of the mountains, the cloudiness is probably in excess of 6.0. The average for the years 1989-91 at a weather station near Oughterard was 6.3. However, this was based only on measurements made at 9 a.m. each day. The true figure, which should be based on hourly measurements, would undoubtedly be somewhat lower.

Wind-shaped hawthorn at Errislannan.

Wind

The air is rarely still in Connemara. It beats in from the Atlantic for much of the year, crashing waves against the islands and the exposed, rocky mainland shores. At times it tears through the valleys, roars over high mountain colls, whips up the lake waters and makes life impossible for all but the hardiest of plants on the exposed hillsides and bogs. It brings a chill to the air and can kill trees a long way inland with the salt which it carries from the sea. Wind is part of Connemara, and Connemara is one of the windiest places in Europe.

The prevailing winds come from the south, the south-west and the west, bringing moist air from the Atlantic. Winds from the north and east are much less frequent but notable for the drier, clearer and crisper weather they tend to bring. Unfortunately, the hazes which nowadays accompany winds from the south and east are most likely to be caused by air pollution from the industrial regions of Europe.

Gales are frequent, with perhaps up to thirty gale days each year at sea-level and no doubt many more on the mountains where winds can be twice or even three times stronger than on the lowlands.

The shape and extent of the mountains greatly influence the speed and direction of the winds. A wind from the north-west will be funnelled down the Inagh Valley between the Bens and the Maumturks, but the valley will be sheltered by the Bens from a westerly gale.

The windspeed can be estimated, either on land or at sea, with a bit of practice, using the

THE BEAUFORT SCALE

This scale was devised by Admiral Beaufort at the beginning of the nineteenth century to differentiate approximately between various wind strengths. The scale, which can be used on land or at sea, employs the effect of the wind on common features in the landscape or seascape to assess its force, which ranges from 0, calm to 12, hurricane. The scale is recognized and used internationally.

Beaufort Number	Short Description	Wind velocity at 10m above ground m/sec.*	Specification for use on land	Specification for use at sea or on large inland waters
0	Calm	<0.3	Smoke rises vertically	Sea mirror smooth
1	Light Air	0.3-1.5	Direction shown by smoke but not by windvanes	Small wavelets like scales; no crests
2	Light Breeze	1.6-3.3	Wind felt on face; leaves rustle; ordinary vanes move	Small wavelets still short but more pronounced; crests glassy and do not break
3	Gentle Breeze	3.4-5.4	Leaves and small twigs in constant motion; wind extends light flag	Large wavelets. Crests begin to break; foam is glassy
4	Moderate Breeze	5.5-7.9	Raises dust and loose paper; small branches move	Small waves becoming longer; more frequent white horses
5	Fresh Breeze	8.0-10.7	Small trees in leaf begin to sway; crested wavelets form on inland waters	Moderate waves and longer; many white horses
6	Strong Breeze	10.8-13,8	Large branches in motion; whistling heard in wires; umbrellas used with difficulty	Large waves begin to form; white crests more extensive
7	Near Gale	13.9-17.1	Whole trees in motion; inconvenience felt when walking against the wind	Sea heaps up; white foam blown in streaks
8	Gale	17.2-20.7	Breaks twigs off trees; generally impedes progress	Moderately high waves of greater length; crests begin to form spindrift; foam blown in well marked streaks
9	Strong Gale	20.8-24.4	Slight structural damage (chimney pots, slates etc.)	High waves; dense streaks of foam; crests begin to roll over
10	Storm	24.5-28.4	Seldom experienced inland; trees uprooted; considerable structural damage	Very high waves with long overhanging crests; surface becomes white with great patches of foam; visibility affected
11	Violent Storm	28.5-32.6	Very rarely experienced; widespread damage	Exceptionally high waves; sea completely covered with foam
12	Hurricane	32.7 and over		The air filled with spray and visibility seriously affected

* Multiply by 3.6 to give km/hr; multiply by 2.2 to give m/hr.

Beaufort Scale (see p. 63). Competence with the scale is a useful addition to the fieldcraft skills of a naturalist in Connemara where the wind can make all the difference between a 'good' day and a 'bad' day studying wildlife.

Extreme winds, of hurricane force, are fortunately quite few and far between. Hurricane Debbie, which struck Ireland on 16 September 1961, lives on in folk memory for the devastation it caused. And a vicious storm at the end of January 1974 is still imprinted on the memories of a group of walkers who, having set out in clear, calm conditions, were, by mid-afternoon, reduced to crawling along one of the high ridges of the Bens into face-stinging hail. The following day, the full impact of that storm became evident. Telegraph poles and lines had been strewn across the roads and in the Maum Valley the prefabricated primary school had been reduced to matchwood, the children's books and paintings scattered to the four winds.

Poison on the wind

Several events in recent years should have made us acutely aware that even a remote area like Connemara is not immune to the discharge of wind-borne poisons from the industrial areas of Europe. Acid rain, that is rain contaminated with oxides of sulphur and nitrogen produced by coal and oil burning and by vehicle exhausts, is not yet a problem, but it could become so if prevailing winds shift as a result of global warming. Many of Connemara's lakes are naturally acidic and additional acid could quickly kill their plant and animal life, as has happened in Scotland and Sweden already.

Radioactivity from the Chernobyl disaster in 1984 reached the west of Ireland, and although assurances were given that it did no lasting harm, the fact that it travelled on the wind as far as Connemara should be a salutary warning to those who have scant regard for the role of wind and rain in carrying pollution around the globe.

The climate in the past

Earlier we saw how the climate of Connemara changed from the time the last glaciers disappeared, about 13,000 years ago, to 2,000 years ago when peat formation began to slow down. There was a climatic optimum between about 7,000 and 5,000 years ago when the average annual temperature throughout Europe was probably around 2°C higher than it is today. Later, between about 4,000 and 1,500 years ago the climate was colder and stormier and rainfall increased. As we have already seen, this story of early climatic changes was preserved in the fossil pollens which accumulated in the lake sediments and bogs of Connemara. After about 2,000 years ago, however, peat became less valuable as a chronicle of climatic change. Fortunately, new evidence was being generated in the form of tree rings, human documents, paintings and other human artefacts which could give a clue to the continuing climatic changes.

There was a second climatic optimum in the early Middle Ages, which peaked around 900 years

Diamond Hill with Tully Mountain in the background.

ago when the average summer temperatures in Europe were about 1°C higher than those we experience today. Then, between about 1430 and 1850 AD the climate took a sharp downturn into the Little Ice Age when the summers were shorter and the winters long, cold and severe. In our own century we have seen a warming into the middle decades followed by a slight cooling and now we may be moving into a further period of warming.

Climate and wildlife

Climate has far-reaching and long-lasting effects on wildlife. These may be on a global scale, with well-defined air-currents sweeping birds along on their migrations, or on a very local scale, with dark and humid rock crevices favouring diminutive liverworts.

In Connemara, with its varied and complex topography, the role of climate in the life of any species cannot be over-emphasised. Why is plantlife richer on one side of a rock than on the other? Why do some plants live only near the tops of mountains? Why do white-fronted geese come to Ireland in winter? How is it that arctic charr can live in Connemara lakes? The questions are legion and the answers will, as often as not, have something to do with climate - directly or, sometimes, indirectly.

The direct impacts of climate are most easily seen in the plant life of the mountains. For example, the tree-line - the upper limit at which native trees will grow naturally - is at about 450 metres (1,500 feet) in Connemara (although there are few trees left to indicate this today). This is most surprising to visitors from the Alps where, although winters are much colder, the tree-line is at 1,500 metres (5,000 feet). This unexpectedly low limit of tree growth in Connemara appears to be controlled by the relatively low summer temperatures which, as we have seen, can be as low as 10-12°C at an altitude of 450 metres (1,500 feet). It is also influenced by the shorter growing season at these heights, where the average temperature remains above the plant growth threshold of around 6°C for only about six months of the year.

Furthermore, it is not just the absolute temperatures which are important to the plants. It is also the cumulative temperature over the growing season which affects their growth and development. Essentially, the cumulative temperature is calculated by adding the daily temperatures which exceed the growth threshold. A short cut is to multiply the appropriate average monthly temperatures by the number of days in each month. In this way we can calculate roughly that in Connemara there are about 1,600 'degree-days' for plant growth at sea-level and only 800 at 450 metres (1,500 feet). On top of Benbaun (730 metres, 2,395 feet) there will be a mere 435 'degree-days' and less than five months in which growth can take place. At 450 metres (1,500 feet) there is up to six months' growing time, whereas at sea-level growth is possible in eleven months of the year. The windier conditions, the wind-chill factor and the greater cloudiness also play their parts in limiting the growth of trees and other plants on the higher mountain slopes, so the figures presented here probably err on the optimistic side.

The climatic effect of increasing altitude is nicely illustrated by some observations on heath rush, which is common and widespread in Connemara, reported by Professor W.H. Pearsall in his fascinating book *Mountains and Moorlands*. With increasing altitude, the length of the flower-stalks diminishes, the number of flowers decreases and the number of ripe seed-capsules produced declines - to zero above about 760 metres (2,500 feet). This effect is evidently due mainly to the slowing down of the development of the flowers and the fruits in response, presumably, to the shorter growing season and fewer 'degree-days' at the greater heights.

Professor Pearsall points out the impact of the changing growth habits of the heath rush on the little rush moth which lays its eggs in the seed-capsules. Briefly, it seems likely that, with increasing altitude, the breeding cycle of the moth gets out of phase with that of the rush, preventing the moth from laying eggs when the capsules are available. As a result no moths are found on the rush above about 200 metres (700 feet). This example not only illustrates a very close inter-relationship but it also points to the fact that, although two species may interact intimately in one set of environmental conditions, they may not necessarily be able to do so in different

Facing page: The essence of Connemara.

conditions because each responds to changing circumstances in a different way. So predicting the impact of climatic change on plant and animal communities is a very difficult task indeed.

Moving from the arctic-alpine extremes of the mountain summits down to the coast, we discover plants and animals which are more commonly found in the warmer climates of southern Europe. Irish heath, which grows sparingly on the blanket bogs, has its headquarters in Spain, while the small, purple sea-urchin, *Paracentrotus lividus*, which is common in suitable inshore habitats, is also of southern origin. These southern species can survive in Connemara, at least in part because of the influence of the warm waters of the Gulf Stream - more correctly called the North Atlantic Drift on our side of the Atlantic. This is a fast-moving body of warm water which has its origins off the Bahamas. From there it streams north-eastwards towards Europe, separating the cold arctic waters of the north from the warmer southern ocean. It keeps our climate and coastal waters warmer than those at the same latitude on the western side of the Atlantic. Yet it has been suggested that, because of global climatic changes, the global ocean circulation system which sustains the Gulf Stream could be about to switch suddenly to a new state in which the Gulf Stream might reach only as far north as Spain. We can but speculate on what effects such a change would have on Connemara's weather and wildlife.

Turning inland again, we discover yet another anomaly in the region's natural history. In the deep, dark, cool waters of several of the larger loughs live arctic charr, relics of the early post-glacial times. In Connemara, the arctic charr, a member of the salmon family, is right at the southern edge of its world range, which otherwise circles the globe in subarctic and arctic latitudes.

The future

Sadly, there is little historical information about Connemara's wildlife from which to draw clues as to how it has changed in the past and how climatic changes might affect it in the future. Most of the changes in wildlife populations which have attracted writers are declines and extinctions wrought by man. Perhaps the closest we can come to 'seeing' historical changes in the natural environment is through accounts of famines, which occurred with considerable frequency, even if only locally. Sir William Wilde listed nearly eighty individual years between 900 AD and the start of the Great Famine in the 1840s when there was famine somewhere in Ireland. Many of these were brought on by adverse weather conditions either directly through storm damage, for example, or indirectly through the fostering of some biological pest such as potato blight. These events must have afflicted Connemara and its wildlife as much as anywhere else.

Future climatic changes, if they are as rapid and extreme as some scientists predict, will bring major changes to the flora and fauna of Connemara. Rapid warming could lead to the retreat and possibly the total disappearance of arctic-alpine plants. A longer growing season could favour the spread of bracken. Drier summers could kill the blanket bogs. Increased storminess and a rise in sea-level could destroy many of the existing seashore communities and make life difficult for already hard-pressed fishermen. Rising sea-levels could flood some of the lower ground around the south coast bays and destroy the low-lying machair grassland west of Ballyconneely. Increased temperatures and changes in rainfall patterns could disrupt the life-cycle of the salmon. On the other hand, warmer summers could benefit Irish oysters, provided the advantages of improved breeding conditions are not cancelled out by storminess and higher sea-levels. In addition, increased temperatures could also encourage the introduced Pacific oyster to breed in the wild, as it has done recently in Britain.

Clearly, we are deep into the realm of speculation when we try to envisage the effects of unknown climatic changes on our wildlife. Nevertheless, it is important to remember that drastic changes may occur; and that these changes should be borne in mind when reading the present-day natural history of Connemara. With knowledge and understanding of our wildlife we may be able to minimise at least some of the adverse effects of climatic change - and perhaps capitalise on others.

Climatic summary

In summary, the climate of Connemara is mild and moist at sea-level, cool and wet in the mountains. Rainfall is moderate at the coast but is two or three times greater in the mountain valleys and more so on the summits. Rain is characteristically frequent but not too often heavy. Relatively dry spells may occur at any time of the year but usually in April and May. Humidity is high and evaporation low, except in exposed situations where even moisture-laden winds can cause excessive evaporation from plant surfaces. Wind is rarely absent and often strong, coming mainly from the south-west and carrying with it moist Atlantic air, the source of Connemara's clouds, high humidity and rain.

The duration and extent of cloud cover is considerable and sunshine is correspondingly low. Temperatures are equable in the lowlands, ranging from 5.4°C in February to 15.5°C in July with an annual average of about 10°C. Mountain-top temperatures are substantially lower, being modified by altitude, strong winds and prolonged cloud cover. The growing season ranges from about eleven months at sea-level to less than five months on the highest summits. The tree-line reaches only about 450 metres (1,500 feet). Ground frost is common but rarely severe. Air frost is infrequent, as is snow, which rarely lies for more than a few days.

Finally, it is worth noting the relative uniqueness of Ireland's climate on a world scale. A quick look at a world climate map in any good atlas will indicate that its pattern of mild winters and cool summers is, in the northern hemisphere, repeated only in Britain, Iceland, south-west Norway and coastal north-west North America. In the southern hemisphere it occurs only in Tasmania, the south of South Island in New Zealand and on the coast of south-west South America.

PLANTS AND THEIR HABITATS

THE MOUNTAINS

At first sight the mountains present a fairly uniform, almost drab face to the naturalist. Vast swathes of bare rock on the Bens and the Maumturks, smooth green slopes on the mountains of Joyce's Country and tedious undulations of purple moor-grass on the Galway Granite hills. But first appearances belie the true botanical interest of the uplands. Yet, enrichment of the botanical senses will not come easily. The seeker of mountain plants will have to endure boot-sucking bogs, slippery rocks, unstable screes, tortuous routes to avoid cliffs and the gales and rain which are part and parcel of mountain exploration. But the rewards will hopefully outweigh the hardships.

A keen eye and a sense of habitat are the first requirements of the mountain botanist. For most of the botanical gems are small, inconspicuous and probably growing on inaccessible ledges. So a pair of binoculars can also be a useful aid to our mountain investigations. To the practiced eye, the distant and fuzzy uniformity of the mountains resolves into an intricate picture of cliffs and slopes, boulders and screes, streams and waterfalls, heathy hollows and mossy flushes, each with its own character, depending on the altitude, aspect and geology.

Summits and ridges

We will start our survey of the mountain flora in the least hospitable habitats, the exposed, quartzite summits and connecting ridges of the Twelve Bens and the Maumturks. Only the sheep farmer and his dogs, passing walkers and occasional naturalists tramp these rugged, rock-strewn and potentially ankle-breaking peaks and passes. Few deviate from the obvious routes to explore

Facing page: Bell heather.

71

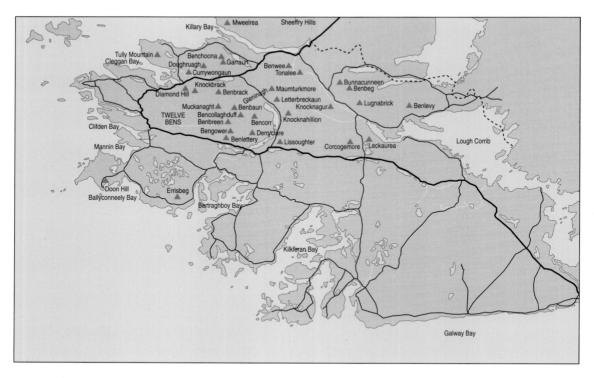

Map 6: Mountains and bays mentioned in the text.

the crags and gullies off the beaten track, so the plant communities at these heights are seldom visited and little known. Their stunted or naturally diminutive members do not rouse passions like some of the lowland species and many remain as unfamiliar to the botanist as to the layman. Nevertheless, the mountain-top plant communities deserve our attention because they include arctic forms that cannot be seen at lower altitudes and because they will be the first to disappear with the advance of climatic warming.

Many of the summits and open ridges are almost devoid of life. But down-slope, where there is a little shelter, plant life has gained a tenuous foothold. On a slope of about 30° at 550 metres (1,800 feet) on the north face of Bengower, on the south-western arm of the Bens, there is a low-growing community of flowering plants, lichens, liverworts and mosses, first described by Dr Derek Ratcliffe, an eminent mountain ecologist. Its members are listed in Table 3.

Heather, also called ling, is the most familiar species and one which occurs frequently on lower ground. Here, however, the harsh conditions prevent it from growing more than about 23 centimetres (9 inches) high. Bilberry, another member of the heath family, grows nearby. Unlike the heather, it is deciduous and sheds its leaves in the autumn. Crowberry, which grows prostrate on the slope, is quite similar in appearance to the heaths but belongs to a different family. It produces

---

Table 3
A high-level plant community on Bengower.

Flowering plants	Lichens	Mosses	Liverworts
Heather	*Cladonia arbuscula*	*Breutelia chrysocoma*	*Adelanthus unciformis*
Bilberry	*Cladonia uncialis*	*Dicranum majus*	*Anastrepta orcadensis*
Crowberry		*Dicranum scoparium*	*Bazzania pearsonii*
Wavy hair-grass		*Hylocomium splendens*	*Bazzania tricrenata*
Velvet bent		*Hypnum cupressiforme*	*Diplophyllum albicans*
Great wood-rush		*Racomitrium lanuginosum*	*Herbertus aduncus*
		Sphagnum capillifolium	*Mylia taylori*
		Sphagnum plumulosum	*Mastigophora woodsii*
		Sphagnum tenellum	*Plagiochila spinulosa*
			Pleurozia purpurea
			Scapania gracilis
			Scapania ornithopodioides

---

small black berries but spreads most effectively by vegetative means, its shoots putting down roots wherever they touch the soil.

Wavy hair-grass, with its hair-like leaves, is frequent in the mountains of Connemara but generally uncommon elsewhere. Typical of cold climates, it is indicative of acid and unproductive soils and produces a long-lasting humus which inhibits further plant growth. It is tolerant of low light intensities and thus well suited to the cloudy conditions in the mountains. Velvet bent (also known as brown bent-grass) is a low-growing grass which, like the wavy hair-grass, is virtually restricted to acidic, infertile, peaty soils. However, it is more widespread and considerably more common in the lowlands where it takes benefits form human activities such as turf cutting, enabling it to colonise newly exposed peat.

Tormentil brings a dash of colour to the community with its bright yellow petals. It is a flower so common in Connemara that further comment might seem superfluous. However, its adaptability to such a wide range of soil and climatic conditions is as noteworthy as the specialisation we find in many other plants

The great wood-rush, with its long, sturdy leaves and tiny brown flowers, is as much at home on the mountains as in its more familiar woodland habitat. In both habitats it grows in wet conditions where nitrogen is available and where grazing sheep and cattle cannot reach it.

Beneath the sheltering canopy

The flowering plants are the most obvious members of the community. But beneath the sheltering canopy of heather and crowberry there is another world, a dark, damp world populated by diminutive lichens, liverworts and mosses - simple plants, but outnumbering the higher forms by four to one in these extreme conditions. Several represent southern and oceanic outliers of arctic-alpine tundra habitats while some have patchy but worldwide distributions.

The two lichens in this community are shrubby in form. *Cladonia arbuscula* (*C. sylvatica* in older texts; *arbuscula* meaning 'little tree' and *sylvatica* 'woody' so both names refer to the same characteristics) is yellowish-grey, with robust stems which curve over in one direction. It forms thick cushions on the ground and is common throughout Connemara. *Cladonia uncialis* is greener, strongly branched and widespread on acid soils and on rocks.

Amongst the mosses there is the distinctive golden-green *Breutelia chrysocoma* with its widely spreading leaves which are narrowly triangular and taper to a sharp point. It is common in the uplands of Ireland and Britain but rare outside western Europe. The *Dicranum* species are green and tufty in appearance. They are also common in woodlands. *Racomitrium lanuginosum* (woolly hair-moss) is the characteristic, greenish-grey moss of the mountain summits, where it can form extensive carpets amongst the rocks.

The liverworts are the least conspicuous members of this high-level community but numerically the most common. They are also represented by more mountain and arctic-alpine species than any of the other groups. Many favour north- to east-facing slopes. The species listed in Table 3 are all regular members of a distinctive liverwort community which is characteristic of the hills of western Ireland and north-west Scotland. Only *Diplophyllum albicans, Pleurozia purpurea* and *Scapania gracilis* occur in any abundance on lower ground.

Mastigophora woodsii and *Bazzania pearsonii* are strongly associated with coastal mountains while *Anastrepta orcadensis, Herbertus aduncus* and *Scapania ornithopodioides,* having a similarly extreme western distribution, also occur at a few stations farther inland.

The speciality of the area, however, is *Adelanthus unciformis*, a leafy liverwort which was first found in Ireland in 1903, on Achill Island. At first it was considered to be a new species, *Adelanthus dugortiensis*, but later it was reclassified because of its similarity to an existing species, *A. unciformis,*

Liverworts living in damp shade beside a mountain stream.

LICHENS, MOSSES AND LIVERWORTS

Lichens, mosses and liverworts are some of the simpler and most ancient members of the plant kingdom, having evolved much earlier than the more familiar flowering plants. They do not produce flowers or seeds but reproduce by means of spores and a variety of vegetative methods. They do not have roots and must absorb their mineral nutrients through their leaves directly from the rain, or from the water or damp environment in which they live. They are all small and no more than a few centimetres high. There are now some splendid photographic guides to lichens, mosses and liverworts, but their identification to species level is generally difficult and really work for specialists.

A lichen is an association of a fungus and an alga or a cyanobacterium (formerly known as a blue-green alga). Basically, the fungus provides the protective structure in which the alga or cyanobacterium can live and the latter supplies the food which the fungus cannot manufacture itself. This relationship, which benefits both partners, is described as symbiotic. It is thought that the fungus cannot live independently of its partner, but that the latter can be free-living. For this reason, a lichen takes the name of the fungal partner. Lichens are extremely slow growing and can live for 100 years or more. Lichens may be encrusting

Lichens encrusting a Connemara fence post.

(crustose) - forming smooth patterns on rocks and tree bark -, leafy (foliose) or even shrubby (fruticose), according to the species. They can be greyish, grey-green, yellow or dark in colour.

Mosses differ from lichens in that they form bright to dark green and sometimes red or yellow cushions of distinctly leafy stems. They can manufacture their own food with the aid of the green pigment, chlorophyll but, like liverworts and lichens, they have no internal vessels (vascular system) to conduct water and food through their tissues, as do higher plants.

Liverworts are generally green, with or without distinct 'leaves' and 'stems' (terms which should, technically, be reserved for more advanced plants). They can be differentiated as lobed or leafy. Liverworts grow on damp surfaces or in water, often where there is heavy shade and are therefore generally less conspicuous than mosses.

Together, mosses and liverworts are known as bryophytes.

which lives in the southern hemisphere and on the Ruwenzori mountain range just north of the Equator in Africa. Its only other station in Ireland is in Donegal where it was found in 1962. How such a southern species arrived here remains a mystery.

This physically undistinguished plant community is, as we have seen, not without its points of interest which could undoubtedly be increased with further study. In fact, as a reference point for the effects of climatic warming, it is essential that it should be monitored over the coming years.

As we noted earlier, the quartzite rocks of the Bens and the Maumturks are particularly infertile. But where the richer, calcareous schists rise to the summit of Muckanaght, more species can thrive, even in the harsh climatic conditions. Several bryophytes which are rare or very local on a national scale grow on this mountain, as do a number of uncommon arctic-alpine flowers, which we will come to a little later. On shaded ledges on the north side there are uncommon mosses like *Orthothecium intricatum* and a variety of *Ditrichium zonatum*, which was discovered in Ireland only in 1968. This is endemic to Ireland and Britain - it occurs nowhere else.

Several notable leafy liverworts also occur on Muckanaght. Of these the reddish-brown *Cephaloziella pearsonii* is one of a group of species with a distribution restricted to the Atlantic fringe of Europe and the highest summits of the Appalachian Mountains in the United States. *Plagiochila tridenticulata*, which has a similar world range, grows nearby, as does *Eremonotus myriocarpus*, which has a similar western distribution in Ireland and Britain. Another small, bluish-grey liverwort, *Anthelia juratzkana*, lives at its southern limit on Muckanaght, its only other Irish station being in Donegal.

The ultrabasic rocks of Doughruagh, above Kylemore Abbey, are also the home of some uncommon bryophytes, including the liverwort *Herbertus aduncus* and the mosses *Oxystegus hibernicus* and *Campylopus setifolius*. *Oxystegus* occurs only in western Ireland and western Scotland while *Campylopus* grows in Spain as well as in Ireland and Britain.

Forgotten ferns

Let us return now to the summit crags of Muckanaght to see some of the uncommon ferns and flowers which grow in the plant community there. Our task has been made a lot easier by Dr Cilian Roden, who has made a special study of mountain plants in Connemara and south Mayo. The mainly arctic-alpine plants that he recorded on Muckanaght are listed in Table 4. This is by far the largest number of such species found on a single mountain in Connemara and the impressive concentration is considered to be related to the relatively high lime content of the schists there. However, contrary to earlier beliefs, many of these species also occur on other mountains. In particular, much the same community occurs on the northern and western slopes of the Sheeffry Hills in south Mayo, just to the north of our area. This is surprising, as the lime content of the Ordovician shales and slates of these mountains is less than that of the Muckanaght schists.

The alpine-clubmoss, although common on Benbreen, some of the Maumturks and several south Mayo mountains, is rare elsewhere, being restricted to the mountains in the northern half of the country, including Wicklow. This clubmoss belongs to an ancient group of plants that superficially resemble mosses but are actually more closely allied to ferns, having a vascular system to transport water and minerals through their tissues. It grows prostrate, with slightly flattened stems creeping over ground to a height of 30-50 centimetres (12-20 inches), the branches forking to give a fan-like, flat-topped appearance.

Ferns are overlooked by most naturalists only a little less frequently than lichens, mosses and liverworts. They have a certain uniformity of appearance rendering them somewhat monotonous to the non-enthusiast and difficult to identify. However, a little extra effort could greatly enhance our enjoyment and knowledge of the Connemara ferns. On the high tops there are four arctic-alpine species worthy of note. The green spleenwort is a fairly small and delicate fern, somewhat similar to the common and widespread maidenhair spleenwort, but distinguishable by its green stalk and lack of a black stripe on the rootstock scales. It favours lime-rich scree crevices and cliffs. It grows on the north face of Muckanaght, on Maumturkmore and Benwee, at the northern end of the Maumturks, on Benbeg in Joyce's Country, on the ancient limestones of Letterbreckaun in the Maumturks and Bengower in the Bens, and on the marble formations of Lissoughter. It is a truly arctic-alpine fern, usually occurring only above about 300 metres (1,000 feet).

The transient moonwort.

Brittle bladder-fern, a delicate, tufted species, has a somewhat similar distribution, but has not been found on Benbeg. It also prefers lime-rich habitats and is, in fact, more common on the limestone of the Burren, in Co. Clare. Like the green spleenwort, it requires shelter and high humidity and the two often grow close together.

Holly fern is a more robust species, with hard, prickly fronds. It is another true arctic-alpine species that is very rare in Connemara, occurring only on Muckanaght, Benbrack, Benwee and Benbeg. It grows only sparingly elsewhere in the extreme west of Ireland and in Britain it is restricted mainly to the central and north-western Scottish Highlands.

Finally, the beech fern is a delicate, distinctly triangular species with fronds the colour of beech leaves in spring and autumn. It is, perhaps, the odd one out in this quartet, being less demanding in its habitat requirements. Elsewhere in its European range it is more common in the deep shade of damp woodlands. In Connemara occasional colonies grow on shaded cliffs on Muckanaght, Benwee, Benbeg and Lugnabrick in Joyce's Country, Doughruagh and on the south-west side of Benchoona.

Table 4
Uncommon plants recorded on Muckanaght and other mountains in Connemara.

	Muckanaght	Other Bens	Maumturks	Joyce's Country	Doughruagh	Garraun	Lissoughter
Alpine-clubmoss*	x	x					
Green spleenwort	x	x	x	x			x
Brittle bladder-fern	x	x	x	x		x	
Holly fern	x		x	x			
Beech fern	x		x	x	x	x	
Alpine meadow-rue	x	x	x	x	x	x	
Welsh poppy	x						
Starry saxifrage	x	x	x	x		x	
Irish saxifrage	x						
Purple saxifrage	x	x	x				x
Roseroot	x	x	x	x	x	x	x
Alpine saw-wort	x	x			x		
Hawkweed	x	x	x	x	x	x	x
Cowberry			x	x			
Bearberry*	x	x					
Thrift (sea pink)	x	x					
Sea plantain	x	x	x	x	x		
Mountain sorrel	x	x	x		x		
Dwarf willow*	x		x	x	x		
Lesser twayblade		x	x				
Stiff sedge*	x		x				
Juniper	x		x		x		

*Species rarely found below an altitude of 600 metres (2,000 feet)

In addition to these specialities, other species found on the mountains include the fir clubmoss, the lesser clubmoss, Wilson's filmy-fern, the finely-dissected parsley fern (of which only one plant has been reported in the last twenty years), the hard shield-fern, the mountain or lemon-scented fern and the often transient moonwort, with its half-moon shaped leaves.

Flowers of the mountains

We have spent some time looking at the lichens, mosses, liverworts and ferns of the mountain tops because, although they receive scant attention from naturalists, they are significant members of this simple but little known plant community. The uncommon flowering plants, on the other hand, have a higher public profile and regularly feature in accounts of Connemara's natural history. It is to these attractive arctic-alpine plants that we will now turn our attention, basing our survey initially on the species which occur on Muckanaght (Table 4).

The alpine meadow-rue is the smallest of the meadow-rues, being short, unbranched and delicate. Its tiny flowers are pale purple with violet stamens and contrasting yellow anthers. Like most arctic-alpine plants, it is a perennial with a rhizome (an underground stem that functions as a food storage organ enabling it to survive the long mountain-top winter). It is abundant on Muckanaght, Doughruagh, Benchoona and Benwee, where it grows on damp scree, cliff ledges and stream-sides, but more local elsewhere, and avoids both quartzite and basic rocks.

The starry saxifrage is a small, slightly hairy plant with a leafless stem and a rosette of toothed leaves at its base. It has white flowers with conspicuous red anthers and turned-down sepals; it grows on damp rocks and by mountain streams. A viviparous form occurs in Gleninagh and probably elsewhere in the Bens. This produces leafy buds in place of some of its flowers - a reproductive adaptation to harsh climatic conditions where successful seed production might not be possible. The Irish saxifrage is a much rarer species in Connemara, being confined to the north face of Muckanaght. It is more common on the limestone pavement of the Aran Islands and the western Burren, but also occurs sparingly from Donegal to the Galtees. Outside Ireland it has been recorded at one site in Wales, very locally in central Europe, but widely in Iceland which is actually its world headquarters.

The third arctic-alpine species of this family is the purple saxifrage, a low, straggling, tufted plant with prostrate stems and purple flowers. It is confined to lime-rich rocks on Muckanaght and other summits in the Bens, on the Maumturks and at a surprisingly low elevation on Lissoughter, which is also its most southerly station in Ireland. It is abundant at all these locations and puts on a spectacular show when it comes into flower from late February to May. Elsewhere in Ireland it occurs only sparingly in south Mayo, Sligo, Donegal and Derry.

A closely related species, but one with a very different distribution, is St Patrick's cabbage, one of Connemara's better-known specialities. Instead of an arctic-alpine range, this saxifrage has its main centre of distribution in north-west Spain and the mountains of northern Portugal. In technical terms it is an Hiberno-Cantabrian species, as is Mackay's heath, one of Connemara's blanket bog species. St Patrick's cabbage has a wider distribution in Connemara than the mountain saxifrages. It can be found on most cliffs in the northern and eastern part of the region. It is less common to the south and west but occurs near Cashel, Screeb and on the Galway Granite hills near Lough Formoyle, Lettercraffroe Lough and amongst boulders beside the upper reaches of the Owenboliska River, north of Spiddle.

There are also several colonies of a natural hybrid between St Patrick's cabbage and kidney saxifrage. The former has spoon-shaped and the latter kidney-shaped leaves while the hybrid has leaves intermediate in shape. Its existence in the region is quite surprising because no pure kidney saxifrage plants remain in Connemara, although they presumably occurred here in the not too distant past. The only kidney saxifrages remaining in the country are confined to Cork and Kerry.

Contrary to popular belief, Londonpride, the popular garden plant, is not St Patrick's cabbage but a vigorous hybrid resulting from cross-breeding between it and the Pyrenean saxifrage, a native of the west and central Pyrenees.

In crevices on high-level wet cliffs, one of the commonest species is roseroot, a member of the stonecrop family. It has grey-green succulent leaves and dull yellow, flat-topped flower heads. It is said to have rose-scented roots, hence its name. It occurs fairly frequently on the Bens and Maumturks and occasionally on the north faces of Doughruagh and Benchoona and the north-

Roseroot - an arctic-alpine plant of mountain and coastal cliffs.

facing cliffs of Lugnabrick and Benbeg in Joyce's Country. Roseroot avoids the Connemara limestone and serpentine but, surprisingly, grows on limestone pavement on Inishmore, the largest of the Aran Islands. Unlike most of the other plants we will meet, it has male and female flowers on separate plants, rather than flowers with both stamens (male) and carpels (female) on a single plant. This seems to be characteristic of the most successful and abundant species in the far north and an adaptation which has, for several complex genetic reasons, enabled them to colonise a wide variety of arctic habitats. In the Icelandic dwarf willow population, which also exhibits this characteristic, nearly 60 per cent of the plants are females, rather than 50 per cent as one would expect. This may be a further adaptation to survival in rigorous conditions. Certainly, it would seem that arctic-alpine plants are not just passive survivors in cold climates. They are a highly specialised group of plants of great antiquity which have evolved a variety of mechanisms to aid their long-term survival. It would be interesting to find out whether roseroot and dwarf willow in the west of Ireland have uneven sex ratios, or whether this characteristic has been lost in the less harsh conditions of the Connemara mountains.

The dwarf willow is common among rocks on the exposed summits of the Bens, the northern Maumturks, Doughruagh, Benchoona and Benbeg, but less frequent on Garraun. It is a small

Dwarf willow - a plant of mountain cliffs and summits.

shrub with prostrate, often herbaceous twigs which are seldom over 7 centimetres (3 inches) long. These arise from a creeping, woody underground rhizome. Its catkins are very small, with few flowers and are produced in June. It is rare elsewhere in Ireland and restricted to the highest mountains.

The alpine saw-wort is a type of thistle. A short, stout, hairy perennial with long, pointed, finely-toothed leaves and purple flowers, it only grows above about 300 metres (1,000 feet) on Muckanaght and Bengower, and in a small colony on Doughruagh which does not appear to flower. Alpine saw-wort is most abundant in the northern corries of the Sheeffry Hills, where it grows on dry ledges and scree. In northern Scotland it also grows on maritime cliffs, a habitat which is also occupied in Ireland by thrift or sea pink.

Of all the mountain flowers growing in Connemara, thrift will be the most familiar to the naturalist; not because it is seen on the mountains very often, but because of its common occurrence on the coast, where it grows down to the edge of the sea. This delightful flower, which produces deep, spongy cushions of 'sea turf', is a familiar sight along coastal and inland cliffs, on seaside grassland and in saltmarshes. Each compact flower head is a cluster of up to twenty individual pink (or, occasionally, white) flowers. In the Connemara mountains thrift occurs on Muckanaght, Benbaun, Bengower, Benlettery, Benbreen, Bencollaghduff and Derryclare, while in the Maumturks it has been seen on Knocknahillion and in the northern corrie of the summit to the south of Maumeen.

Thrift is primarily a coastal plant and it only ascends the mountains close to the west coast where the prevailing salt-laden winds can reach. It can adapt to a range of moisture and grazing conditions by modifying the form of its rosette of leaves. In dry conditions, or where there is heavy grazing, it masses its leaves in a dense cushion which minimises the evaporation of water from its leaf surfaces and reduces the scope for grazing. In damper conditions, free from grazing, it adopts a more diffuse habit with longer and more loosely arranged leaves,

Sea plantain is another plant which is found both on the coast and on the western mountains. Its presence in such contrasting habitats is difficult to explain. It may have something to do with the post-glacial spread of woodland. This forced the then widespread species to retreat into two different habitats, both of which satisfy an important requirement, lack of shade. The sea plantain, unlike the more familiar garden varieties, has long, narrow, fleshy leaves. But, like its close relations, it is most unimpressive in bloom, its brownish-pink flowers brightened only marginally by the projecting yellow anthers. In Connemara sea plantain grows on dry and wet rocks on Muckanaght, Bengower, Benwee, Maumturkmore, Benbeg, Garraun, Doughruagh and on the summit of Errisbeg.

Bearberry, a member of the heath family, is a low-growing evergreen shrub with stout, woody, trailing stems. It produces clusters of small pink flowers which give rise to scarlet berries. The Bens are its only mountain refuge in Connemara, where it is common above 400 metres (1,320 feet) on Derryclare, growing with juniper and crowberry, on Muckanaght, Knockbrack, and Diamond Hill in the Connemara National Park. Comparing its current distribution with that of the nineteenth century, it appears that it may be diminishing. It has not been ascertained why this should be. Elsewhere, it occurs on heaths, moors and rocky places near the coast from Antrim to Clare where, rather surprisingly, it has its largest Irish concentration in the Burren. Another member of the heath family, crowberry, is very rare and only a few plants occur high up on the hills to the north and south of Lough Nafooey.

Mountain sorrel is a small member of the dock family with kidney-shaped leaves and green flowers which produce small fruits surrounded by a reddish, membranous wing. It occurs on cliff ledges on the north face of Muckanaght, on the north-west face of Bengower and at about 360 metres (1,200 feet) on Doughruagh. This is certainly one of Ireland's rarer plants, occurring as it does at only a handful of sites in the mountains of Kerry, Connemara, Mayo, Sligo, Donegal and Tipperary. In Britain it is confined to the Highlands of Scotland, the Lake District and the mountains of north Wales.

An even more tenuous link with Wales is the Welsh poppy, which may or may not still inhabit its only Connemara station on the north face of Muckanaght. It was not found by Dr Roden in the early 1980s but had been reported there during the previous twenty years. This poppy, with its large (6-7.5 centimetres, 2-3 inches across), bright yellow flowers, would look quite incongruous on the smooth slopes of Muckanaght in June and July. The same must surely be true in the mountains of north Wales where it is a recognised member of the arctic-alpine community. In south Wales, however, it grows in the cool shade of rich lowland woodlands. It is a rare species internationally, growing naturally only in northern Spain and western France. However, it is a popular cultivated plant and many records in lowland Ireland must be of garden escapes. In 1993 it was found beside the ruins of an old cottage in the hills south of Oughterard.

Yellow flowers which the naturalist is more likely to encounter on the mountains, are hawkweeds. They occur on most of the mountains but generally appear to avoid the pure limestone and serpentine outcrops. These dandelion-like plants are exceptionally variable and very difficult to name because they have developed into a very large number of micro-species - recognisable populations of plants that have developed from a single parent and are all, therefore, genetically similar.

Juniper at 500 metres (1600 feet) on Derryclare.

A less obtrusive member of the arctic-alpine flora is the stiff sedge, a small plant with a creeping stem and stiff, sharply three-sided, down-curved leaves. Its flowers, like those of all the sedges, are rather plain, the males in one spike above two or three spikes of female flowers. It occurs on the summits and higher ledges of the Bens and on the Maumturks, where it lives in similar habitats to the dwarf willow but is somewhat rarer. It occurs on other mountain ranges in Ireland but is generally rare, being here at the southern edge of its circumpolar range.

Juniper is the only conifer growing at high levels in Connemara. It is scattered throughout the Bens and the Maumturks and on Doughruagh, and is particularly common on Derryclare, Benbreen, Knockbrack and Diamond Hill. Juniper grows in a prostrate form, hugging the rocks in sheltered cracks and crevices. The mountain juniper, which is generally confined to acid rocks, is said to be slightly different from the lowland plant and has been distinguished as a sub-species *Juniperus communis alpina* (alpine). The lowland plants have the scientific name *Juniperus communis communis* (common) and are usually found on limestone. Juniper is a shrub with flaking red-brown bark, greyish-green needle-like leaves and green flowers which, in the female, give rise to green berry-like seed-bearing cones which turn blue-black in their second year. It was one of the first plants to colonise Ireland after the Ice Age, but whether the plants growing on the Connemara mountains are relics of that time is not clear.

The tiny green lesser twayblade grows amongst moss at the base of heather stems at altitudes of up to 490 metres (1,600 feet) on several of the western Bens, including Diamond Hill, and at lower levels on the Maumturks and an adjacent hill to the east. It is a northern plant, found occasionally in the northern half of Ireland, in the British uplands, in Scandinavia and Iceland, and sparingly in continental Europe. Being inconspicuous, it is likely that this orchid, which flowers from June to August, has been overlooked in the past. So we should keep an eye out for it in the future.

In addition to the strictly high-level plants just described, there are several others which occur in summit cliff communities. But as these occur commonly on lower ground, they will not be discussed in detail here. This group includes marsh hawk's-beard, wild angelica, meadowsweet, cuckoo flower, harebell, mountain everlasting, yellow-rattle, primrose, smooth lady's-mantle, intermediate lady's-mantle, hairy lady's-mantle, opposite-leaved golden saxifrage, stone bramble, northern bedstraw, early-purple orchid, eyebright, water avens, hairy rock-cress and glaucous sedge.

In conclusion, the flora of the Connemara mountains is sufficiently widespread to permit the detection of habitat preferences in several species. The main factor influencing species distribution appears to be rock type. The arctic-alpine species show a strong preference for lime-rich mica-schists and the limestone and serpentine outcrops; they are uncommon on the quartzite. Height is also an important factor. Few of the mountain species occur below 400 metres (1,300 feet) and a small group (marked * in Table 4) are rarely found below 600 metres (2,000 feet).

It is encouraging to note the stability of the mountain flora which seems to have changed little in species composition since the first botanists, H.C. Hart and N. Colgan, reported on them in 1883 and 1900 respectively. However, there is little doubt that intensive grazing has restricted the mountain plants to the less accessible cliffs and crags, a trend which is unfortunately not likely to be reversed in the forseeable future except, perhaps, in the Connemara National Park. On the other hand, increased erosion on the Maumturks ridge, presumably caused by walker pressure, has, perhaps surpringly, created new habitat for the alpine clubmoss, which has increased in abundance in recent years. Clearly, there is still much to be learned about our mountain-top plant communities. In addition to collecting further basic information on species distributions it will be necessary to find out how each species responds to climatic and land-use changes and how human intervention can, if necessary, ensure that these fascinating communities survive into the twenty second century.

On the way down

Leaving behind the stark and windswept summits, we must carefully descend the steep and rocky slopes characteristic of the Connemara mountains. Easily dislodged and slippery boulders are everywhere, awaiting the careless foot. But the ground improves as we descend onto shallow peat with sedges, grasses and patches of stunted heather. Sheltered gullies and streamsides provide cover and sustenance for a greater variety of plants. Stunted rowan trees begin to appear. So do sheep. Now we can be certain that we have left behind any semblance of 'natural' vegetation and have moved into a plant community totally controlled by a human activity - sheep farming. Occasional crags and gullies, inaccessible to sheep, can harbour a greater variety of plants, including specialities such as St Patrick's cabbage. But generally, our botanical diet, like that of the sheep, will be grasses and rushes.

On the drier slopes, where the soils are shallow peaty podsols and the grazing is heavy, mat-grass is the most common species. This is a fine-leaved, densely tufted perennial which reaches only 10-30 centimetres (4-12 inches) in height. It is well adapted to living in conditions of considerable infertility and heavy trampling. However, its foliage is low in calcium and generally unpalatable to sheep, although they will eat it in winter when other food is scarce. If winter

Common bird's-foot-trefoil.

grazing is reduced, mat-grass is likely to spread and replace more palatable species. Other plants which grow in association with mat-grass include grasses such as common bent, sheep's-fescue and heath rush. In areas fenced off from grazing heather returns and common bird's-foot-trefoil becomes prominent in the community.

On lime-rich soils, in the Maumturks, for example, plant communities are more diverse. Heather tends to be quite common and species such as ribwort plantain, selfheal and cat's-ear are important members of the community. Mountain avens occurs at its only station in Connemara on magnesium-rich schists on Lissoughter at a height of about 300 metres (1,000 feet).

Before we leave the mountains, mention should be made of the wet flushes which punctuate the hillsides, usually with bright green, moss-rich communities. Many a walker, not recognising the danger, has plunged into one of these deceptively benign 'sponges' and spent the rest of the day cursing this misfortune. Many of the flushes surround emerging springs which bring mineral-rich water from the eroding upper slopes. Their vegetation is quite variable and depends on the slope, aspect and drainage. They harbour peat mosses and mosses such as *Campyllium stellatum*, *Fissidens adianthoides* and *Bryum pseudotriquetrum*, liverworts and sometimes mountain plants which normally grow only at higher altitudes. Unfortunately, it is not possible to go beyond such a general statement because Connemara mountain flushes appear to have received little attention, although they undoubtedly offer scope for study, particularly by the bryophyte enthusiast.

BRACKEN AND GRAZING

Bracken lives on lime-free, acid mineral soils which are well drained and fairly dry. It is characteristic of undergrazed or abandoned farmland, but it also invades sheep pastures where it now causes considerable concern to hill farmers.

Bracken is a highly successful and aggressive species with a worldwide distribution. It was originally a plant of the woodland floor, where its distribution was limited by dense tree cover. However, since deforestation, it has increased its range substantially, and in recent times it has reached pest proportions in some areas. In the past there were probably more people in upland districts who put bracken to many uses and grazed more cattle on the high ground in the summer. In colder conditions, too, late spring frosts destroyed both underground stems and new shoots so the rate of spread was limited. The present very high ratio of sheep to cattle and repeated burning have harmful effects on bracken's main competitors, such as trees, shrubs and heather, and thus favour its spread. Furthermore, bracken itself prevents the regeneration of other species by producing a dense covering of dead material in autumn which is slow to decay and disappear.

Bracken shows up clearly in early autumn.

Bracken is toxic to livestock and many other animals, and its spores are said to have the potential for causing cancer in people who are regularly and heavily exposed to them. So overall, at the present time it must be viewed as a nuisance, rathern than the asset it used to be. Attempts to control bracken chemically may not be of long-term benefit. It may be more desirable, and certainly more environmentally friendly, to revert to physical control by cutting and more appropriate grazing regimes.

Large numbers of sheep, through their heavy grazing and trampling, have serious impacts on the hills. They graze vegetation down to ground levels, often exposing peat or mineral soil, which is then washed away by heavy rainfall. On some slopes they follow regular routes and this has lead to the formation of distinctive terraces. On the terrace faces, heathers tend to be common and grow in the company of a variety of flowering plants, but on the flat terrace tops they tend to be replaced by mat-grass, creeping bent and heath rush.

INTO THE LOWLANDS

From the mountain slopes our view is one of broad expanses of blanket bog, filling the valleys and stretching southwards to Galway Bay. Yet, before we reach the bogs, we must pass through a mixture of cultivated land, dry heath, scrub and rock, roads and tracks, stone walls, bridges, quarries, cuttings and the embankment of the old Galway to Clifden railway line. This miscellany of sub-habitats offers much for the enquiring botanist, but will not detain us long now.

One of the most pleasing sights in Connemara in late summer is the colourful mosaic of western gorse, heather and St Dabeoc's heath growing in low hummocks, tight up against the roadside rocks. The rich, golden-yellow gorse flowers provide a striking backdrop for the pink-purple bells of the heathers.

Western gorse is very similar in most repsects to gorse. Both have dark green, spiny leaves and typical pea-family flowers. However, western gorse forms only low bushes, flowers in late summer and is common only in Connemara and the southern and eastern upland and coastal regions of Ireland. Gorse, on the other hand, grows to several metres in height, flowers from September (at the very earliest) through to late July, and occurs throughout the country. With both species present in Connemara, we are at least guaranteed a cheering splash of yellow through the whole year.

Western gorse and heather bring a welcome dash of colour to the rocky landscape of Gorumna Island.

St Dabeoc's heath is one of Connemara's special plants. It occurs only here and in south Mayo, the next colony being near the west coast of France. Otherwise its main centre of distribution is in west and central Spain and north-west Portugal. It grows only on acid soils and never ventures onto any of the lime-rich Connemara soils or eastwards onto the limestone. It differs somewhat from the other heathers in having larger, glossy leaves, large flowers and weak straggling branches which gain support from the heather or gorse through which they usually grow. It prefers a mild oceanic climate with a high rainfall, but it is not sensitive to frost and can grow at elevations of up to 580 metres (1,900 feet) on the Bens and the Maumturks. The first published reference to St Dabeoc's heath appeared in 1699 but pollen studies now have shown that it was, like rhododendron and Mackay's heath which we will meet later, present here during the last interglacial period.

Recent introductions

Although rhododendron occurred in Ireland before the last Ice Age, it did not return naturally and was introduced by man some time in the late eighteenth century after first being introduced to Britain in 1756 from the cool mountainous areas of Lebanon and Turkey. It was planted in hedgerows, but in suitable locations spread rapidly, invading the oakwood behind Kylemore Abbey, for example, and forming such dense stands between the trees that light can hardly reach the ground. This choking growth prevents the development of young oak trees so, although the oakwood looks healthy from the outside at present, once the older trees die off there will be no young oaks to replace them. Shading by the rhododendrons also prevents the growth of other species, reduces the variety of epiphytes (plants which grow on the oak trunks) and fungi and destroys the habitat and food supplies of a range of animals. It provides few substitute habitats and, because its leaves are poisonous, it can be eaten by only a small number of invertebrate species. All in all, this large member of the heath family, so admired by visitors when it is in bloom briefly in May and June, is a major nuisance. But because it is so difficult and expensive to control, it looks as if it will remain part of the Connemara scene for a long time to come.

Fuchsia enlivens Connemara hedgerows from mid-summer through to the autumn.

Fuchsia is another well-loved roadside species with its drooping, deep purple and crimson flowers. It blooms in late summer and early autumn, bringing welcome colour to the shortening days. It, too, was introduced to Ireland for hedging. But, unlike rhododendron, fuchsia rarely reproduces here and generally stays where it was planted. It does not sucker widely and rarely, if ever, produces fruit. Therefore, the occasional naturalised bushes must have developed from detached twigs which took root. Nearly all of the fuchsia hedges in the west of Ireland are composed of a horticultural variety which apparently arose in a Scottish nursery some time before 1850, though the original species is actually a native of Chile and Argentina.

Another plant which catches the eye of many a visitor is giant-rhubarb. This large-leaved herb grows in roadside ditches, along stream-sides and on grassy banks such as we can find near the playing field on the road down to Clifden pier. It produces a rich brown, cylindrical flower head, somewhat reminiscent of a slim pineapple. Its leaves can be up to a metre (3.3 feet) in diameter or even more in garden specimens. It is not known when and how giant-rhubarb reached Ireland from its native South America, but it was first recorded by Robert Lloyd Praeger in 1939, when he found it growing plentifully in the hills near Leenaun. The seeds seem to be spread partly by sheep and partly by water and it is steadily expanding its range in Connemara, west Mayo and, to a lesser extent, other parts of western and southern Ireland.

Stone walls

Stone walls form an important element of the Connemara landscape. They are a very effective means of marking boundaries, enclosing livestock, providing shelter for crops and animals and, as often

Giant rhubarb - an eye-catching South American introduction.

as not, of identifying indirectly the underlying rock type. They are also significant plant habitats. In an interesting study carried out about twenty years ago, P.G. Holland looked at the patterns of species density on stone walls which were over 100 years old. He found an average of fourteen flower and fern species for every 10 metres (33 feet) of wall. Walls on slopes exposed to the south-west had fewer species than those facing the north-east. The greatest density of species occurred in mid-slope locations, the least on flat ground, and intermediate densities on upper and lower slopes. Stone walls in exposed coastal situations had few species and many of the old walls along the shores of Galway Bay were completely bare. Species density increased towards the east, possibly because more limestone was being used in the walls.

Holland encountered a total of 133 species on 1,650 metres (1,805 yards) of which half were restricted to fewer than one tenth of the walls and only 3 per cent were found on more than 50 per cent of the walls. He observed regional patterns in the distribution of several species. For example, sheep's-bit is a frequent but localized member of stone wall communities in areas of heath vegetation. English stonecrop and wild thyme are common along exposed coasts but rare inland, while navelwort is most common on walls leading down to Lough Corrib. Many of the plants are typical of disturbed sites, but the species composition of any wall generally reflects the neighbouring vegetation, the aspect of the wall and its degree of exposure to winds from the sea. A follow-up study on the lichens and mosses of old stone walls would be welcome!

Europe's tallest fern

There is one more species which deserves our attention - the royal fern, an impressive plant which can grow to a height of 2 metres (6.5 feet), making it Europe's tallest fern. Its central leaves are so thickly covered with spores that, as they turn golden brown, they begin to look like the flower spike of a

Royal fern - a distinctive species common only in the west of Ireland.

flowering plant. The royal fern prefers wet, peaty conditions and is common in drains at the edge of the bog and beside loughs and rivers. It thrives best where there is some shelter and freedom from grazing by livestock. The rhizomes from which new plants sprout each year can be very large (over 2 metres, 6.5 feet in diameter in exceptional cases) indicating that it ranks amongst the longest-lived of our native ferns. Royal fern is most common in the west, where it is of particular interest to visitors from the Continent where it is now very scarce.

THE BLANKET BOGS

To dig deep into a blanket bog is to cut through time, to expose the history of the landscape, to link the present with the past. But to walk quietly, alone, across a pristine bog on a clear summer morning is a timeless, tranquil experience. The spongy peat slows your progress to the pace of the bog and the humid air eases away the tumult of the outside world. Now you can be at one with the heather, the lichen-capped hummocks, the dark, ominous bog pools and the distant, bubbling trill of the curlew; this is the world of the bog.

The Connemara blanket bogs stretch southwards from the foot of the Twelve Bens and the Maumturks to the north shore of Galway Bay and westwards from Barna to Mannin Bay. There is a northward extension from Clifden towards Letterfrack and Cleggan, another through the Inagh Valley to Killary Harbour and an isolated outlier in the Maum Valley. They mainly occupy the low ground, but extend over the granite hills, rising to more than 300 metres (1,000 feet) in places. The specialist can detect differences between the plant life on the lowland blanket bogs and the mountain blanket bogs into which they merge at about 150 metres (500 feet). But for our purposes, we will consider them as a single habitat.

The blanket bogs, as we saw in Chapter 1, are composed of compacted layers of waterlogged peat and a surface layer of living vegetation. The peat consists of plant and, to a lesser extent, animal remains that have accumulated over thousands of years. Blanket bogs survive only where the rainfall exceeds 1,200 millimetres (47 inches) and occurs on well over 200 days per year. In these circumstances the rainfall, for most of the year, exceeds the evaporation of water from the bog surface and from the plants, with the result that the bog remains waterlogged throughout most of its depth. The waterlogging prevents the decomposition of the plant remains and causes considerable stress to the plants which live on it by excluding air from the peat and by generating very acid conditions. Furthermore, the peat is very deficient in plant nutrients which are generally supplied only by the rain. Only if there is high ground nearby will more fertile water flow into the margins of a blanket bog and enrich the conditions for plant life.

To counteract these extreme conditions bog plants, though widely different in their forms and origins, have developed a great variety of adaptations which enable them to survive, albeit often in stunted and less robust forms than in richer habitats. Some have become carnivorous and obtain

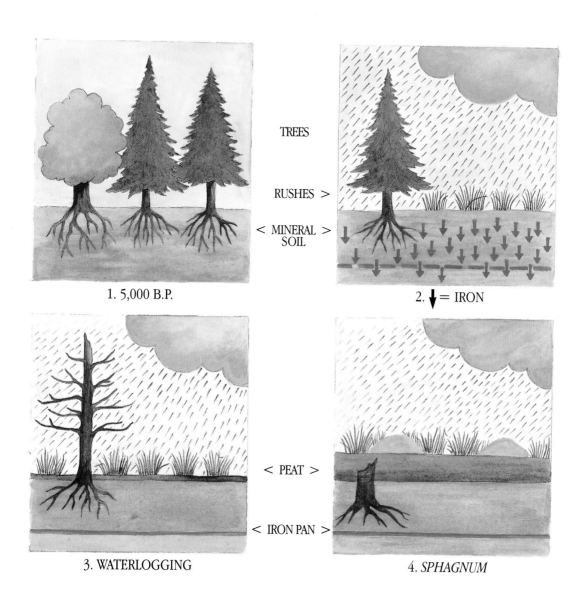

TREES

RUSHES >

< MINERAL >
SOIL

1. 5,000 B.P.

2. ↓ = IRON

< PEAT >

< IRON PAN >

3. WATERLOGGING

4. *SPHAGNUM*

Figure 8: Blanket bog development.

part of their food from insects and other small animals which they trap in a variety of ways. Others have developed symbiotic relationships with micro-organisms in the peat. Many are very economical in their use of water and nutrients; some have tiny leaves which reduce water loss through transpiration (the evaporation of water from the leaf surface after it has carried nutrients up through the plant from its roots), while others withdraw food from their leaves in autumn and store it in underground bulbils until growth starts again the following spring. The roots of some bog plants can function in the absence of oxygen (they are anaerobic) by performing special metabolic reactions while others develop tissue called aerenchyma - an open meshwork of living cells separated by a complex of oxygen-rich air spaces.

Blanket bog at Recess in July.

While many plants have to work hard to live with the acidity of the bog, the peat mosses (*Sphagnum* species) actually increase the acidity of their own surroundings and, in doing so, of course make them less habitable for other species. They do this by exchanging the hydrogen in their tissue fluid for minerals in the rain, which is their only source of nutrients. The hydrogen, when released into the surrounding water, then adds to its acidity unless there are any basic (alkaline) substances such as bicarbonate to neutralize it.

As we will see shortly, the peat mosses, the evergreen dwarf shrubs and the tussock-forming grasses, sedges and rushes are the plants which have been most successful in coming to terms with the extremes of life in the bog. That is not to say that other groups, such as the more common flowering plants and the occasional tree species, have not had some success in colonising the blanket bog. They have, but even a brief walk across a summer bog will indicate how meagre that success has been.

But success is a relative thing. And if we measure the weight of different types of plants in a bog at the height of the growing season in the middle of the summer, we will find that the algae and bryophytes make up over one third of this weight and that the non-woody flowering plants, excluding the grasses, sedges and rushes, contribute only a fraction of 1 per cent. Even the grasses, sedges and rushes contribute only slightly more than this to the above-ground weight of plant material, although the weight of their roots and swollen stems below ground make up nearly one third of the total. All this suggests that bogs are very unproductive habitats. This is confirmed by the fact that the vegetation on 1 square metre will produce only about 300 grammes (11 ounces) of new material above ground each year compared with the 1,100 grammes (2.5 pounds) produced each year by meadow communities growing on reclaimed peat. But of course it should be remembered that the greater productivity on the reclaimed peat can be achieved only with considerable effort and expenditure.

From a distance, a bog surface looks fairly uniform and uninteresting. But if we look closer we will find that it is really a rich mosaic of hummocks and hollows, sedge lawns, flushes and bog pools. In some places the peat may be reasonably firm, in others it may be totally waterlogged and quaking. The hummocks may be composed of peat mosses topped by lichens or heather, while the wetter hollows and flushes will harbour a variety of mosses and liverworts. Sedges can form extensive lawns while some of the taller rushes grow into distinctive tussocks. The bog pools are dark and relatively infertile, but they can contain interesting communities of algae as well as flowering plants such as the bogbean. So the bog community is richer than might at first be imagined, and its inhabitants are well worth looking at in some detail.

Plants of the blanket bog

Black bog-rush is a common member of the blanket bog community and easily recognised by its blackish-brown spikelets, each with one to four flowers. It grows up to about 60 centimetres (2 feet) in height on permanently waterlogged peat. Its presence on the acid peats of the west of Ireland is a source of amazement to botanists from the Continent, who know it only as a plant of alkaline fens. And, indeed, it also occurs in fens in Ireland. There is no consensus on why it should be present on blanket peats. One suggestion is that minerals derived from sea spray carried on westerly winds might facilitate its growth. Another, more recent, idea invokes the species' vulnerability to aluminium as an explanation for its unusual distribution. In the base-poor mires in the drier east of Britain, accumulation of aluminium in the soil excludes the bog-rush, but in the very wet climate of the west of Ireland, aluminium is leached from the soil, allowing the plant to grow in spite of the peat's acidity. There are also conflicting views about why the black bog-rush is so abundant on west of Ireland bogs. On the one hand, it has been suggested that the low levels of grazing and the low incidence of fire have allowed it to survive on the bog. However, the opposite has also been argued quite convincingly. Grazing and fire, which have been features of land-use in Connemara for several thousand years, lead to compacting of the bog surface and to the creation of areas of bare, waterlogged peat suitable for black bog-rush. Its relative scarcity on islands where grazing and fire have been absent or minimal seems to support the latter argument.

There is nothing controversial about purple moor-grass, except, perhaps, its replacement of

Purple moor-grass in winter.

heather where burning has been excessive. The species is so common and widespread on the bogs and peat-covered lower hills of south Connemara as to make it one of the most striking features of the landscape, particularly in the autumn when it turns a rich, reddish brown. Purple moor-grass often grows in large tussocks up to a metre (3 feet) across and sometimes as high. It prefers to live on damp peat but can tolerate wet conditions for at least part of the year, although it cannot survive waterlogging, possibly because of its deep root system, which can penetrate down to at least 80 centimetres (32 inches) - a depth at which waterlogging is likely to be quite frequent. In areas with a relatively sharp transition between wetland and dryland, purple moor-grass often occupies the transition zone. It has considerable food value for livestock, having a higher nutrient content than many other bog plants, but at the same time is extremely sensitive to grazing and can disappear quickly if regularly and heavily grazed. However, it is not adversely affected by fire and can survive regular burning. Another feature which distinguishes purple moor-grass from its associates is that it can tolerate, or perhaps requires, a high iron supply and, as a result, can be found in iron-rich flushes which are characterised by deposits of red-brown ferric-iron deposits.

Two species which regularly grow in association with purple moor-grass are deergrass and the attractive and aromatic bog-myrtle. Deergrass (like cottongrass) is actually a member of the sedge family and at one time it was called deer-sedge. Why it is now officially called deergrass remains one of botany's little mysteries. Deergrass is a relatively low (15-30 centimetres, 6-12 inches), tufted sedge which forms conspicuous tussocks. It is widespread and abundant throughout Connemara and, like purple moor-grass, can tolerate repeated burning. It is moderately valuable as winter food for sheep, as it was, perhaps, for red deer herds when they once roamed the hills and valleys of Connemara.

Bog-myrtle is one of the real delights of the bog and is abundant in Connemara. In the past it was also known as sweet gale, in deference to its sweet, resinous fragrance, which kept fleas away and gave flavour to ale or beer before hops became popular. Today, bog-myrtle mead can be pleasing to the palate and gentle on the head. It is one of the few woody shrubs to grow on the blanket bog where the orange male and shorter, reddish female catkins add welcome colour. Male and female catkins usually occur on different plants but a plant may change sex from year to year. It is deciduous and can range in height from 50 to 120 centimetres (20-50 inches).

Bog-myrtle is one of the few bog plants that can utilise atmospheric nitrogen, through its symbiotic relationship with bacteria which live in nodules on its roots. In this it is similar to legumes but, unlike these

Male catkins of the fragrant bog-myrtle.

plants, it can operate in quite acid conditions (pH 4.5). It can fix nitrogen at pH levels as low as 3.8, but below this the symbiotic relationship apparently ceases and the bog-myrtle fails to thrive. In addition to the difficulties of survival under very acid conditions, it is likely that the nodules may suffer oxygen deficiency in waterlogged conditions. However, this is overcome by the production of vertically growing roots which are rich in air spaces. But, if the oxygen supply to these roots is restricted, the plant's capacity to fix nitrogen is reduced.

THE pH SCALE

Acidity and alkalinity are measured on a pH scale ranging around 7, which is neutral.
Water with a pH below 7 is acid, above 7 it is alkaline.

The nodding, white, cottony heads of common cottongrass are familiar to all who pass through or by the bogs from August to late September. It is particularly abundant on areas of wet cut-over bog where it invades the newly exposed peat surfaces after they have developed a covering of algae. Hare's-tail cottongrass is also common and widespread in Connemara and can be distinguished by the fact that it produces a single flower head on each stem, compared with several heads in the common cottongrass.

Two other cottongrasses occur in Connemara, but these are rare and more difficult to identify. The broad-leaved or fen cottongrass, as its latter name suggests, grows where the water supply is base-rich and is, as would be expected, very limited in its distribution in Connemara. There is a small colony to the west of Roundstone, one in the Connemara National Park at Letterfrack and another near Maam Cross. Not far from Oughterard, just outside our chosen eastern boundary, it grows on an area of bog adjacent to Burren-like limestone pavement. Elsewhere in Ireland and Britain it is widespread but rare.

The most significant species in this group, from a conservation point of view, is the slender cottongrass. This is so rare, not only in Connemara, but also throughout Ireland and Britain, that it has been included in the *Irish Red Data Book* on rare and endangered plants and is protected under the Flora Protection Order of 1987. Since it was first recorded in Connemara in 1966 it has been found at nineteen sites here, two in Kerry, one in Mayo and one in Westmeath. Its main centre of distribution is in central and northern Europe, where it is considered to be vulnerable - a higher category of endangerment than in Ireland, which emphasises the importance of the Connemara population.

Dr Micheline Sheehy Skeffington and her colleagues in the Botany Department at University College Galway have found that the favoured habitat of slender cottongrass is floating rafts of vegetation which develop around the edges of lakes. It seems to spread from rhizomes and rarely produces seeds. It also grows occasionally in very wet areas of bogs and fens. In coastal lakes, within 2 kilometres (1.2 miles) of the sea, it grows in rich communities that include water mint, marsh cinquefoil, common marsh-bedstraw, gipsywort and marsh willowherb. At inland lakes slender cottongrass lives in less diverse communities with great fen-sedge, pipewort, white water-lily, many-stalked spike-rush and bog pondweed. In areas of very wet quaking bog, which in many ways are similar to the lake margin habitat, the slender cottongrass is found in communities dominated by blunt-flowered rush and slender sedge.

Why should there be these different habitat preferences in a species which is so rare and sparsely distributed? One suggestion is that the decrease in water nutrient levels the further one goes from the sea influences its behaviour and distribution. On the other hand, it is also suggested that winds from the east, which carry dust containing calcium and magnesium, may

Facing page: Common cottongrass.

contribute to the survival of the slender cottongrass in Connemara. It is known, however, that it only thrives in habitats that are waterlogged for most of the year. Its survival in the long term could therefore be threatened by the natural in-filling and eventual drying out of the lakes in which it currently occurs and it will be important to keep a close watch on the slender cottongrass as land-use and climate inevitably change. The survival of any species can never be a foregone conclusion.

That lengthy digression may have seemed unnecessary for such an uncommon species in the Connemara landscape - a species which most of us will never actually see, or recognise even if we do. But, hopefully, it will have illustrated some of the problems facing conservationists who are trying to ensure the survival of rare and endangered species. First of all a species must be identified - a rather obvious point, but a significant one, bearing in mind that the slender cottongrass was not recorded until 1966. (In a world conservation context this is an extremely significant point because the majority of the world's plants and animals have not been identified and named!) Then it must be studied to determine the details of its habitat requirements, its behaviour and so on. And finally, methods must be developed, using this knowledge, to manage both the species, its habitat, and human behaviour in such a way as to ensure its long-term survival. Clearly, wildlife conservation is a very difficult task, more so with the economic and political obstacles that continually bedevil it.

From the rarest of the rare let us now return to something more common, the bog asphodel, a species that we can all see and admire throughout Connemara. This delightful flower is a member of the lily family and has long, grass-like, pointed leaves and bright yellow, star-like flowers with striking orange anthers and, later, deep orange fruits. Its colourful flowers are a clear sign that it is pollinated by insects, unlike many of the drab-flowered grasses, sedges and rushes amongst which it lives. These rely on the wind to carry their pollen from plant to plant.

Bog asphodel can tolerate quite acid conditions and tends to inhabit sites where water is moving through the peat. It is common throughout Ireland on the uplands and bogs but in Britain it is restricted mainly to the western and northern uplands whilst on the Continent it occurs only in suitable habitat along the western coastal fringe from northern Norway southwards to Portugal.

Like many scientific names, *Narthecium ossifragum* tells us more about the plant than its common epithet, bog asphodel. *Narthecium* means 'little rod', which describes the perky, upright stem quite well. *Ossifragum*, meaning 'of broken bones', is more intriguing. As often as not there is some good practical reason behind the naming of plants. In this case, it is because farmers associated the presence of bog asphodel in pastures with cattle breaking their legs. However, any direct connection between the misfortune of the cattle and this apparently innocuous little flower was for a long time rejected by 'objective' scientists who preferred to ascribe the brittle bones to a lack of minerals, and particularly calcium, in the habitat. Even the layman might have suggested that cattle walking over the bog would be at some risk of injuring themselves by sinking into the soft peat. However, recent research has vindicated the link suggested by the Latin name and it is now believed that bog asphodel contains a substance that blocks the production of vitamin D in cattle and, in so doing, causes rickets in extreme cases. The lesson here is for the naturalist (and the scientist, for that matter) not to shun the difficult and often unpronounceable scientific names but to get hold of a book that explains them. A few minutes browsing will be well rewarded with many unexpected insights.

The heath family

Heather is widespread on the drier parts of the blanket bogs but much less abundant than it used to be, having fallen victim to uncontrolled burning, over-grazing, extensive turf cutting and afforestation. It makes a welcome, but brief, reappearance when bogs are drained and fenced off for forestry, but once the canopy of young conifers closes it soon disappears again. As we have seen, its range extends from the lowlands right up to the summits of the higher mountains where dwarf plants form protective canopies for rich and interesting communities of bryophytes.

Heather is easily distinguished from the other members of the heath family which live

Heather - a widespread but declining species.

on the bogs by its tiny, tightly packed, scale-like leaves. These have a lot in common with the leaves of plants which grow in arid conditions. This might seem surprising at first, considering the general wetness of the blanket bog environment. But during the height of a dry summer the bog surface dries out and so it becomes necessary for the heather to conserve water by minimising losses through its leaves. In winter, when the bog freezes over and water is unavailable to its roots, the heather must also counteract the drying effects of the wind. The smallness of the leaves is the first line of defence. Additionally, these are protected by a thick, waxy cuticle and a covering of long hairs over furrows and pits which house the stomata - the pores through which water escapes to the atmosphere and carbon dioxide is taken in to fuel the process of photosynthesis.

Cross-leaved heath is a more straggly plant with longer leaves set in whorls of four which are widely spaced and erect near the top of the stem. The leaves have a greyish tinge and the compact clusters of flowers are a watery pink. It grows in wetter situations than heather. In contrast, the dark-pink-flowered bell heather grows on drier ground than either of the other two species. Apparently, all grow best in moderately wet conditions but the low tolerances of cross-leaved heath and bell heather to drought and flooding, coupled with their inability to compete with heather, means that they are excluded from the moderately wet sites where the heather grows with greatest vigour.

While the species just discussed are the most common heaths in Connemara, it is the rare species that have earned the region its special reputation. Indeed, it is quite unique for such a combination of heaths to be found in such a small area.

Irish heath is a tall, hairless plant with leaves in whorls of four and tiny pink flowers set among them. It grows on wet bog, lakeshores and stream-sides at one site on the north side of Errisbeg and by drains and among rock outcrops near Lettergesh, on the coast to the south of Killary Harbour. It flowers from March to the end of April, much earlier than the other heaths, and will consequently be missed by the visitor coming to see the heather in bloom in late summer. Unlike the other two rare heaths, it is fertile and reproduces by seed. Outside Connemara Irish heath grows only in Mayo, France, Portugal and Spain, a distribution which is difficult to explain. However, after detailed studies of its ecology, distribution and history Dr Peter Foss and Dr Gerry Doyle suggest that it could have been introduced by man about 500 years ago when the warmer weather would have favoured the spread of this frost sensitive species. There were direct trade links with Spain and Portugal at that time and the presence of Irish heath close to pilgrimage shrines and abbeys in Spain, France and Ireland reinforces the possibility that this attractive plant was intentionally transplanted by visitors to Ireland. A further possibility, stemming from its current use as animal bedding in Galicia, is that it arrived in Ireland in a trading vessel in which it was used for that purpose or as packing material.

Clearly, we may never know exactly how Irish heath arrived in Ireland, but the uncertain history of the species should serve to remind us of the complex ways in which our present-day flora has come into being. We can be certain, however, that Mackay's heath has had a long and natural history in Ireland, its remains having been found in interglacial deposits near Gort. And although there is some doubt that this rarity was present in post-glacial deposits at Roundstone, there seems to be little question that it arrived here unassisted by man. It is very like cross-leaved heath in appearance but tends to be more compact and bushy, with broader leaves which are not erect or widely spaced below the flowers, which are purplish-pink.

The Irish populations of Mackay's heath are sterile and do not produce seed. They spread by layering, so populations over a considerable area consist of a single clone (genetically identical plants). However, to complicate matters, they can hybridise with cross-leaved heath to produce plants which are often difficult to distinguish. These are common and, needless to say, live close to their parent plants. Mackay's heath lives mainly in an area to the north of Errisbeg around Lough Nalawney and the adjacent hillock, unnamed on maps but known locally as Craiggamore. From

Mackay's heath - a Connemara speciality.

here its distribution extends discontinuously north-westwards towards Clifden and then down to an area near Carna where there is another small colony. Outside Connemara, the species is found only in Mayo, Donegal and in the province of Oviedo in north-west Spain. By a strange coincidence it was discovered almost simultaneously in Spain and Ireland in the summer of 1835.

Dorset heath is by far the rarest member of the family in Connemara, occurring in only one tiny colony near the bog road south-east of Clifden. The plants are low and straggly and tend to be choked by soft rush and purple moor-grass. Like Mackay's heath, it does not seem to set seed but, unlike the latter, it does not spread by layering, so the chances of it ever expanding its range naturally appear to be minimal. Outside Connemara it occurs only in Cornwall, Devon, Dorset, west and central France, Spain, Portugal and north-west Morocco.

Insectivores

Not far from these heaths, growing on damp, bare peat, we will find the tiny round-leaved sundew. Its reddish leaves are fringed with long glandular hairs, each tipped with a transparent, sticky globule. Its flowers are white and are carried on a long stem well above the rosette of leaves. The

101

Oblong-leaved sundew - an inhabitant of wet peat and bog pools.

sticky globules on the leaves act as traps for small insects which are then digested by enzymes produced by the leaves. The sundew gains valuable nitrogen, phosphorus and potassium from this 'meat', which supplements its more natural plant diet gleaned from the peat by its roots. It can survive without insect food, but grows much better when it is available. Among the insects known to be trapped by round-leaved sundew are small caddis flies, damselflies, beetles, ants and butterflies.

Two other sundews are common in Connemara. The great sundew, which has long leaves and a flower stalk arising from the centre of its rosette of leaves, often grows among peat mosses. Oblong-leaved sundew also has long leaves, but these taper to a shorter stalk. It also differs from the great sundew in that the flower stem is curved at the bottom and arises from between two of the leaves rather than from the centre of the rosette. Also, it is found on very wet peat or growing in bog pools.

An even more inconspicuous insectivore is the pale butterwort, no more than 3-4 centimetres (1.25-1.5 inches) across, which grows on the peat surface under an open canopy of sedges or rushes. Its dull greyish-green, in-rolled leaves are also sticky fly traps. It has a lilac flower with a yellow throat and a down-turned cylindrical spur. The pale butterwort is another Atlantic coast species, occurring mainly in the western half of Ireland, on the west coast of Scotland, in the south-west of England and on the west coasts of France, Portugal and Spain, south to Morocco. Its larger, more common, blue-flowered relation, the common butterwort, is, on the other hand, much more widely distributed in Europe but mainly away from the western fringes, at least in France, Portugal and Spain. In Ireland it occurs mainly in the northern half of the country where it is found on lakeshores, in wet meadows and marshes as well as bogs.

Before we leave this fascinating group of insectivorous plants, mention should be made of the bladderworts. These, too, are inconspicuous plants that live submerged in pools and drains, except for their delicate creamy flowers which show above the surface in mid-summer. Two species, the lesser and the intermediate bladderwort, occur in Connemara. Unlike the butterworts and the sundews that capture their prey passively on sticky leaves, these are active insect trappers. The microscopic bladders on their underwater stems have trapdoors that are kept shut while the plant removes some of the water, thereby creating a partial vacuum in the bladder. When an unsuspecting planktonic animal such as a water-flea touches the trigger hairs attached to the bottom of the trapdoor, the tension is broken and the reduced pressure inside causes water and victim to be sucked inwards. The door closes and the extra water inside the bladder is slowly pumped out over the next couple of hours, during which digestive enzymes are released and the prey is consumed.

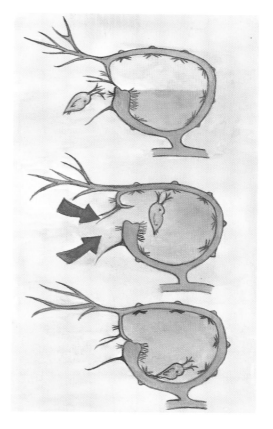

Figure 9: How the bladderwort traps its prey (*after* Guidelines for keeping and using animals and plants - carnivorous plants, *Centre for Life Studies, Zoological Gardens, Regent's Park., London NW1 4RY*).

The blanket bog community contains many more interesting flowering plants, such as heath milkwort, with its bright blue, pink or white flowers, the distinctive lousewort which obtains part of its food parasitically from the roots of grasses, the ubiquitous tormentil and the delicate white beak-sedge which is an important winter food source for Greenland white-fronted geese. These, and many more, could fill another chapter. However, we must move on. But, before leaving the blanket bogs, we should turn again at the lower plants - the algae, mosses, liverworts, fungi and lichens - whose role in the community is probably far more significant than their stature would suggest.

The lower plants
Much of Connemara's blanket bog is covered with deposits of slimy algal material which can cover the surface to a depth of 10 centimetres (4 inches) in places. This mass (or mess, as it might be more appropriately described) can contain up to sixty different species. However, the major

---

Table 5
Some common plants in a Connemara bog community.

Flowering plants	Mosses	Liverworts	Lichens
Black bog-rush	*Campylopus atrovirens*	*Odontoschisma sphagni*	*Cladonia arbuscula*
Purple moor-grass	*Sphagnum palustre*	*Calypogeia sphagnicola*	*Cladonia portentosa*
Deergrass	*Sphagnum papillosum*	*Pleurozia purpurea*	
Common cottongrass	*Sphagnum magellanicum*	*Mylia anomala*	
White beak-sedge	*Sphagnum capillifolium*		
Heather	*Sphagnum tenellum*		
Cross-leaved heath			**Alga**
Bog-myrtle			
Bog asphodel			*Zygogonium ericetorum*
Round-leaved sundew			
Great sundew			
Heath milkwort			
Lousewort			
Tormentil			
Common butterwort			
Pale butterwort			

---

constituent is usually an alga called *Zygogonium ericetorum* which is one of the first plants to colonise newly exposed peat at the bottom of bog pools. The algal mat produced by it may create a barrier to colonisation by other plants and especially to the germination of seeds. In addition, it may help to arrest the growth of peat by producing oxygen which can be seen bubbling up from the bottom of a pool. This oxygen saturates the water and promotes a process called corrosive oxidation which retards and impedes any further accumulation of peat. bog pools have been maintained in this way in some areas for up to 2,000 years.

The peat mosses are also associated with very wet conditions. Although they are not as abundant in the blanket bogs as in the midland raised bogs, there are more than twenty species growing in Connemara. However, they are notoriously difficult to identify so it is best just to remember initially that they occur in a range of colours from various shades of green through to pink and red and exhibit different life-styles which relate, for example, to the wetness or exposure of the area they inhabit. The red variety of *Sphagnum capillifolium* is a hummock-forming bog moss, although it can crown hummocks formed by other species because it can tolerate dry conditions. *Sphagnum palustre*, which is normally pale green or yellow-brown, is a shade-tolerant species which forms loose carpets or tussocks, while *Sphagnum tenellum* is small and yellow and grows among other species. The very uncommon *Sphagnum pulchrum* forms hummocks in the blanket bog at Roundstone. *Sphagnum magellanicum* is a large, chunky moss, pale green to wine-red in colour. It is widespread, but often localised in nutrient-poor habitats, where it usually grows in association with *Sphagnum papillosum* and *Sphagnum capillifolium*. *Sphagnum magellanicum* is more susceptible to damage by fire and drainage than *Sphagnum papillosum* . So bearing in mind how intensive these activities are in Connemara, we can see again how human activity can affect the structure and balance of a plant community by damaging some species and favouring others.

There have been changes in the bog moss community in the past, too, probably as a result of climate change. This is indicated by the widespread occurrence of the remains of *Sphagnum imbricatum* in the surface peat. Today this species is very restricted in its distribution. The main peat-formers at the present time are *Sphagnum papillosum*, *Sphagnum palustre*, *Sphagnum recurvum*, *Sphagnum cuspidatum*, *Sphagnum subnitens* and *Sphagnum auriculatum*.

The one thing that all the bog mosses have in common (and which distinguishes them from most other plants) is their capacity to retain large quantities of water. Both living and dead plants have this capacity, so it is just as dangerous to step into a carpet of dead bog moss as it is to tempt fate with a carpet of living moss. They can also, as we have seen earlier, acidify their environment by releasing hydrogen ions into the water after exchanging these for the mineral nutrients which they require for their life processes. This, of course, adds to the problems of other plants in an environment which is already stretching their tolerances to the limit.

Another moss which makes a significant contribution to the blanket bog scene is *Campylopus atrovirens*. This is a striking species, with bright yellow tips to its leaves which rise from a contrasting brown-black base. It lives among the bog mosses and can make up 5 per cent or more of the living cover. *Odontoschisma sphagni* is a dark green, round-leaved liverwort which, as its name suggests, also lives with the peat mosses, particularly *Sphagnum papillosum*. It is characteristic of rain-fed bogs, where it can form patches on wet peat, on the base of tussocks and on decaying vegetation. In Connemara it occurs widely but, with its peat moss companion, does not cover an extensive area. On saturated peats it is sometimes locally prominent with other bog liverworts such as *Mylia anomala* and species of *Cephalozia*.

Calypogeia sphagnicola grows among hummock-forming bog mosses such as *Sphagnum capillifolium* and *Sphagnum papillosum* and to a lesser extent at the edge of hollows with *Sphagnum auriculatum* and *Sphagnum cuspidatum*. *Cephalozia loitlesbergeri* is a rare species which has been found in a bog near Tullywee Bridge, at Recess.

Among the liverworts, the red, earthworm-like strands of *Pleurozia purpurea* are most impressive. This is a rare species confined mainly to the western blanket bogs of Ireland, Scotland and the English Lake District. It can be especially abundant where the bog is relatively

IMPORTANT BLANKET BOGS IN CONNEMARA MAP 7
(Source: Irish Peatland Conservation Council)

NAME	GRID REFERENCE	AREA (Hectares/) Acres)	FEATURES
Internationally Important			
1 Roundstone	L7145	4,250/10,200	This area consists of infertile lakes, streams, rivers, flushes, and fens with well-developed blanket bog. Greenland white-fronted geese feed and roost on the bog. Part of it is in the Connemara National Park.
2. Derryvickrone	L740470	468/1,123	This has extremely wet quaking areas and is a Greenland white-fronted goose feeding site. It has been damaged by private afforestation.
3. Lettershinna	L850450	995/2,388	This bog is studded with loughs. It has inter-connecting pools and well developed hummocks. It is a feeding site for Greenland white-fronted geese. Part of this bog is a state Nature Reserve.
4. Maam Cross / Lettercraffroe / Screeb / Cashel / Glendollagh Lough	L9040	27,000/64,800	This extensive area supports several rare plant species. There are six Greenland white-fronted goose feeding sites within it.
5. Shannavara	L920410	1,127/2,705	This bog contains excellent pool/hummock lawn complexes with a rare peat moss. It is a Greenland white-fronted goose feeding site.
6. Leame	M010430	855/2,025	This is an intact and extensive area of mountain and lowland blanket bog where Greenland white-fronted geese feed and roost. Part of it is a state Nature Reserve.
7. Bealacooan	M090280	1,396/3,350	This is the most extensive, largely undamaged bog in east Connemara. It has pool complexes, flushes and interconnecting pool/lawn systems. It is a feeding site for Greenland white-fronted geese.
Nationally important			
A. Cashel Bog	L800450	597/1,433	This bog contains rocky ridges and interconnecting pools and lawns containing a rare peat moss.
B. Dooletter	L800340	393/943	This bog has lakes, flushes and wet, quaking / lawn complexes.
C. Gowla	L840410	238/571	A bog with numerous wet flushed areas with a rare peat moss.
D. Bunsharriff	L940450	192/461	This bog is situated on Connemara marble and contains an iron flush.
E. Knockadav	L950430	355/852	This bog contains quaking peat basins with a rare peat moss.
F. Derroogh North	L960440	390/936	This bog features flushes and interconnecting pools in the low-lying areas.
G. Derroogh South	M000270	220/528	This bog has quaking *Sphagnum* lawns, interconnecting pools and a flush with a rare peat moss.
H Knocka	M170280	21/50	This bog is intermediate in character between a blanket and a raised bog with well developed hummock and hollow patterns.

undisturbed and the growth of *Sphagnum* is poor or unhealthy. Only female plants occur in Ireland, although elsewhere in its world range individual plants produce both male and female inflorescences (reproductive structures). *Pleurozia*, *Campylopus* and black bog-rush form a grouping which is characteristic of the western blanket bogs.

Peat is surprisingly rich in fungi, although of the smaller, microscopic kinds, which would more generally be called moulds, like *Mucor*, of school textbook fame. In a study carried out in the 1960s in a raised bog in Kildare, the commonest fungi in the peat belonged to the genus *Penicillium*. Whether this is also the case in Connemara bogs is not known. Larger mushrooms and toadstools are scarce on the bog, probably being most common on animal droppings. However, as virtually nothing is known about fungi in Connemara, there would seem to be plenty of scope for field research, both amateur and professional, on this little-known but ecologically very important group.

The lichen flora is equally sparse on the bogs, although *Cladonia arbuscula* and *Cladonia portentosa* do grow luxuriantly amongst the heather. Where this is burned, however, *Lecidea granulosa*, *Lecidea uliginosa* and, again, several *Cladonia* species appear on the peaty soil.

Map 7: The location of blanket bogs in Connemara.

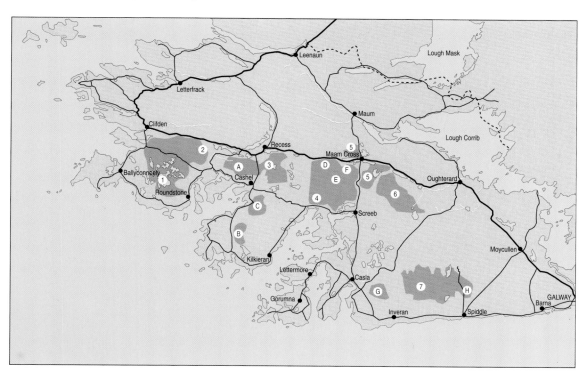

WOODLAND

We have spent quite some time looking at the blanket bogs, the most extensive habitat in Connemara. Now let us turn to one of the least common habitats, the deciduous woodland. We can move out of the wind into the calm ambience of the oakwood where we will find a host of plants and animals which cannot tolerate the exposure of the mountains or the acidic infertility of the bog.

As we saw in Chapter 1, thousands of years have passed since Connemara was heavily wooded and hundreds of years since the last remnants of natural woodland were destroyed. The small areas of woodland we see today (see Map 8), at Kylemore, Derryclare and Spiddle, for example, have grown only within the past 200 years. Nevertheless, they have had time to mature and develop flora and fauna which we can describe as semi-natural. And, whatever their botanical purity, we should be grateful that these woods still exist, and do all in our power to ensure that they are protected and maintained in a healthy state.

A woodland nature reserve

Derryclare Wood is situated beside Derryclare Lough on the south-eastern flank of Derryclare, one of the Twelve Bens. The oak woodland covers about 8 hectares (19 acres) of a 19-hectare (46-acre)

Rowan with holly.

Statutory Nature Reserve which is the responsibility of the National Parks and Wildlife Service of the Office of Public Works. The reserve is hemmed in on the landward side by a state coniferous plantation, a monument to less enlightened times.

Sessile oak is the most common tree species in the woodland, with some rowan, downy birch, willow, ash and pedunculate oaks bringing variety to the canopy. Beneath the tall trees, in the shrub layer, hazel is dominant, with holly and hawthorn scattered throughout the wood. In addition, there are some large sycamore, beech and horse-chestnut trees, which were planted near the now-ruined Derryclare Lodge. Analysis of their tree rings has shown that the oldest were planted between 1830 and 1840.

The sessile oak is a magnificent tree, tall with widely spreading branches and grey, finely fissured bark. Its life may span five centuries or more, during which many generations of other plants will come and go and landscapes will change beyond recognition. It is the commoner of the

---

CLIMATIC CLIMAX VEGETATION

Oak woodland has for a long time been considered to be the climatic climax vegetation of Connemara - that is to say, in the current climatic conditions, oakwood is the final stage in the progressive development of the vegetation from the lichens which first colonised the bare rocks of the region. This is a simple concept which assumes that once the vegetation has reached its climax it will remain stable until the climate changes, dying individuals being replaced all the time by new individuals of the same species. And if we look down on an oakwood, with its long-lived trees, we will see little change in the appearance of the canopy during a human lifetime. So it is easy to accept the idea of climax stability on the basis of this short-term and superficial view.

However, forest ecologists now realise that stability is something of an illusion, that disturbance and change are frequent within communities such as the Connemara oakwoods and that the concept of a single climatic climax vegetation for a region is no longer valid. In fact, it is more realistic to think of a series of climax types, merging into one another across the landscape as the environment changes. Thus, the lichen community on the rocks at the seashore is just as much a climax type as the oakwood, the blanket bog and the dwarf heather community on the mountain tops. However, we should also realise that change is going on continuously within each of these communities, even if we cannot detect it with our short-term observations. When a plant dies it is not necessarily replaced by another of the same species, so absolute stability does not exist. This last point is worth bearing in mind when we consider the conservation of natural communities. Is it possible, or even desirable, to try to conserve communities in exactly the form in which we find them now? Or should we just let nature take its course and sit back and enjoy the spectacle of unfettered ecological change? These are questions well worth thinking about. The answers to them are legion, often contradictory, and discussion of them is certainly beyond the scope of this book.

It is also worth remembering that when we are studying nature we must always consider the ecology of a particular species in terms of its own life span, be it several hundred years, as in the case of the oak or a lichen, or merely a few hours or days as in the case of a tiny aquatic plant such as a diatom. It is hard to shake off the tendency to think in terms of the human 'three score years and ten', but it must be done if we are to get a better grasp of how nature works.

---

two species of oak growing in Connemara and can be distinguished from the pedunculate oak by examining its acorns which are attached directly, or almost directly, to the twigs. In the pedunculate oak the acorns are attached by long stalks called peduncles. Sessile oak is native to Connemara and is undoubtedly the species which was present during the heyday of west of Ireland oakwoods. Most of the pedunculate oaks, however, are likely to have been introduced or to be the offspring of introduced trees. Where they grow together the two species interbreed to form hybrids which are intermediate in some or all of their characteristics. Although we tend to think of oaks as typically Irish, Ireland is, in fact, the northern outpost for these trees, which belong to a large group of species which live mainly to the south in warm temperate and even tropical mountain regions.

Other trees of interest growing in Derryclare Wood include two large yew trees. The presence of just two of these fine trees reflects clearly the general scarcity of this species in Connemara, and in Ireland as a whole. (We should not be misled into thinking it is common by the numerous churchyard yews; they are an upright cultivated variety which was discovered in Fermanagh in 1750.) One of these could be about two hundred years old and may be one of the oldest surviving members of Derryclare Wood. Fortunately, one tree is a female and the other a male and, since the wood was fenced off in the 1970s to prevent grazing, several seedlings have become established, thereby raising hopes that this uncommon species will be able to re-establish itself naturally within the reserve.

Holly is quite a rare species in Connemara and its status is reflected in Derryclare Wood. However, since the wood was fenced off from grazing sheep and goats, many seedlings have appeared, giving us a clue to the reason for its absence elsewhere. Because it retains its leaves during the winter it is attractive fodder for grazing livestock in spite of its prickles. Holly is also attractive to the human predator during the Christmas period and in recent years many berried trees (not just branches) have been felled to supply a growing demand for decorations. This poses a serious local threat to the species because male and female flowers occur on separate trees. All the trees which are felled are females, leaving only males which, of course, cannot propagate the species by themselves.

Table 6
The flora of Derryclare Wood.

Group	Number of species
Flowering plants	124.*
Conifers	3 **
Ferns and clubmosses	16
Mosses	40
Liverworts	14
Lichens	98
Lichen parasites (fungi)	8
Fungi	?
Algae	?

* including three species known to have been deliberately planted

** including two species known to have been deliberately planted

Figures based on the studies of Dr David Ferguson and Professor Victor Westhoff, and of Dr Ann Quinn and Professor Michael Mitchell.

Ivy is common on the trunks of many of the larger trees and it is estimated that some of the plants could be up to eighty years old. Honeysuckle, another climber, is present too, but rarely found in the trees, being most common trailing through the plants on the ground.

The flowers growing on the floor of the wood include common species such as wood-sorrel, common dog-violet, meadowsweet, sanicle, wood avens and enchanter's-nightshade. Among the rarer Connemara plants found in Derryclare are woodruff, creeping soft-grass and tufted hair-grass. Interestingly, English stonecrop, a plant which normally avoids lime-rich habitats, grows on the limestone at the edge of Derryclare Lough, indicating, it is suggested, that the climatic conditions in the west of Ireland enable it to tolerate these unusual circumstances. A species which is fortunately not present is rhododendron which, as we have seen, can cause severe long-term damage to oak woodlands in the west of Ireland.

Wilson's filmy-fern and Tunbridge filmy-fern, two small and delicate species, are notable members of the fern community in Derryclare Wood. Although they are fairly common in Connemara these ferns are rare in Ireland, except in the south-west, and are very local in occurrence elsewhere in Europe.

Mosses, liverworts and lichens are also well represented. The lichens and their parasites were

Map 8: Oakwoods in Connemara.

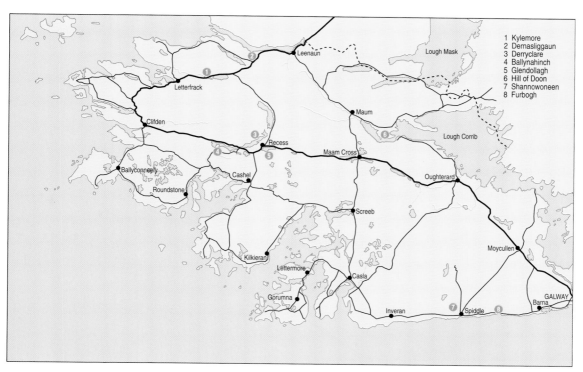

studied in detail in the late 1960s by Dr Ann Quinn (née Folan) and Professor Michael Mitchell of University College Galway. They recorded nearly 100 species of lichens and several species of fungi growing parasitically on some of these lichens. Some of the better-known lichens include species of *Cladonia*, *Parmelia*, *Peltigera* and *Ramalina*. Among the parasites, the record of *Hemigrapha astericus* was the first for this species in the northern hemisphere, it being a native of Australia and South America.

Derryclare Wood has a rich and varied flora and within its bounds occur more than one fifth of the flowering plants, ferns and clubmosses known to live in north-west Connemara. The numbers of species recorded so far, with the notable exception of fungi and algae, are presented in Table 6.

Shannawoneen Wood

Shannawoneen wood lies in the valley of the Owenboliska River, just to the north of Spiddle. It covers 33 hectares (82 acres) and, like Derryclare Wood, has sessile oak as its main canopy species. Occasionally, downy birch rises to the canopy level which ranges in height from 6 to 12 metres (20-40 feet), the exposed, western fringes being conspicuously lower than the rest. The shrub layer is well developed with ivy, downy birch, rowan and beech. On the eastern bank of the river hazel scrub is dominant in the shrub layer. Bilberry is frequently the dominant member of the ground

Rowan and oak - Shannawoneen Wood.

flora, although ivy and honeysuckle are also common. The herb layer is rich in ferns, with the hay-scented buckler-fern being particularly abundant. The two filmy-ferns mentioned earlier are important members of the community, as are mosses and lichens which grow on the walls and rocky outcrops within the wood and as epiphytes - plants growing on the trees themselves. Of the epiphytes recorded by Dr Noel Kirby and Dr Michael O'Connell, eight were flowering plants or ferns, notably herb-robert, wood-sorrel and common polypody, thirty-two were mosses, fifty-six were lichens and four were parasitic fungi.

As a result of recent surveys by Dr Reitze ten Cate and his colleagues working from the Corrib Conservation Centre, we can now add a further thirty or more species of fungi to the plant list for Shannawoneen Wood. These include species like the blusher (*Amanita rubescens*), several species of *Mycena* which grow on birch and hazel, six species of *Russula* and three species of *Lactarius* which produce 'milk' when broken. Undoubtedly, there are more fungi waiting to be recorded and further surveys here and in the other deciduous woods of Connemara will bring dividends of further knowledge and great pleasure.

JENNY'S MUSHROOM

On the morning of 16 September 1991, while searching for fungi with her grandfather and some friends, Jenny, then aged 7, came across some violet-capped mushrooms. They were almost hidden amongst the heather at the edge of a bog near Oughterard. Dr Reitze ten Cate, the grandfather, took a specimen of the striking and unusual mushroom back

to the Corrib Conservation Centre for identification. But, after detailed examination under a microscope and a lengthy search of several identification guides, he could not identify it. Unfortunately, this was the last day of his visit to Ireland so it was not until July 1992 that a return visit yielded another specimen of this perplexing species.

Further attempts to identify the mushroom failed, although it was clear that it was a species of *Entoloma* . So Dr ten Cate took the specimen to an expert on fungi of this type, Dr Machiel Noordeloos, at the Rijksherbarium in Leiden, in the Netherlands. He examined the mushroom in great detail and made drawings of its diagnostic features. He searched the world literature for clues to its identity, but could find none. Eventually, after some delay (because he broke an arm in the meantime - the course of science rarely runs smoothly), he concluded that it must be a species new to science and, just as this book was being completed, named it *Entoloma jennyi* Noordel and ten Cate, in honour of the young lady who found it.

Some woodland fragments

Less is known about the fragments of birch woodland and scrub which remain, for example, on the hillsides near Oughterard and Moycullen. The small wood at Newtown, near Moycullen, contains birch and hazel with some oak and hawthorn and a rich moss and lichen flora. It is small, only about 3 hectares (7 acres) in extent, and, like the similar small wood at Rusheeny, to the west of Oughterard, is being gradually depleted by land reclamation.

Island communities

Less vulnerable are the scrubby woodlands that have developed on lake islands, many of which have been left ungrazed, unburned and unexploited for many decades. The species found on the islands are, of course, the same as those living on the nearby mainland, but in the undisturbed and often better-drained conditions of the islands, communities can develop in a more natural manner and species which, for example, are held back by grazing on the mainland can grow to their full potential on an island. The contrast between a well-vegetated island and the bare, over-grazed mainland just a few metres away across the water is striking, and should be a constant reminder to us of how much of the Connemara countryside has been abused over the centuries.

Lake islands in south Connemara usually have a heath zone on the windward (west) side, dominated either by western gorse or by heather and purple moor-grass. This merges eastwards into woodland which, on the larger islands, covers most of the area. The woodland tends to be very dense, with trees up to 11 metres (36 feet) high, and has rather a sparse ground flora. The commonest trees, as in the mainland woods, are sessile oak, rowan, downy birch, willow, holly and yew. Where there is sufficient soil and light for the ground flora to develop, we can find heather, St Dabeoc's heath, ivy, honeysuckle, bramble, bilberry, great wood-rush, common dog-violet, royal fern, bracken and broad buckler-fern. Bryophytes are common on most islands, especially in the woodland zones, and lichens are fairly abundant as epiphytes on the trees.

The photogenic Scots pines, conveniently growing on an island in Derryclare Lough beside the Maam Cross-Clifden road, are not typical of lake island woodlands and are likely to have been planted some time last century.

While the vegetation of most lake islands is now free from disturbance by people and livestock, some islands do not escape the damaging effects of nesting cormorants and, to a lesser extent, breeding herons. After several years of regular nesting, a cormorant island, such as the island in Lough Aroolagh, near Rosmuck, becomes a scene of utter devastation and desolation, with a smell to match. The vegetation is covered with murderous guano and, at the height of summer, instead of being in full leaf the trees are merely bare and fragile skeletons. However, when cormorants eventually desert an island - as they must when they have destroyed all their nesting trees - the vegetation does recover, but very slowly, perhaps taking a century or more to reach its natural climax again.

St Dabeoc's heath. Inset shows the flowers of St Dabeoc's heath pierced by a bumblebee in search of nectar.

The study of island plants and animals illustrates an interesting ecological principle. If we count the number of plant species living on different islands and relate these figures to their areas we will find that generally, and not really surprisingly, the smaller islands will have fewer species than the larger ones. The same principle applies to breeding bird species, the number of which tends to decline with the decrease in size of the islands on which they nest.

The study of island ecology need not just apply to communities living on isolated rocks in the middle of lakes or in the sea. Most habitats are, in fact, 'islands', isolated from similar 'islands' by different habitats. Derryclare Wood is an 'island' separated from Shannawoneen Wood by a 'sea' of blanket bog. The summit of Muckanaght is an 'island' separated by a great expanse of fresh air from the nearby summit of Benbaun.

This is a significant point to remember in relation to conservation. If, for example, Derryclare Wood is reduced in size, or the arctic-alpine plant communities are forced to retreat upwards to smaller summit 'islands' by climatic warming, the number of species in each of these habitats is likely to decline.

Coniferous plantations

Before we leave the subject of woodlands it is important that we should give some consideration to coniferous plantations. They are, after all, an expanding habitat in the Connemara landscape. Already they cover a considerably greater area than all of the semi-natural deciduous woodlands in the region and, if current projections are fulfilled, they will continue expanding for the forseeable future. Whether we like them or not, they are here to stay and, as naturalists, we should start to take an interest in them for their own sake and not just because of the damage - real or apparent - which they cause to other elements of the Connemara countryside.

The unnaturally straight edge of a coniferous plantation.

In early 1993, the state forestry company Coillte owned 16,520 hectares (39,648 acres) in Connemara. Of this total, 12,991 hectares (31,178 acres) were planted with conifers. The balance of 3,529 hectares (8,470 acres) was made up of plantable land, unplantable land and water. Statistics for private planting in Connemara are not available. However, the total area under private plantations in County Galway at the end of 1992 was 10,046 hectares (24,110 acres). This suggests that private plantations still represent a small proportion of the total area under conifers in Connemara, but with the growth in private afforestation and the cessation of state planting on bogs, their relative impact on the landscape is set to increase.

Most of the plantations in Connemara have been established on blanket bog or on the poor soils of the lower slopes of the mountains. As there are no native trees which can grow sufficiently fast for commercial purposes, two North American conifers have been planted in this region and generally throughout Ireland. These are sitka spruce, a shapely, but sharp-needled species, and lodgepole pine, a less elegant tree but one with softer foliage. Both grow naturally on the slopes of the mountains on the north-west coast of North America, where they live in communities rich in plants and animals. When they are grown in Connemara, however, they must do so in the absence of their natural associates. And because they have been cultivated in Connemara for less than a century, there has been insufficient time for them to build up new associations, so we find very few local plants and animals living in any sort of close relationship with them.

When the bogs are fenced and drained and the young trees first planted, typical bog plants such as black bog-rush and bog asphodel disappear, soon to be replaced by vigorous stands of purple moor-grass and heather. Wood mouse numbers increase as well. However, after a few years the branches of the closely planted trees intermingle to create an almost light-proof canopy and life disappears from the floor of the plantation for several years, perhaps decades. Only when the trees are thinned out or felled can light return to encourage the regeneration of the local flora. Fortunately, though, there are usually areas within plantations which cannot be planted and these can harbour interesting plants, as can the forest roads, particularly where they have been covered with stones from outside the locality. For example, limestone chippings laid in a granite area can, just like the limestone blocks used to face bridges, bring unexpected species to a plantation.

Perhaps if we begin to show a more positive interest in the natural history of forestry plantations, forest managers might be encouraged to take a broader view of the huge areas of countryside under their control. It is worth a try.

SOME FRESHWATER PLANTS

Although Connemara is well endowed with lakes, its freshwater plant life is considered by botanists to be rather sparse. But as we shall see later, it does support some notable and intriguing species. The larger lakes are deep, steep sided and frequently lacking in suitable shoreline habitat, while the smaller lakes, often no more than large bog pools, are poor in nutrients and too acidic to support even a modest flora. Only near the coast, where the lakes and pools receive a regular supply of nutrients in the sea spray from the Atlantic will we find more impressive assemblages of water plants. It is estimated that the water in some of these lakes contains something like 0.1 per cent of seawater. In lakes very near the coast, calcium-rich sand, blown in from nearby beaches, also adds significantly to the fertility of the water.

The rivers and streams of Connemara are not good hunting grounds for the water plant enthusiast either. Most are short, fast flowing and infertile. However, submerged boulders and shady banks are usually home to a variety of mosses and liverworts, and these could repay the attention of bryophyte specialists.

The most conspicuous and attractive water plants are the water-lilies. The white water-lily is common on lakes and slow streams and its large, white, sometimes pink-tinged flowers are a

White water-lily - common on lakes and slow-flowing streams.

117

delight to behold when set against the dark water of a Connemara lake. Even after the flowers have gone, its large, circular leaves are still prominent on the water surface, and especially so when a breeze curls them over like the page of a book.

The yellow water-lily, while it occurs in lakes, is more frequently encountered in slow-flowing streams and bog pools. It has a compact, yellow flower which is held a few centimetres above the water surface. The flower is about 5 centimetres (2 inches) across - half the diameter of the white water-lily flower. It has broadly oval leaves, some of which remain submerged while others float on the surface.

Another common but much less conspicuous species is the bog pondweed. We will come across this regularly in bog drains, flushes, small lakes and streams. It, too, has both floating and submerged leaves. Those reaching the surface are short, stubby and often translucent, while the leaves which remain submerged are long and lance-like. Unlike the water-lilies it has a most unimposing spike of small, green, petal-less flowers.

Alternate water-milfoil is a slender, fragile, fine-leaved plant that is found frequently in lakes and rivers, particularly in north Connemara. It has tiny flowers on a spike which is raised above the water where pollination can be effected by the wind. The flowers at the top of the spike are male, those at the bottom female, while those in between are hermaphrodite. The slender, fragile stems are quickly broken by any violent disturbance of the water, rapid currents, strong winds or foraging animals, and great masses of fragmented milfoil are often stranded on the shore in the wake of any of these events and also at the end of the growing season as the plants die back. This species was one of the first to reappear in Connemara as the Ice Age was coming to an end. Alternate water-milfoil is a regular member of shallow water and littoral (lakeshore) communities which include the characteristically scented water mint, the familiar yellow iris, common reed, marsh pennywort, marsh St John's-wort, purple-loosestrife and several species of rush, sedge, stonewort, horsetail and moss.

Pipewort - an aquatic species which has its main centre of distribution in eastern North America.

Also living in these communities in some Connemara lakes are a number of species that would turn the heads of even the most seasoned botanists. Pipewort is one such species. This small plant grows in shallow water at the margins of lakes from Barna out to Inishbofin. It has a dense basal rosette of leaves from which it produces a long, leafless stem which carries a tiny, white button-like flower at its tip. It is an insignificant plant and, unless it is growing in dense stands at the height of the flowering season in July and August, it can easily be overlooked. But why should such an unimpressive plant turn the heads of naturalists? The main reason is that in Europe pipewort occurs only in the west of Ireland, from west Kerry to Donegal, and sparingly on the west coast of Scotland. Its main centre of distribution is in eastern North America. This raises the question of whether or not it is native to western Europe and, if not, how it got here.

At one time it was suggested that the European plants were different from their American counterparts because they had twice as many chromosomes. However, this case-clinching evidence foundered when later investigations showed that the American plants had just as many chromosomes as those in Ireland and Scotland. Evidence from pollen studies near Roundstone indicate that pipewort was present in Ireland nearly 6,000 years ago, long before there was any possibility of it being brought here by human agency. So, it would seem that it is a native species but one of a small number which have a very restricted range in western Europe and an extensive range on the other side of the Atlantic. Interestingly, there are other species such as bog pondweed, alternate water-milfoil and oblong-leaved sundew which exhibit the reverse distribution pattern, being

The delicate flowers of the water lobelia.

widespread in Europe and restricted to a narrow range in eastern North America. How these asymmetrical distributions came about still remains to be explained satisfactorily.

Growing close by pipewort in many lakes we will find the delicate-flowered water lobelia. This, too, has a submerged rosette of leaves which gives rise to a leafless stem and a graceful head of pale mauve flowers in July and August. Like pipewort, it occurs on both sides of the Atlantic but in Europe it is more widespread, with populations in western Britain, western France, the Netherlands, Germany, Denmark and Scandinavia eastwards.

Awlwort is another rare species which grows near pipewort in the shallow waters at the edge of Glendollagh Lough. It is a small plant belonging to the cabbage family, with grass-like pointed leaves and small white flowers. Outside Connemara it occurs sparingly only in the south-west, on the shores of Lough Neagh, in the west of Britain and in Scandinavia.

Another very rare water plant goes by the delightful title of the slender naiad. It is a small, annual plant with slender, brittle, branching stems. Its leaves are only 1-2.5 centimetres (up to 1 inch) long, straight and very delicate and arise in threes at intervals along the stem. It produces tiny green flowers. The slender naiad grows in relatively deep water and generally is only seen when fragments are washed up onto the shore. Outside Connemara, it occurs at only a handful of sites in Kerry, Donegal, Scotland and the English Lake District and very sparsely over a wide area of Europe. Like the previous two species it also occurs in North America.

One of the haunts of the slender naiad is Rusheenduff Lough near Rinvyle. Here it lives in a community containing many of the species already mentioned, but with one addition, hydrilla, an extremely rare species with quite a complicated history.

Hydrilla is an underwater plant that resembles the Canadian waterweed (*Elodea canadensis*), a species which will be familiar to most of us as an aquarium plant. Hydrilla was discovered in 1935 by Professor W.H. Pearsall, whose book *Mountains and Moorlands* has already been mentioned. Since its discovery, however, there has been some uncertainty about its true identity and it has been called *Hydrilla verticillata*, *Hydrilla lithuanica* and *Elodea nuttallii* - the latter not surprisingly since it is very similar in appearance to *Elodea canadensis*. Eventually, however, after a very detailed examination of the species by Maura Scannell, formerly of the National Botanic Gardens in Dublin, it was decided to call it *Hydrilla verticillata* variety *pomeranica* because of its similarity to plants found in Esthwaite Water in the English Lake District and in north-west Poland. This name distinguishes it from slightly different plants which grow in eastern Poland, Lithuania and Russia. The plant now seems to be extinct in Esthwaite Water and in north-west Poland and its long-term prospects in Rusheenduff Lough can hardly be considered secure. The lough is separated from the sea only by a low shingle bar and, with increasing storminess, the sea floods into the lough with greater frequency and vehemence, putting the whole freshwater community at risk.

How did hydrilla arrive in Rusheenduff Lough? Maura Scannell largely rules out human introduction and surmises that it may have been introduced by birds, perhaps in fairly recent times. We now know that ducks such as the pochard migrate from eastern Europe to spend the winter in the west of Ireland each year, so it is plausible, if only remotely so, that a bird could have brought fragments of hydrilla and the slender naiad to Rusheenduff Lough from eastern Europe or possibly from Esthwaite Water where, significantly, the two species lived together in the past.

Finally, brief mention should be made of a tiny, very rare fern called pillwort, found only in marshy ground at the edge of Glendollagh and beside the Ballynahinch River. It has thread-like, yellow-green leaves, coiled in a fern-like manner when they are young. Pillwort grows at only a few other sites in the west and north-west of Ireland and is rare in Britain and the rest of Europe, where it has suffered from pollution and habitat loss.

The freshwater plant life of Connemara may be sparse, but it does not entirely lack fascination.

COASTAL FLOWERS

The coastal grasslands of Connemara are some of the most attractive habitats in the region during the summer when they are carpeted with a wealth of colourful flowers. Table 7 lists some of the species that can be seen on the sandy grasslands and beaches around Mannin Bay. Similar communities can be found at Aillebrack in the vicinity of the Connemara Golf Course, on the tombolo and island enclosing Dog's Bay and at several other locations between Clifden and Gorumna Island.

Many of the flowers are common and widespread, but no less attractive for that. There are also some which are not widespread either in Connemara or Ireland as a whole. The bulbous buttercup, readily identified by its sharply down-turned sepals, occurs only on dry pastures, sand-dunes and rocky ground and is, therefore, rare in Connemara away from the dry coastal grasslands. It flowers and sets seeds earlier than the other common buttercups and usually dies back from mid-July onwards, surviving through the remaining dry summer conditions as an underground stem. The bulbous buttercup is encouraged by over-grazing and its seedlings take full advantage of any bare areas created by trampling.

Common scurvygrass - one of the earliest flowering plants on the coast.

Common scurvygrass is strictly a coastal plant in Ireland. Its small white flowers are some of the first to appear, often before the chill of winter has passed. Scurvygrass was so named because sailors, in times gone by, used to eat it to prevent attacks of scurvy while they were at sea. Only in more recent times has its effectiveness been linked to the high concentration of vitamin C in its leaves.

The sandhill pansy, as its name suggests, lives mainly in sandy places. It is a sub-species of the wild pansy and its flowers are blue-violet, yellow or a combination of these colours. It is scarce in Connemara, as elsewhere in Ireland, and is confined to the coast. Sea sandwort is another strictly coastal plant which grows on loose sandy and gravelly shores. It is a small, creeping, yellowish-green perennial with oval, fleshy leaves and greenish white flowers which produce fruits like little green peas.

Sea sandwort - a small plant of sandy beaches.

121

Irish eyebright and blue moor-grass, species more commonly found in the Burren, are also quite at home on the lime-rich sandy soils of the coastal grasslands and dunes. Although the eyebrights are very difficult to identify, Irish eyebright can be distinguished by its narrow, jagged-toothed leaves, its usually deep bronze stem and leaves and its bushy outline. Blue moor-grass flowers in April and May, earlier than most other grasses, and is quite distinctive with its slate-grey-bluish flowers.

The name English stonecrop belies the true distribution of this attractive white-flowered little plant. It is actually rare in most of England, its main centres of population being in Cornwall, Wales,

Biting stonecrop - formerly called wall-pepper because of its peppery taste.

the English Lake District, western Scotland and the south and west of Ireland. Biting stonecrop, probably still better known to naturalists by its old name, wall-pepper, is a low, creeping plant with yellow flowers and leaves which have a peppery taste. It is more widespread than English stonecrop and grows on sandhills, walls and in dry, rocky places.

The orchids bring some style to the grassland flora. The pyramidal orchid, with its distinctively shaped head of small, bright pink flowers is especially pleasing. It is frequent on the dunes around Slyne Head but is otherwise rare in Connemara, being a species which is strictly confined to lime-rich soils. It is really a southern species and Connemara is very close to the northern limit of its European range. The green-winged orchid, with its distinctive hood of green-veined sepals, is quite common in the area, but elsewhere in Ireland is has suffered a catastrophic decline which has led to its inclusion in the plant *Red Data Book* (see Chapter 6). Like the pyramidal orchid, this delicate species is at the very northern edge of its European range. The dark-flowered early-purple orchid, probably best known for its exceptional abundance in the Burren, is also common on the coastal grasslands of Slyne Head but uncommon elsewhere in Connemara. The common spotted-orchid, with its light pink flowers and broad, heavily spotted leaves, is far more common in the area. The sweet-smelling fragrant orchid is, however, rare in Connemara and confined to the Slyne Head peninsula.

The dense-flowered orchid, sometimes called the Irish orchid, is a small, inconspicuous plant with greenish-white petals, often streaked with dull purplish pink. It is found mainly on lime-rich grasslands such as occur in the Burren. However, in the early years of this century, Dr Lloyd

Praeger and his wife found it growing around Dog's Bay and on the Slyne Head peninsula. But it was not reported again until the early 1970s when it was rediscovered on the grasslands beside Mannin Bay by John Dawkins, father of the well-known and controversial biologist Richard Dawkins. Another species which is restricted to basic ground, often in shallow pockets of peat soil, is the pyramidal bugle. In Ireland it has been found only in the Burren, west Connemara and, recently, County Antrim. It is a softly hairy plant with pale violet-blue flowers arranged in a spike, growing to a height of 15 centimetres (6 inches).

Sea-holly, as its name suggests, has prickly leaves. Plants are often found growing in isolation, on shores where the sand is loose and mobile. Here they are anchored by roots which can be up to 2 metres (6.5 feet) long. Sea-holly is a xerophyte (from the Greek *xeros,* meaning dry), that is a plant which can tolerate long dry periods. It manages this by having long roots which can reach a distant water table and by having leaves which minimise the loss of water to the atmosphere. Other species, such as sea sandwort and prickly saltwort, which occur, for example, on the beach at Dog's Bay, have fleshy, succulent leaves which store water. Some species which normally occur inland also develop some of these characteristics when they live in dry, coastal habitats. A good example is the sea campion. This has fleshy leaves and is the coastal form of the well-known bladder campion.

Table 7
Some flowers of the grasslands and beaches beside Mannin Bay.

Bulbous buttercup	Sea-holly	Common centaury
Common scurvygrass	Rock samphire	Speedwell
Common milkwort	Heath bedstraw	Irish eyebright
Sandhill pansy	Devils'-bit scabious	Water mint
Ragged-robin	Daisy	Wild thyme
Common mouse-ear	Yarrow	Selfheal
Sea sandwort	Sea mayweed	Pyramidal bugle
Common stork's-bill	Oxeye daisy	Pyramidal orchid
White clover	Common ragwort	Green-winged orchid
Kidney vetch	Harebell	Early-purple orchid
Common bird's-foot-trefoil	Thrift	Common spotted-orchid
English stonecrop	Sea-milkwort	Fragrant orchid
Biting stonecrop	Brookweed	Dense-flowered orchid
Purple-loosestrife	Yellow-wort	Yellow iris
		Blue moor-grass

Some plants, like annual sea-blite, live so close to the sea that they are regularly washed by spray. Such plants are known as halophytes (from the Greek *halos*, meaning seasalt), because they seem to be able to tolerate salt, or perhaps, in some cases, need some of it to thrive. They also tend to have fleshy leaves, like many xerophytes, probably because they also need to protect themselves against the drying effects of the seawater. Because the seawater contains more salt than the water within the plants, it can draw the freshwater out by the process of osmosis, thus having the same effect as strong sunshine or a dry breeze.

Machair

Some of the grasslands and sand-dunes in west and south Connemara are of particular interest to the conservationist because they represent a scarce type of habitat called machair, a name commonly used in the west of Scotland where it was first described. The name is derived from the Gaelic word *magh*, meaning a field or plain. In Irish, *machaire* means plain, stretch of level ground or links. Machair can be found on the west coast from north Donegal to the Aran Islands, but there are only about fifty machair sites on this very long stretch of coastline. In Connemara we find machair at Aughrusbeg, Omey Island, Leagaun, Mannin Bay, Aillebrack, Ballyconneely, Doolan, Dog's Bay, Mason Island, Mweenish Island and Finish Island see (Map 9).

Machair and sand-dunes at Mannin Bay.

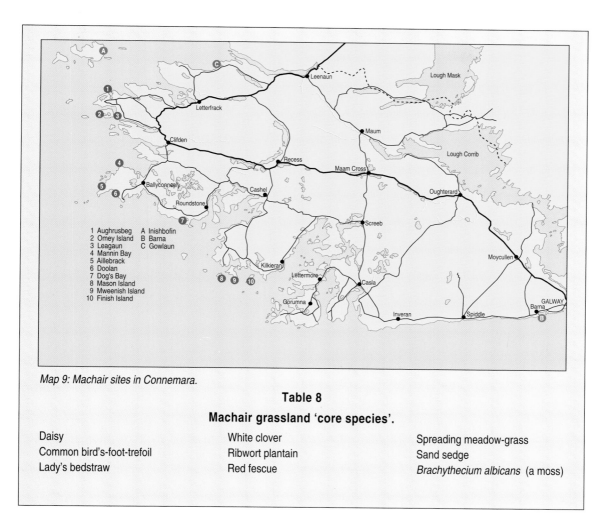

Map 9: Machair sites in Connemara.

Site list on map:

1 Aughrusbeg   A Inishbofin
2 Omey Island   B Barna
3 Leagaun   C Gowlaun
4 Mannin Bay
5 Aillebrack
6 Doolan
7 Dog's Bay
8 Mason Island
9 Mweenish Island
10 Finish Island

Table 8
Machair grassland 'core species'.

Daisy	White clover	Spreading meadow-grass
Common bird's-foot-trefoil	Ribwort plantain	Sand sedge
Lady's bedstraw	Red fescue	*Brachythecium albicans* (a moss)

Machair grasslands are usually flat and found on soils which are rich in lime derived from shell fragments. They are subjected to intensive grazing which keeps the vegetation short and allows a large variety of flowers to flourish. Until recently, most machair sites would have received little artificial fertilizer, another factor contributing to the high density of their flora. Machair grasslands are characterised by nine core species (see Table 8), according to Dr Tom Curtis and his colleagues in the National Parks and Wildlife Service, and usually support all those listed for the coastal grasslands.

Many machair sites are now threatened by fencing, reseeding and artificial fertilisation and in places like Mannin Bay they are being damaged by excessive visitor use and the removal of turf for horticultural purposes.

THE OFFSHORE ISLANDS

Of all Connemara's offshore islands, only Inishbofin seems to have received much attention from botanists. It was first surveyed in 1875, then again in 1911, 1965 and most recently in 1987 by Drs Juliet Brodie, Micheline Sheehy Skeffington and Pat McCarthy (lichens). The island now supports between 300 and 350 flowering plants and ferns, most of which are also present in mainland Connemara. Notably, the island generally lacks any native trees and shrubs more than about 30 centimetres (1 foot) high and there is therefore an almost complete absence of shade and shelter.

While the number of plant species recorded during this century has not changed much, some elements of the flora have altered quite significantly, particularly during the last two decades. Drainage and turf cutting have taken their toll of several wetland species and the decline in tillage and the possible increase in the use of herbicides and artificial fertilisers may account for the reduction in, or extinction of, weeds typically associated with arable land. Overgrazing by rabbits and livestock is probably causing a decline in the dune and upland heath vegetation although, ironically, this baring of the soil may be benefiting the growth and spread of annual plants such as the rare spotted rock-rose which is still at least as common as it was in the 1960s.

The spotted rock-rose is one of two rare species growing on Inishbofin, the other being the grass, wood small-reed. Both are included in the plant *Red Data Book*. Elsewhere, spotted rock-rose occurs only in south Connemara, on Inishturk to the north of Inishbofin, in west Cork, in north Wales and on the Channel Islands. Its main centre of distribution is in west, south and central Europe. Wood small-reed is also very rare in Ireland, though widely distributed in England, most of Europe and temperate Asia. It is clearly a continental species and therefore an unusual plant to find on an offshore island like Inishbofin.

Inishbofin has a rich lichen flora, with nearly 200 species recorded so far. Most of these grow on bedrock, peat or soils derived from the silica-rich bedrock. The remainder grow on mortar, cement, wooden fence-posts, old heather stems, elder bushes and single planted specimens of sycamore, hawthorn and pine. Three of the species, *Catapyrenium cinereum*, *Opegrapha paraxanthodes* and the parasitic *Lecidella umbonella* variety *alumnula* are known in Ireland only from west Galway.

Studies of the flora and fauna of small islands are always valuable because the numbers of species on them are usually small enough to permit complete recording and monitoring. This in turn allows the ecologist to make reliable assessments of the changing fortunes of individual species and communities over short and, as we have seen with Inishbofin, quite long periods of time. From such studies it is possible to put forward tentative suggestions as to how richer and more complex communities on the mainland behave. The studies of Inishbofin and other inhabited islands off the west coast, such as Clare Island and Inishmore, are both interesting and valuable. Comparable studies of uninhabited, uncultivated and ungrazed islands would be equally useful.

ANIMAL LIFE

BIRDS

Birds of the mountains

First there is calm and a clear blue, May sky. Then, from a distance, a subdued screech breaks the silence, growing rapidly louder and soon erupting into a full-blooded, menacing 'cacking' as a slate-grey form hurtles over the sparkling rim of the sheer quartzite cliff at the head of a deep valley at the heart of the Twelve Bens. We can be in no doubt that the male peregrine has returned to his nest site, though where it is on the face of the vast cliff is hard to tell. The raven, which had been patrolling the cliffs in a leisurely manner, is in no doubt either that his peace is about to be shattered. But more of that in a while.

The peregrine is one of Connemara's least-known birds, in spite of the species' high public profile at a national and international level. It nests on remote mountain cliffs, mainland sea-cliffs and uninhabited offshore islands. And when it is not advertising its presence with its unmistakable call and spectacular flying displays it is sitting tight on a small ledge, well camouflaged against the backdrop of rock and vegetation. There are, perhaps, ten or more pairs of peregrines in Connemara, with three or four pairs in the mainland mountains and the rest on coastal and island cliffs. In the mountains peregrines probably feed on woodpigeons and members of the crow family. On the coast they also take seabirds such as kittiwakes. A cliff-top peregrine kill can easily be recognised by the wide scattering of feathers and the characteristic notches it makes in the breastbone of its prey. Outside the breeding season peregrines range quite widely and it is then that we can see them flying over the lowlands. One peregrine, in particular, takes up winter residence at the wildfowl sanctuary at Rostaff Lake, near Headford on the east side of Lough Corrib. Here it probably feeds on the smaller ducks such as teal.

The recent history of the peregrine is well known and need not be recounted in detail. But it is worth reminding ourselves of it for the important conservation lessons it contains. The peregrine population in Ireland and Britain declined drastically in the 1960s as a result of pesticide poisoning which manifested itself in the thinning of eggshells which were then easily broken on the nest by the incubating birds. The discovery of the link between pesticides and the peregrine decline was made after painstaking research by Dr Derek Ratcliffe, the mountain ecologist to whom reference has already been made in connection with the Connemara flora. Fortunately, the offending pesticides were withdrawn in time and the peregrine population has recovered, so succesfully that the Irish population is probably now at an all-time high.

But how is it that the peregrine could have been affected by pesticides which were used primarily to protect cereals against insect and fungal attacks? The reason lies in its position at the top of the food web. Birds such as woodpigeons fed on the poisoned seeds and absorbed some of the poison which was later taken up by peregrines, whose diet consists mainly of birds of that size. Although the concentration of poisons in the woodpigeons was not sufficient to kill them, it built up in the peregrines as they ate more and more affected birds. In many cases the peregrines were not killed either but their ability to produce strong eggshells was reduced and this led to the loss of eggs and the rapid population decline of the 1960s. We can be thankful that the destruction of the peregrine (and many seed-eating birds) was halted. Lessons have been learned and new practices implemented with regard to the use of pesticides. Nevertheless, our predatory birds are still not entirely safe from them. Continuing vigilance will be required to secure their long-term survival. The details of the classic piece of conservation detective work which led to the reprieve of the peregrine can be found in Derek Ratcliffe's newly revised book *The Peregrine Falcon,* along with much interesting and valuable information on the life of this fascinating species.

The raven is a regular associate of the peregrine, often nesting nearby, in mountain or coastal habitats. But the relationship between the two species is hardly the best, consisting as it does of periods of strained tolerance interspersed with outbursts of substantial aggression which can culminate in dramatic talon-grappling rolls which often break up only just before the two interlocked birds hit the ground.

The raven is more common and widespread than the peregrine and often nests at lower altitudes on the mountains. In the vicinity of Maum, not far from the main roads radiating from the village, for example, there are several nesting sites on well-hidden ledges. In 1986 there were at least twenty-three nests in the region.

The raven, the largest member of the crow family in Ireland, is easily recognised by its size, dark, shiny-black plumage, black bill and deep croaking call. It is one of the earliest nesting species in the region and some birds start laying eggs in February. Its varied diet includes carrion, soil-living insects, small birds and mammals, and the eggs of other species. Ravens are quite sedentary and tend to stay in their breeding areas throughout the year, although in the autumn and early winter some occasionally venture eastwards across Lough Corrib. Outside the breeding season some form communal roosts. One such roost of over thirty ravens has been seen in woods near Ashford Castle, at the north-eastern boundary of Connemara.

The raven's reputation for killing sheep was exaggerated in the past. It is now generally accepted that the species is no great threat to a sheep farmer's livelihood. In fact, the high mortality of sheep on the hills which has accompanied serious overstocking has probably benefited the raven and other carrion-eating species such as the hooded crow and the fox.

The hooded crow is met with regularly in the mountains but it nests most frequently in the lowlands, on low, isolated trees on the blanket bog and in trees on lake islands, often in close proximity to nesting herons or gulls. There were over 60 nests in Connemara in 1986. Its diet is similar to that of the raven, though it is unlikely that the two species compete for food because their habitats do not overlap to any great extent. Hooded crows also have a reputation for killing lambs though this, too, has been exaggerated. Detailed research in Scotland has shown that they kill only a minute proportion of the lambs on which they feed, the majority of these having been dead at birth. However, hooded crows do take quite a lot of birds' eggs. They can have an adverse effect on the breeding success of some gamebirds and colonially nesting species such as terns. Just as ravens have benefited from increased carrion on the mountains, hooded crows, like gulls and common rats, have taken advantage of the disgraceful volumes of rubbish we produce today. If we want to see hooded crows at close range (something worth seeing because they are beautiful birds in their own way) all we have to do is head for a rubbish dump. Unfortunately, a dump is unlikely to be very far away from any particular point in Connemara.

Outside the breeding season hooded crows may form flocks, sometimes containing up to one hundred birds, such as the one seen in the hills to the south of Oughterard in May 1990.

A chough with characteristic red bill.

The chough, readily identified by its red bill and legs, is also a bird of the mountains and coastal cliffs, but with the added capacity for nesting in deserted buildings. It is scarce in Connemara, living only in the extreme west of the region. A survey in 1992, organised by the Irish Wildbird Conservancy and the Royal Society for the Protection of Birds, revealed a total of twenty-five pairs nesting in Connemara. Of these, eleven pairs were confirmed to be breeding while six were probably breeding and eight possibly breeding. In addition there were twenty-three non-breeding birds, giving a total population count of seventy-three birds, about 3 per cent of the national total. Only one pair was possibly breeding inland, in the Twelve Bens, which is a drop on the four recorded in a previous survey in 1982. Five pairs were nesting on Inishbofin and one on Inishshark. Overall, there had been an increase of 6 per cent in numbers since the last full survey in 1982. This was perhaps a little disappointing in view of the fact that the chough population had increased nationally by 34 per cent during the decade between the two surveys.

The chough feeds mainly on insects, in short turf habitats such as we find on the coastal fringe and on offshore islands. The machair habitats are particularly important in this respect, and the international scarcity of the chough is a further reason for their conservation.

In Ireland, the chough is only found near the north, west and south coasts from Antrim to Wexford. Its stronghold is in Kerry and Cork where 1,608 of the 2,633 total were recorded. Outside Ireland, it is a scarce species in Britain and France, but becomes moderately common again in Spain and Portugal. Clearly, we have a responsibility to conserve it in Ireland by ensuring that its localised habitats are protected.

The only other species we will meet regularly on the higher mountains is the meadow pipit. This rather nondescript little bird, with its plaintive call is one of the most common and widespread species in Ireland. It nests on the ground in areas of low vegetation, in both mountains and lowlands and especially on the bogs where it is sometimes the only species to be seen. In winter it often occurs in flocks of over fifty birds. Despite its abundance, we know very little about this bird. It is becoming apparent that we should investigate its ecology, as large areas of its habitat are being destroyed by afforestation. While the loss of such

Meadow pipit.

habitat may not seriously diminish the national population of meadow pipits, it could have an indirect local effect on the merlin, a scarce bird of prey which includes large numbers of meadow pipits in its diet. The cuckoo, too, could be affected because, in Connemara, it lays its eggs mainly in the nests of meadow pipits.

During the late autumn and early winter, before the weather gets too cold, we may flush a woodcock or two from the heathery middle slopes of the Bens or the Maumturks. The woodcock is a species that has greatly benefited from afforestation in the west of Ireland and the numbers wintering and presumably breeding here have increased during recent decades.

A rare but welcome sight is the colourful snow bunting, sometimes seen on migration northwards through the mountains during the winter months and occasionally going south in late summer. Rare, too, is the ring ouzel, a relation of the blackbird, distinguished by its white throat patch. Individuals are reported occasionally in Connemara, rather surprisingly in the winter. It is usually a summer visitor to Ireland and breeds in the mountains of Donegal, Kerry and Wicklow. Though it bred in Connemara in the last century, nesting has not been reported here for many decades.

The twite is a small finch which nests on heather and bracken covered hill slopes. At one time it was plentiful in the mountains of west Connemara, but now it is very scarce indeed. In fact, it may be on the verge of extinction as a breeding bird in Connemara. Outside the breeding season small flocks are regularly seen near the coast, for example near Rinvyle. The twite is rare in Ireland as a whole, with a population of less than 1,000 pairs, confined mainly to the uplands on the west coast from Donegal to Kerry. It has been included in the *Irish Vertebrate Red Data Book*.

Another species closely associated with heather is the red grouse. Once this popular gamebird was more common in Connemara, but, with the decline in the heather cover caused by excessive burning and over-grazing, it has become very scarce. In 1986, Dr Paul Haworth estimated the minimum population to be only fourteen pairs. Small parties are occasionally encountered on the lower hills and drier parts of the bogs in the south of the region. Its life is so closely bound to heather, which it eats and requires for shelter, that only an extensive programme of heather moorland rehabilitation could restore the population to its previous level. As such a programme, which would also greatly benefit many other species, is unlikely to be undertaken in the forseeable future, the continuing decline of the red grouse population is inevitable.

It is obvious then that the high mountains, and even the lower hills to the south, are very poor indeed in bird life in spring, summer and especially winter, when a day's walking might raise just a couple of meadow pipits and perhaps a raven. This should not surprise us, of course, in view of the harsh climatic conditions and the poor vegetation at the highest altitudes. We must find shelter and richer vegetation on the lower ground if we want to see more birds.

Birds of the lowlands and blanket bogs

In late February or early March, on the lower slopes of the Bens, we are likely to meet the first wheatear of the year. The male has a grey back and buff underparts, the female has a brownish back and both have distinctive white rumps. They will be flitting between boulders on the heavily grazed, drier slopes or keeping an eye on us from the safety of a distant outcrop where they perch with their typical upright posture. They may be birds just arrived on their breeding grounds or they could be long-distant migrants taking a refuelling stop en route to Greenland or even

Canada, for wheatears are the world's smallest long-distance migrants. They spend the winter in Africa, south of the Sahara Desert, and breed from the latitude of the Mediterranean north to Greenland, west to the shores of Hudson's Bay in eastern Canada and east around the globe to north-west Canada. The two edges of their breeding range in Canada are separated only by about 1,600 kilometres (1,000 miles). The Greenland race of the species, which winters in West Africa, may fly up to 21,000 kilometres (13,050 miles) via northern Europe to Alaska. And of course they make these enormous journeys twice a year, some over a life span of seven years or more.

Wheatears nest under rocks and screes and in dry stone walls. They feed in areas where the vegetation is kept short by grazing. This ensures easy access to their insect food and good visibility all round. Having arrived in Connemara early, they tend to leave early too, usually by mid-July. But we can often see individuals moving south through Connemara well into the autumn. These are likely to be members of the Greenland race perhaps on their way from Hudson's Bay.

Wheatears are reasonably common in Connemara, on the mainland and on the offshore islands, although it has been suggested that their numbers have declined in recent decades. As we have no up-to-date information on their numbers or distribution, it could be very rewarding for an enterprising bird-watcher to undertake a long-term study of this fascinating and attractive species.

In complete contrast, the Irish dipper is a real 'stay at home' species, often living out its life on the same stretch of stream or river. Irish dippers belong to a distinct race, *Cinclus cinclus hibernicus*. They have darker upper parts and less chestnut-brown underneath than their British counterparts. Typically, the dipper is seen briefly as a flash of wings as it flies upstream low over the water or bobbing on a rock in the centre of a fast-flowing stream. Its life is strictly confined to the water and rarely will we see one fly over land, even to short-cut a bend in a stream.

The dipper feeds under water, collecting mainly insects while it walks along the stream bed. Its nest, perhaps under an overhanging river bank or under a bridge, is a characteristic ball of moss and grass, lined with leaves and resembling that of a wren. It is rather scarce in Connemara, limited in its distribution by a lack of suitable streams and the infertility of those streams which are satisfactory in other respects. However, a dipper can be seen easily on the Owenriff River at Oughterard where it often perches on rocks beside the parking area opposite Sweeney's Hotel.

Because the dipper relies on a diet of aquatic insects, any environmental change which affects the latter inevitably has repercussions on the population of the former. In Wales, for example, the acidification of upland streams has seriously reduced the dipper population. Concern is now being expressed that similar effects could soon be seen here, especially where coniferous plantations are being established in areas where the rocks and streams are already fairly acidic. The hills of south Connemara are a case in point. It is important that we keep a close watch on the small number of dippers in that area.

The grey wagtail is often found living close to the dipper, although it is more common on the

A dipper at its nest.

lower reaches of rivers and streams and beside lakes. It is sometimes mistakenly called a yellow wagtail but it has very little yellow plumage compared with the real yellow wagtail, which nowadays is only a very rare summer visitor, mainly to the south and east of Ireland. The grey wagtail is less restricted in its habitat than the dipper and in the winter some birds appear to move out of the mountains and closer to the coast.

By far the scarcest of the Connemara river birds is the kingfisher. It hardly requires description, except to say that it is smaller than is suggested by the close-up photographs with which we are all familiar. It is actually much smaller than a blackbird and only just a little larger than a chaffinch. It requires soft earth river banks to nest in and overhanging branches to fish from. These features are uncommon in Connemara so we do not see many kingfishers in the region. Outside the breeding season they are met most frequently on the coast or beside some of the larger lakes in the east.

In mid-April, the arrival of the common sandpiper, often with the whimbrel, the cuckoo and the first terns, marks the beginning of spring. The sandpiper is a small brown wading bird with a shrill, piping call. It distinguishes itself on a river bank or lakeshore by the way it constantly bobs its head and tail. It flies with rapid, shallow wing-beats alternating with brief glides on down-curved wings showing conspicuous white wing-bars. Connemara is one of the common sandpiper's strongholds and it is estimated that at least 150 pairs breed in the region.

The common sandpiper is the only wading bird to fly north from Africa and stop to breed in Ireland. (Most of our waders are winter visitors which fly north from here to their breeding grounds.) The whimbrel also comes from Africa, but merely passes through Ireland, stopping from time to time to feed and rest on its way to Iceland. Locally it is known as the May-bird because it is most numerous in that month. It can also be seen, and more often heard, in April and June and then again in August and September on its return journey to the coasts of southern Africa. In Connemara, it is most often seen on coastal headlands and islands, but it also visits short-cropped lakeside pastures. The whimbrel is closely related to the curlew but differs in appearance and call. It has a relatively short, slightly down-curved bill and prominent stripes running backwards across its head. Its migratory call is shorter than that of the curlew, usually with fewer notes in any sequence.

The other notable spring arrival is the cuckoo which, as we have already noted, lays its eggs in the nests of meadow pipits, and possibly those of skylarks, as seems to be indicated by an observation made beside the Sky Road, outside Clifden. Here, towards the end of July, eleven meadow pipits and one skylark were engaged in feeding one juvenile cuckoo which was perched on a fence post. Each small bird, in quick succession, perched briefly on the shoulder of the cuckoo which turned its head sideways to accept the insect food from its hosts. Such splendid views of cuckoos are not uncommon in Connemara, where the general absence of tree cover forces them to spend more time in the open than they would do in many other parts of the country.

Skylarks are widespread during the breeding season but only numerous on the bogs where their familiar songs fill the wide open skies. Unlike the pipits, most of them leave the bogs after the breeding season. In fact, most leave the region entirely, returning from the south-east in the following February.

The bird community of the blanket bogs is small, but highly significant from a conservation point of view. The declining red grouse has already been mentioned. Other important species are the golden plover, the merlin and the Greenland white-fronted goose.

Although over 200,000 golden plover spend the winter in Ireland, only about 300 pairs breed in the country. Of this total, forty pairs were recorded in south Connemara in a survey by Dr Paul Haworth in 1986. In 1989, Michael Miller, then working at the Connemara National Park, found about twenty-five pairs breeding on the bogs north of Roundstone, an encouraging increase on the 1986 counts in that particular area.

The largest concentration of breeding birds occurs on the bogs north of Roundstone, where the majority nest in areas of very wet, hummocky, intact bog. These areas provide superior cover for nesting and invertebrate food for newly hatched chicks. In addition, the wetness of the areas may confer some immunity to the effects of fires, which are common in spring and early summer when set to burn off dead grass. Most of the remaining pairs nest on partially or totally cut-over bog while a few pairs in the east of the region occupy territories on drier, uncut but heavily grazed blanket bog. The second largest concentration is on the bogs north of the Spiddle-Inveran road. Elsewhere, a few pairs may nest on the hills of north-west Connemara.

When the breeding season comes the golden plover casts off its drab brown winter plumage and takes on an immaculate livery of golden, spotted upper parts and a blackish face and underparts, separated by a whitish-yellow stripe from the forehead along the neck and sides and down to the flanks. This is a wonderful sight, but one which could rapidly disappear unless effective measures are taken soon to protect the breeding habitats of this *Red Data Book* species; habitats which, it should be recalled, are also internationally important for their flora and other elements of their fauna.

The only notable flocks of wintering golden plover reported in Connemara have been on Omey Strand, Roundstone bog and in the vicinity of the Connemara Golf Club near Ballyconneely, where several hundreds feed and roost in the autumn and winter. And, in passing, it should be noted that the

Above: A golden plover on its nest.
Below: A golden plover nest in heather.

latter site is also important for other waders during the winter and during the early autumn when birds such as the ruff use it as a stopping place on their southward migration.

The merlin is Ireland's smallest and probably most elusive bird of prey. The male, which is slate-blue above and rufous-striped below, is only slightly bigger than a blackbird. The larger female has dark brown upperparts and a barred brown and creamy tail. Merlins require open ground for hunting, have a preference for drier areas of the bog where there is still heather and bracken and avoid wetter areas with common cottongrass and purple moor-grass. They nest in lake island scrub, or on the ground, in dense heather and bracken, and, in recent times, in conifer plantations. Occasionally, they lay their eggs in the disused nests of hooded crows. In the mid-1980s it was estimated that there were at least fifteen pairs in Connemara, of which about half successfully reared chicks. This represents about 15 per cent of the national total.

Merlins fly fast and low over the bog in pursuit of their prey, which includes meadow pipits and other small birds and, on occasions, woodmice, dragonflies and day-flying moths. This behaviour renders them very hard to see, either by their prey or by human observers. It also makes them extremely vulnerable to collisions with the many newly erected barbed-wire fences, hazards which most of us would not have predicted until they began to appear in such abundance.

Outside the breeding season, merlins travel widely and can be seen most frequently on the coast, chasing flocks of pipits and finches.

The blanket bog is a quiet and lonely place in the early autumn. Only a few pipits and the occasional red grouse or Irish hare keep us company. But the arrival of the white-fronted geese from Greenland in mid-October changes all that. Though not as numerous or widespread as in former times, their unmistakable cackling can fill the air as they fly high between their roosts and feeding areas. They feed in some of the wettest areas of the bog, areas into which we venture at our peril - to be sucked into an ice-cold, metre-deep quagmire, several kilometres from the nearest road is, at worst, extremely dangerous and, at best, very uncomfortable. Their feeding signs are obvious. Sedge plants are strewn across the bog surface where they have been uprooted, their nutritious bulbils torn from them and eaten. At dusk the geese return to their roosts, usually remote lakes in the bog or, more likely these days, within some of the extensive forestry plantations which now occupy their former ranges.

In the 1950s it was estimated that there were about 600 geese in Connemara. They made up several distinct flocks which were found on the bogs north-east of Roundstone and east of Ballyconneely, in the Maum Valley, Gleninagh and on the hills north of Spiddle. But by the 1970s the flocks north of Spiddle and in Gleninagh had disappeared and the total Connemara population reduced to between 140 and 205 birds as a result of drainage, turf cutting, afforestation, road construction and considerable shooting. In the winter of 1983-4 there were only about 100 birds left, but by 1988-9 there had been an increase to 134-140. This increase, however, merely reflected the growth in the national population and not any real improvement in the situation in Connemara.

The national population of white-fronted geese now stands at over 15,000 birds, about half of which spend the winter on the Wexford Slobs on the south-east coast of Ireland. Ireland holds about 50 per cent of the world population of the Greenland white-fronted goose, which is one of the rarest sub-species of geese in the world. The other half winters in Scotland and Wales. Clearly, Ireland has an international obligation to conserve the goose and its habitat, not only on the Wexford Slobs, but also at its other haunts around the country. That the Connemara population should have been allowed to dwindle to about 100 birds is a tragedy which reflects the equally tragic loss of so much of our blanket bog. It is to be hoped, therefore, that the decline of both can be stemmed and that conservation measures can be put in place to secure the future of Connemara's remaining intact blanket bog and white-fronted goose flocks.

The numerous lakes which punctuate the blanket bog are generally rather infertile, but they do support small numbers of breeding teal, mallard and red-breasted mergansers. In the mid-1980s there were at least fourteen pairs of teal, thirty-three pairs of mallard and twelve pairs of mergansers nesting beside these isolated lakes. In addition, there is a large colony of cormorants on an island in Lough Scannive in the middle of the bog to the north of Roundstone. In 1970 this contained 150 nests, by 1974 it had grown to 209 and by 1985 there were 218.

Little grebes breed on many Connemara lakes, too, but their small size and diving habits sometimes make them hard to find. They feed on small fish and insects and nest on floating platforms of water plants anchored to submerged vegetation. Like the red-breasted mergansers, most of them move down to the coast after the breeding season.

The heron saga

Standing motionless beside a stream or lake, or in the shallows at the edge of the sea, herons are a familiar sight throughout Connemara. They eat many kinds of fish including eels and trout in freshwater and wrasse at the coast. They also take common frogs, small mammals and birds when they come across them.

They usually build large nests in the tops of tall trees. However, in Connemara, where tall trees are few and far between, they have to make do with low trees and bushes, usually on lake islands. Though the nests and the birds themselves are large, it is remarkably difficult to find either. An island with only one heron visible from the mainland might prove to have four or five nests on it when thoroughly investigated. It is therefore necessary to search every likely island for nests if an accurate count of the population is to be made. Dr Karl Partridge did this in the mid-1970s, Dr Paul Haworth repeated the survey in the mid-1980s and Pádraic Reaney and I conducted a third count in 1989 to see if the population decline between the first two surveys had continued. The overall results of the three surveys are presented in Table 9. This shows that there was a dramatic decline in the number of nests between 1977 and 1986 followed by a partial recovery up to 1989. What could have caused the 57 per cent decline in nest numbers? The first suggestion was that, because herons are known to catch fish at fish farms, the managers of the local fish farms, which had been established between 1977 and 1986, might have been killing them off to protect their stocks. Clearly, this was likely to be a contentious issue and not one that could be resolved by merely asking the fish farmers whether they had killed the herons, because killing herons without a special licence is an infringement of the Wildlife Act. There could, of course, be other reasons and, to cut a long story short, when we examined the weather records for the period back to 1960, we

Table 9
The Connemara breeding heron population, 1977, 1986 and 1990
(based on Partridge 1984, Haworth 1987, Whilde 1990a)

	1977	1986	1989
Number of heronries	29	27	31
Number of nests	269	116	159
Number of nests per heronry	9.3	4.3	5.1

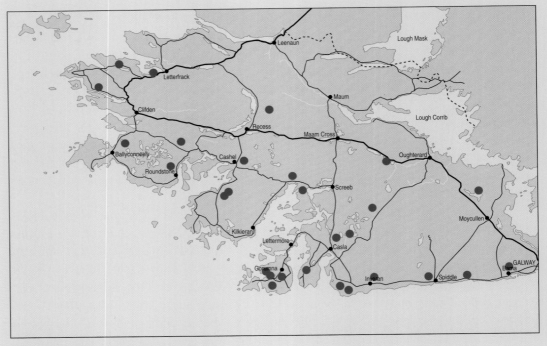

Map 10: Location of heronries in Connemara.

noticed that the weather in January 1985 and February 1986 was by far the coldest since the very severe winter of 1962-3. In that winter the heron population in England and Wales (and presumably in Ireland) suffered a serious decline, primarily due to a shortage of food which affected young and inexperienced herons in particular. It seemed likely, therefore, that the cold winter weather in the mid-1980s reduced the Connemara population, first by killing off the young birds which could not catch fish in frozen streams or down at the coast where their prey had moved offshore into warmer

Heron chicks on their nest.

water, and secondly by adversely affecting the breeding condition of the remaining adults. Thus a potentially unpleasant confrontation was avoided and a lesson well learned that disasters in nature can have natural as well as human causes.

Nevertheless, we do know, from rings returned to us by fish farmers, that herons do 'die' on fish farms. But it is also clear that the numbers lost in this way could not account for the decline between 1977 and 1986. Co-operation between fish farmers and conservationists in the collection of information about a common problem is the obvious way to make progress in dealing with that problem.

The ringing of Connemara herons has shown us that many of them stay in the region, although winter counts suggest that some move into inner Galway Bay during that period. Just a small number of the birds ringed in the 1970s study moved elsewhere in Ireland. Only one was recovered outside the country, in southern Scotland. One tagged with a yellow ring near Rosmuck in June 1989 was seen near Barna Pier in September and October of the same year. Otherwise, recoveries of recently ringed birds have been from within the west Connemara nesting area.

Waterbirds

Although Connemara has many freshwater lakes and a very long coastline, it supports relatively few wintering ducks, geese, swans, waders or other water birds. This point is made very clearly by the figures in Table 10 which are based on a comprehensive survey carried out by members of the Galway Branch of the Irish Wildbird Conservancy in January 1986. Although Connemara holds over 60 per cent of the freshwater lakes in County Galway, these held only 2 per cent of the freshwater birds and only 1 per cent of all the waterbirds counted in the county. Likewise, only 58 per cent of the freshwater species were found on the Connemara lakes, and this figure translated into a mere 40 per cent of all the waterbird species recorded in the county. Combining the freshwater and coastal totals, Connemara held 75 per cent of the species in County Galway, but only 8 per cent of the total number of waterbirds.

The Connemara coast is much richer in species and numbers of birds but still not as productive as the coastline of inner Galway Bay running from Barna southwards to Ballyvaghan on the north Clare coast, which is about one third of the length of the coast of Connemara.

Undoubtedly, more birds do occur in Connemara on occasions. Furthermore, it is likely that some birds are missed in counts. This must be true particularly for ducks like the wigeon which spend a lot of time on the sea around the islands, where they are not easily visible from the mainland, and waders such as sanderling, which are known to occur on the sandy beaches from time to time.

Table 10
County Galway Waterbird Count - January 1986.
(based on counts by the Galway Branch of the Irish Wildbird Conservancy - *In* Whilde 1987)

WETLANDS	CONNEMARA FRESHWATER	EAST GALWAY FRESHWATER	TOTAL FRESHWATER	CONNEMARA COAST	INNER GALWAY BAY	TOTAL COAST	GRAND TOTAL
Number of wetlands with birds	54	61	115	1	1	2	117
Number of wetlands without birds	80	26	106				106
Total number of wetlands	134	87	221	1	1	2	223
Percentage of wetlands	61	39					
BIRDS							
Number of species	19	32	33	31	37	38	48
Number of birds	697	37,017	37,714	3,487	12,322	15,809	53,523
Percentage of total birds	1	69		7	23		

Table 11
Waterbird species recorded in Connemara in January 1986.
(based on counts by the Galway Branch of the Irish Wildbird Conservancy - *In* Whilde 1987)

SPECIES	FRESHWATER	NUMBERS OF BIRDS COAST	TOTAL
Great northern diver	-	4	4
Little grebe	9	16	25
Cormorant	19	63	82
Shag	-	17	17
Heron	12	32	44
Mute swan	37	180	217
Whooper swan	69	-	69
Greenland white-fronted goose	21	-	21
Brent goose	-	7	7
Wigeon	-	18	18
Teal	23	45	68
Mallard	10	32	42
Pochard	367	80	447
Tufted duck	43	-	43
Goldeneye	-	7	7
Red-breasted merganser	3	58	61
Coot	2	-	2
Oystercatcher	-	180	180
Ringed plover	-	187	187
Golden plover	-	105	105
Grey plover	-	5	5
Lapwing	-	235	235
Dunlin	-	153	153
Snipe	1	1	2
Bar-tailed godwit	-	41	41
Curlew	27	238	265
Redshank	-	59	59
Greenshank	-	3	3
Turnstone	-	36	36
Black-headed gull	4	213	217
Common gull	6	142	148
Lesser black-backed gull	2	-	2
Herring gull	24	1,070	1,094
Iceland gull	-	3	3
Glaucous gull	-	8	8
Great black-backed gull	18	249	267
Total	**697**	**3,487**	**4,184**

Some interesting observations were made during the survey. Several of the whooper swans seen in the 1986 survey had numbered leg bands which had been attached to them on their breeding grounds in Iceland. The sight of such ringed birds in the wild is an infrequent and exciting experience. It confirms for us in a very real way, the fact that these birds have travelled considerable distances to reach Connemara. And, importantly, it should heighten our feeling of international responsibility because these birds are clearly not just 'ours'; they are members of an international community.

The only species of swan which occurs consistently in relatively large numbers in Connemara is the mute swan. Throughout the winter there are usually well over 100 and sometimes more than 200 in the region. The largest numbers occur in a single flock on upper Camus Bay, most often in the vicinity of Screeb, where over 120 have been recorded on occasions. Smaller flocks occur in Ballyconneely Bay and at the head of Cleggan Bay. These numbers dwindle as spring approaches and some of the birds presumably return to their nesting territories. In late spring there may be as few as forty immature or non-breeding mute swans remaining in Camus Bay.

As with the herons, it is surprising how difficult it is to locate big, white swans in their nesting areas. The nests are well camouflaged and birds may lie very flat when they are incubating, which can make the identification of nests on distant lake islands particularly awkward. Be that as it may,

Mute swans.

a survey of breeding mute swans was carried out by members of the Galway Branch of the Irish Wildbird Conservancy in 1992. This yielded a total of fifteen pairs and five individuals which may have been nesting, suggesting a minimum breeding population of twenty pairs. In addition, there was a minimum of ninety-four non-breeding and immature swans in the region. These figures indicate that the summer population is about 140 birds, to which can be added an average of about three young birds per brood, giving a late summer total of about 200, which matches fairly closely the autumn and winter figures referred to above.

It is likely that there is some movement of mute swans in and out of Connemara. However, this is probably not a major factor influencing the population size. Mute swans are generally fairly sedentary in Ireland and so far no swans ringed in Galway, Cork or Dublin have been seen in Connemara.

Some uncommon gulls were also reported in the 1986 survey. For example, Iceland and glaucous gulls were seen on the coast. These gulls, which in adult plumage notably have no black on their wings, are northern species. The former nests only on the coasts of Greenland and arctic Canada, while the latter has a circumpolar breeding distribution above latitude 60° north. Although they regularly visit north European waters in small numbers, their appearance in the west of Ireland is always noteworthy. Also noteworthy is the appearance in winter of the lesser black-backed gulls. Although these breed in large numbers in the west of Ireland, they travel south after nesting, returning usually only in March and April.

Common gulls are not as abundant in Ireland as their name suggests. In the winter they occur all around the coast, with the largest concentrations in county Cork. In the breeding season, however, they concentrate in the four western counties of Galway, Mayo, Sligo and Donegal. There are moves afoot to change the name from 'common' to 'mew' gull, in line with American practice. This seems sensible as the term 'mew' describes the call of this species very well.

During the breeding season common gulls in Connemara nest in very small colonies, sometimes of only one or two pairs, mainly on rocks and small islands in freshwater lakes. A few pairs nest on coastal islands. In 1992 there were sixty-three pairs nesting in twelve inland colonies. This contrasts with 104 pairs in 1986 and 107 pairs in ten colonies in 1977. The substantial decrease between 1986 and 1993 is mirrored elsewhere in Galway, Mayo, Sligo and Donegal. The reason would seem to lie outside the breeding grounds as the breeding success of common gulls on nearby Lough Corrib has been consistently high from 1980 to 1992. One possibility is that Irish birds have moved to a colony in the north-east of Scotland which has increased from about 5,000 pairs in the 1970s to between 25,000 and 40,000 pairs at the end of the 1980s. Why Irish birds should move to Scotland remains to be explained.

Most of the herring gulls in Connemara in 1986 were recorded at Rossaveel, where the Galway fishing fleet is based. Since then their population has continued a decline which started in the late 1970s. The numbers in the region today are only a fraction of those present in the mid-1970s when the population was at its peak. This decline is most likely to have been caused by botulism, a form of poisoning which the gulls pick up at rubbish dumps. The poison, which causes paralysis and dehydration, is produced by a bacterium called *Clostridium botulinum,* which thrives in the airless conditions of the black plastic bags we all use to dispose of our rubbish, and in the puddles which develop on and around rubbish dumps. A decline of such proportions in any other species would have caused an outcry amongst conservationists and the general public. But gulls were abundant in the past and considered to be pests in some quarters. Now the tables have been turned and it is time to reassess our attitude to these birds and to ask if conservation measures are needed to halt the population decline resulting from our wasteful and negligent behaviour.

Black-headed gulls are seen infrequently inland in Connemara, where the damp pastures they favour for winter feeding are scarce. Nor do they breed in large numbers inland or on the coast. In 1992 there was only one major colony, on an island in Lough Naskanniva, to the west of Inveran and that only about 1 kilometre (less than a mile) from the sea. There were 110 nests in this colony which is similar to the total of 113 nests found in two colonies in 1977 - one on Lough Naskanniva and the other on Loughauneveneen, just across the road to the west.

Nesting with the black-headed gulls on Lough Naskanniva, in 1977 and in 1992, were up to sixty pairs of common terns. These are birds which are more commonly seen on offshore islands. We will meet them again when we move down to the coast.

Birds of the coast and coastal lowlands

Connemara has an incredibly long and complex coastline. To get some idea of its length and complexity let us make some comparisons, taking Barna in the south-east and Aasleagh Falls at the head of Killary Harbour in the north as the starting and finishing points of the Connemara coast (see Map 2).

If we flew in a straight line over land our journey would be 53 kilometres (33 miles). If we sailed around the coast, taking the safest route around Slyne Head and keeping well out from any dangerous rocks and islands, we would cover about 130 kilometres (81 miles). If we considered walking along the shore, a very rough estimate of the distance, taken from the Ordnance Survey 1/2inch to 1 mile map, would be at least 440 kilometres (275 miles) - over eight times the straight-line distance.

But, if we actually tried to walk the shore, we would find that, as soon as we had passed Inveran, our estimate would quickly go astray because the actual shoreline is much more intricate than any map can show. It is so intricate, in fact, that Tim Robinson suggests that the stretch of shoreline between Rossaveel and Roundstone is at least 400 kilometres (250 miles) long! So how long might our total journey on foot be? Seven or eight hundred kilometres (450-500 miles), perhaps? Whatever the exact length of the mainland shore, we would have to add to this figure the shoreline lengths of all the islands if we wanted to know how much seashore habitat is available for coastal wildlife. A thousand kilometres (600 miles)? More? We will probably never know.

We do know, however, that examining wildlife on such a long and complicated coastline is extremely difficult. Birds are particularly hard to study as their mobility adds greatly to our logistical problems.

Let us start our coastal investigations at a quiet spot on the south-western tip of Gorumna Island. Here there is diverse habitat with rocky shore, saltmarsh and maritime turf, a brackish pool, low heath with rocky outcrops, willow scrub and stone walls. It is a sunny afternoon late in July - not the most exciting time for bird-watching, but good enough for us to be able to pinpoint the main members of the summer bird community. Our attention is first caught by the characteristic, strident alarm call of an oystercatcher as it flies off to a distant rock. Other oystercatchers are less concerned by our presence and continue feeding on the maritime turf. They are regular members of the community throughout the year, nesting on the shore and feeding in the inter-tidal area when the tide is low and roosting and feeding on the maritime turf when the tide is in.

A brackish pool at the southern tip of Gorumna Island. An attractive habitat for a variety of birds throughout the year.

Several mallard paddle quickly between the seaweed-covered rocks in a sheltered cove. They are the only ducks we are likely to see on this part of the coast all the year round, though teal and red-breasted mergansers may make an appearance from time to time.

Nearby, perched on a low cliff, just above the high-tide line, there is a small brown bird with dark legs and a thin bill. It is uttering high-pitched notes, similar to some we have heard in the mountains and on the blanket bogs. This is a rock pipit, a close relation of the ubiquitous meadow pipit. But while the meadow pipit is found almost everywhere inland, the rock pipit lives only on the coast where there are rocks, cliffs or stone piers. It is usually safe to say that a pipit seen close to the water is a rock pipit, but this can be confirmed by its slightly larger size, darker plumage and very dark legs.

As we approach the marsh-fringed, brackish pool there is a sudden flurry of wings accompanied by a rasping call. A snipe zig-zags away, quickly diving into cover behind a distant wall. This is typical habitat for snipe, with damp soil which it can probe for its food and low cover for security. Snipe are common, though not abundant, in Connemara during the breeding season.

They can be located by their 'drumming', a vibrating sound produced by air passing between their tail feathers as they dive obliquely during display flight. They are also common and widespread during the winter when more birds arrive from northern latitudes. Although we have no detailed population figures it seems likely that, as their wetland habitats shrink in the face of drainage and land reclamation, their numbers are declining.

Suddenly, as if out of nowhere, we first hear the 'pee-wit' of the lapwing and then catch a glimpse of a single bird flying erratically over the turf, flapping its broad and very rounded wings in typical lapwing fashion. It is joined by a second bird which suggests that they have nested somewhere nearby on the short cropped turf. Lapwing are widespread, although their numbers in Connemara during the breeding season are small. In winter they are scarce, unless very cold weather forces birds westwards. Then large flocks may appear for the duration of the cold snap. While the lapwings perform their graceful aerial manoeuvres a wheatear lands on a rocky outcrop but soon moves on. It may have been breeding in the area but, at this time of the summer, it is more likely to be moving through on its southward migration.

High up the shore, on the drier turf, there is a large flock of starlings feeding busily and noisily in a tight formation. This is a regular sight from mid-summer onwards as the adults and young of the year come together to form effective foraging groups. Although the winter numbers of starlings in Connemara are not large, the local population is probably augmented by immigrants from the Continent and together they form large roosts, often in conifer plantations.

Down at the tideline, well camouflaged against the mottled, decaying seaweed, we can see several linnets picking seeds from the ground. These small finches breed along the coast and throughout Connemara. But after the breeding season they tend to move out of the area and gather in large flocks inland or along more productive stretches of coast such as occur around inner Galway Bay.

Moving inland about 200 metres (220 yards) to the shelter of the hills, we find low scrub growing on the drier ground beside the walls. Here there is a family of stonechats, a colourful male, a dullish female and four brown, streaked and speckled juveniles flitting in and out of the foliage. Occasionally one of the adults flies up from a bush to pluck an insect from the air. Male stonechats

A male stonechat - a common species near the Connemara coast.

are among the most distinctive small birds in Connemara with their black heads, broad white half-collars, rich chestnut under-parts and whitish rump patches. They often perch in the open, on the tops of bushes and frequently on telephone wires, uttering their persistent, scolding 'taccing' call. Connemara stonechats also undertake significant local movements after the breeding season. Most of the inland breeding birds move down to the coast where we can often find large numbers of them within a few hundred metres of the sea during the winter months.

The stonechat has a western distribution in Europe, breeding commonly only in Ireland, western Britain, western France, Iberia and eastwards around the Mediterranean. To the east it is replaced by the whinchat which is somewhat similar in appearance but distinguished from the stonechat at all times of the year by the white (male) or light (female) stripe above the eye. Occasionally, whinchats are seen near the coast on passage in September, and two pairs probably bred in the vicinity of the Connemara National Park in 1990. The sighting of a male at Dog's Bay in July 1992 suggests that breeding might also have taken place in that area.

A little further inland, where the willow scrub is getting higher, we meet a robin, one of the commonest hedgerow and woodland birds in the west of Ireland in winter and summer. In the more exposed coastal areas where hedges and scrub are scarce, the robin is scarce, too. However, there are few areas of any size in lowland Connemara without their resident birds. The same can be said for the dunnock, the wren and the only species smaller than the wren, the goldcrest. All are reasonably common and widespread in Connemara throughout the year.

This is not true of the yellowhammer singing in bushes on a crag beside Ballynakill Lake. This species, once common in the west of Ireland, appears to have declined in numbers in recent decades, though the Connemara coast seems to remain one of its strongholds. It was also common on Inishbofin early in the century but by 1943 there was only one pair left and by the mid-1970s there were no yellowhammers breeding there. In the winter the yellowhammer disappears from most of Connemara, presumably moving south-eastwards to winter elsewhere in Ireland or perhaps in the south-east of England.

Almost hidden amongst the branches of one of the taller bushes are a male blackbird and a song thrush. These two familiar species are often linked together in our minds. They are common hedgerow and garden species which are always around. However, familiarity should not stop us taking an interest in them. As with all plants and animals, their populations fluctuate - sometimes for natural reasons and sometimes as a consequence of human activities.

Anecdotal information suggests the song thrush is declining in the west of Ireland and the blackbird might be on the increase. Unfortunately such information, without figures to back it up, is almost impossible to evaluate. But it seems there could be substance to the anecdotes if information coming from Britain is anything to go by. There, bird-ringing records have shown that fifty years ago there was just one blackbird for every three song thrushes. Now the reverse is the case and breeding blackbirds outnumber song thrushes by three to one. It could be argued that this change is due to an increase in blackbirds. But experts are more inclined to believe it is due to a major decline in the breeding song thrush population. Cold winters could have killed off more song thrushes than blackbirds because they are smaller birds and therefore less resistant to freezing conditions. The growing use of toxic slug and snail pellets could be a contributing factor - echoing the cause of the peregrine decline in the 1960s. The abundance of broken snail shells at a song thrush's 'anvil' is testimony to the importance of these animals in its diet. Some people suggest that predation of chicks by magpies, also members of this coastal community, could be damaging the song thrush population as well. However, research has shown that the breeding success of song thrushes in Britain is increasing rather than decreasing, even where there are large magpie populations, so the magpie, a universal scapegoat, cannot be blamed in this case.

What is the situation in Connemara? Are song thrushes really declining? If so, by how much, how fast and why? We need to monitor such common species as well as the rarities if we want to keep our finger on the pulse of environmental change.

Finally, a question about blackbirds. Where do all the females go in winter? Observations in east Connemara in recent years have indicated that from October to February most of the blackbirds in the area are males. Is this the case throughout Connemara? Are there really more males than females or are the females less conspicuous or using different habitats? Do females leave the area after the breeding season? Is the bias in favour of males caused by an influx of males from Britain and the continent? These are just a few questions we can ask about a species we all think we know well. Is it not chastening to contemplate our ignorance of all the species we do not know well?

Contrary to what one might expect, Connemara's long coastline does not attract large numbers of shorebirds each winter, as is evident from the figures presented in Table 11. We will not see the large flocks of waders and wildfowl familiar to ornithologists on the east and south coasts of Ireland. Why should this be?

First, fewer birds generally migrate to the west coast either from eastern and northern Europe, or along the west coast between their northern breeding grounds and their winter quarters to the south. Secondly, Connemara lacks large rivers with extensive tidal estuaries. Thirdly, those rivers which do discharge at the coast are relatively infertile and do not supply the nutrients required to generate the food supplies wintering and migratory birds need. Fourthly, Connemara lacks the extensive areas of sandy or muddy shore favoured particularly by waders. Much of the shoreline is composed of seaweed-covered boulders. Such habitat, though attractive to some birds like turnstones and curlews, does not produce sufficient food to support large numbers. Finally, much of the shoreline is exposed to strong, prevailing south-westerly winds and rough seas. Because many shorebirds need to feed for the maximum number of hours possible each day, it is in their interest to spend as much time as possible on sheltered shores where feeding is not affected by strong and cooling winds.

Most of the wading birds listed in Table 11 can be found in small numbers in many of the bays between Killary Harbour and Inveran and on sheltered shores between Inveran and Barna. However, counts have not been made on a sufficiently regular basis at enough sites to allow detailed discussion of the distributions and behaviour of these species. Nevertheless, it appears that Omey Island strand is a favoured resort, particularly for ringed plovers. Ringed plovers are also plentiful on the sandy beaches of Ballyconneely Bay and Dog's Bay. Lapwing, snipe and common sandpipers nest on the coastal grasslands, as do small numbers of dunlin and possibly redshank.

Oystercatchers can be seen all around the coast, but usually in small numbers. Likewise redshank, bar-tailed godwits and curlew, but these tend to be well spaced out along the coast, and often difficult to see against the background of brown and golden seaweed. Turnstones, with their shorter legs, are even harder to pick out as they forage through the seaweeds near the edge of the water. Although turnstones do not breed in Ireland, migrating and non-breeding birds can often be seen on remote headlands and on offshore islands during the spring and summer.

Dunlin are very scarce on the Connemara coast in winter, although it is encouraging to note that small numbers breed on the coastal machair. This is also a favoured haunt of golden plover and lapwing and, during the autumn migration, small numbers of ruff can be seen on these sandy grasslands near the golf course at Aillebrack. Birds which favour the sandy beaches, and are seen nowhere else, are sanderlings. These small, plump and extremely active birds are easily recognised by their whitish plumage and the manner in which they race down the beach after retreating waves. Finally, among the waders, we can look out for purple sandpipers, as they migrate westwards, in late winter and early spring, along the south Connemara shore and then northwards around the coast. Occasionally, they have been seen on offshore islands in late summer, presumably on their southward migration. In contrast to sanderlings, we are only likely to see purple sandpipers on rocky shores where their very dark upper parts, contrasting white underparts, yellow legs and yellow base to the bill ensure their identification.

Birds offshore

The birds we see offshore during the winter include ducks like the red-breasted merganser, wigeon, teal, mallard and, occasionally, long-tailed duck, known more evocatively in North America as oldsquaw. The long-tailed ducks we see will probably have bred in Iceland. Another northern species, which visits Connemara waters very occasionally indeed, is the eider. That we do not see them more often is rather surprising as the nearest breeding colony is not very far away on Inishmurray, off the coast of Sligo.

Great northern divers are regular visitors to several of the bays and we might chance to see one or two in almost any month of the year. Red-throated divers are scarce visitors, but, like black-throated divers, they are being seen increasingly in Galway Bay, so it is quite likely that they will be reported in winter in some of the south Connemara bays before long. On 9 June 1980 Jim Fox saw two red-throated divers flying from the direction of the Roundstone bogs towards Mutton Island, off Dog's Bay, fuelling speculation that they might have been breeding in the area. No further sightings have been reported, although the habitat north of Roundstone is similar to that in which red-throated divers have bred and may continue to breed in Donegal.

Cormorants and shags, so difficult to tell apart at a distance, especially in the poor light of winter, are common although rarely numerous off the Connemara coast. Shags breed mainly on the west coast and offshore islands and are more likely to be seen in more open waters than cormorants which, as we have already noted, nest in several large colonies on inland lake islands. Little is known about the shag population. Any professional research which has been conducted on coastal fish eating birds has usually been concentrated on cormorants because of their reputation for eating game and commercial fish species. So there is ample opportunity for an amateur research project on the ecology and behaviour of shags.

A cormorant on its nest in a tree.

Let us now visit an uninhabited offshore island to see what bird-life we can find. The swell is up, but fortunately it is coming from the north-west and there is little wind so we can make our undignified landing onto the steep, skin-grazing cliff in the sheltered south-facing cove. On the opposite side of the cove fulmars cackle on the cliff ledges, responding to their partners which are gliding gracefully on the updraft near the rim of the cliff. The month is July and this remote cliff-girt island is full of life. Rabbits scamper into their burrows as we ease ourselves up onto the short maritime sward which covers the island. Great black-backed gulls croak above our heads as they glide rather lazily towards their colony at the end of the island.

This is a good day, one of the few when landing is fairly easy and we can stand upright on the top of the island, for, like all the others on the Atlantic fringe of Ireland, it is battered by strong winds and heavy seas for much of the year. Still, this is an advantage for the seabirds which are here because they can live and breed undisturbed by people or mainland predators. At one time sheep were kept on the island, but now only the rabbits are left to graze the vegetation down to snooker-table smoothness, and to provide food for the great black-backed gulls. Rabbits were introduced into Ireland by the Normans in the thirteenth century and seem to have been released onto most of the larger offshore islands where they have had a devastating effect on the ecology by over-grazing the vegetation and undermining the thin soils with their burrows.

However, some of the rabbit burrows have been put to good use by the Manx shearwaters which nest in them. Nest is perhaps the wrong word because the shearwaters lay just a single egg on the bare soil of burrows which are located on a slope, usually quite close to the cliff. Manx shearwaters, with their legs set far back under their bodies, are very clumsy on land, so living on a slope close to the cliff edge makes taking off and returning to their burrows quick and easy. This is important because, although they return at night, great black-backed gulls are always ready to attack and devour a hapless shearwater on the ground. In the air, though, Manx shearwaters are the masters. Using the up-draughts of air created by the waves, they can travel endlessly, gliding, low across the water, flapping occasionally and characteristically showing alternately the white of their underwings and the dark of their upper parts. Outside the breeding season and during the first six or so years of their lives, before they settle down to breed, the shearwaters roam the Atlantic Ocean along a regular route which takes them south to the east coast of South America, then north again to the waters off eastern North America and finally back across the Atlantic to Europe. No wonder they are seen as masters of ocean navigation as well as efficient, economical flight.

The tiny storm petrel is a close relation of the manx shearwater and leads a similar nomadic life. Each pair rears a single chick in a hole under a rock or in a wall. The adults take it in turns to go on feeding expeditions as far south as the Bay of Biscay, so the sitting parent and the chick sometimes have to survive several days without food. They are well able to do so, but it does mean that it takes the chick longer to develop to the flying stage than in many other species. However, by the time they are ready to leave the island, the chicks have stored up so much food that they are substantially bigger than their parents. They need these food reserves to carry them through the first few weeks at sea while they are developing their feeding skills. Petrels pick their food, small planktonic animals, from the surface of the sea. As they search for food they let their feet hang down, giving the impression that they are walking on the water, hence the name petrel, derived from St Peter. In Irish they are known as peadairín na stoirme , 'little Peter of the storm'.

Like Manx shearwaters, storm petrels only come to the island at night. They arrive in waves starting about 11 p.m., and from then on birds will be coming and going continuously until four or five o'clock in the morning. Not all the visitors are breeding on the island. Some are young birds, just prospecting, others may be non-breeding adults 'touring' the colonies of Ireland and Britain. One such bird which turned up on this island had a shiny new ring on one of its legs. To the amazement of all concerned, it had been ringed only twenty-four hours earlier on an island on the west coast of Wales!

On dark, moonless nights the petrels can return to their breeding holes in reasonable safety. But when the moon is bright they become easy prey for the great black-backed gulls which are nesting nearby. Evidence of the great black-backed gulls' predatory behaviour comes in the pellets they regurgitate. These are composed of the feathers and bones which they cannot digest. Yet in spite of their depredations, the gulls do not seriously affect the storm petrel or Manx shearwater populations.

The gulls also feed on fish, and are capable of swallowing large herrings and mackerel in one go. Outside the breeding season we will see them more often on the mainland, often at rubbish dumps or sometimes, in small numbers, far up the valleys in the Twelve Bens where they scavenge salmon which have died after spawning.

Fulmars are closely related to Manx shearwaters and storm petrels. But they have a different life-style, one we can study in less discomfort because they are visible throughout the day. They are also clumsy on the ground, but the gulls pay no attention to them because the fulmars are bigger and nest on fairly inaccessible cliff ledges. They are ocean-roaming birds, too, but many return in winter to their nesting cliffs, on the mainland as well as on offshore islands. Fulmars, like many seabirds, are long-lived, some reaching the age of fifty or more. They tend to return to the same nesting ledge year after year, sometimes for several decades. We should remember when visiting a fulmar colony that these birds may well out-live us!

Shags are nesting on the rocks near the bottom of the cliff. And close by are several black guillemots, made visible only by their distinctive white wing patches. When they take to the water we see that the rest of their plumage is black and their legs and feet bright red. These features distinguish them from the more familiar guillemot which has a white breast and black feet. The two species have different nesting habits, too. The black guillemot nests in cracks and crevices in the cliff, while the guillemot breeds, often in large, tight-packed groups, on large open ledges. There are no ledges like that on this island and we will have to go to Inishmore to see the nearest guillemot colony.

A few pairs of herring gulls nest along the cliffs and several pairs of lesser black-backed gulls nest on the fringe of the great black-backed gull colony. There are also oystercatchers, mallard, rock doves, wheatears, starlings, hooded crows, meadow pipits, rock pipits and a pair of peregrines on the island. Ravens and choughs appear from time to time but do not seem to nest here. Nor do the curlews, whimbrels and purple sandpipers which stop off briefly on their southward migrations.

At the western end of the island, by a lake, there are small piles of well-decayed droppings. Clearly, they have been here for some time - since the winter, in fact. They are the only signs to indicate that the island is visited in the winter by barnacle geese. These birds, which breed in north-east Greenland, come to uninhabited west coast islands each winter. They are rarely seen on the mainland of Connemara or elsewhere, except in Co. Sligo where a flock regularly uses the state nature reserve at Lissadell, on the north shore of Sligo Bay. The Irish headquarters of the barnacle geese is the Inishkea Islands, a few kilometres to the west of the Mullet in Co. Mayo.

If we are a little less adventurous we can visit an inhabited island like Inishbofin. Here we will find fulmars, but not Manx shearwaters or storm petrels. We will also find a greater range of land

Table 12
The bird community of an offshore island.

	RESIDENT	BREEDING	WINTERING	PASSAGE MIGRANT*	VISITOR
Fulmar		x			
Manx shearwater		x			
Storm petrel		x			
Shag	x				
Barnacle goose			x		
Mallard					x
Peregrine		x			
Oystercatcher	x				
Purple sandpiper				x	
Whimbrel				x	
Curlew				x	
Black guillemot		x			
Rock dove	x				
Meadow pipit	x				
Rock pipit	x				
Wheatear		x			
Chough					x
Raven					x
Starling		x			

* Undoubtedly, many more species use the island while on migration but we would have to spend considerable periods on the island in spring and autumn to record them.

birds including such rarities as the corncrake and the corn bunting, species which we will consider in more detail in Chapter 6. The bird-life of Inishbofin has been well documented by two of Ireland's leading ornithologists, Clive Hutchinson and Major R.F. Ruttledge, and their paper in *Irish Birds*, Ireland's main ornithological journal, should be consulted by any bird-watcher visiting the island.

For those lucky enough, or hardy enough, to take a boat trip offshore, there can be further ornithological delights in store. In spring great, pomarine, long-tailed and arctic skuas can pass close to the coast. Gannets, too, start to appear and their numbers build up as the summer progresses. And in August, the Manx shearwater flocks are often joined by sooty shearwaters and occasional Cory's and great shearwaters.

Birds on inshore islands and rocks

For once the sea is calm. Looking out from the shore we can see a distant undulation which, according to our chart, is a small island. Over the next ten minutes, as we speed towards it in a deceptively sturdy and safe inflatable dinghy, the undulation gradually takes form. The island is low, no more than 10 metres (33 feet) at its highest point, and rocky with a fringe of brown, tangled seaweeds which merge into a jumble of lichen-encrusted angular boulders and rocky outcrops. Only on the high ground, near the summit, can we see any green vegetation. Nothing stirs on the island. No birds are visible. Are we wasting our time?

Suddenly there is an explosion of noise, louder even than the engine, as four oystercatchers express their raucous displeasure at our approach. We are not surprised, as there are oystercatchers nesting on most of the small offshore islands. We cut the engine and continue drifting silently towards the island. The oystercatchers settle down again and peace returns, nothing moves. Then, when we are within four or five boat lengths of the shore, there is an eerily silent white eruption. Scores of terns take to the air and fly low out over the water in a tight flock. They wheel and most return to the shore behind the ridge where they become invisible to us again. A few settle on prominent boulders at the edge of the water. The quietness of the display is uncanny. It fills a brief but special moment in our experience of Connemara wildlife.

The silent birds are mainly arctic terns with just a few common terns blending in with them. When they fly between us and the bright blue sky we can distinguish the two species fairly easily. The arctic terns have a distinct, narrow black band on the trailing edge of their otherwise white wings while the common terns have dirty-looking, indistinctly marked underwings. If we are lucky enough to see the two species perched side by side on a rock we will notice that the arctic tern has a dark blood-red bill, while the common tern has a lighter, orange-red bill with a black tip. If we see them at the right angle it will also be clear that the arctic tern has longer tail streamers, projecting a little beyond the end of its wing tips.

The arctic terns are found more commonly on these remote islands, although they are quite fickle in their behaviour, shifting from island to island between seasons. Common terns are usually easier to locate because most of them nest on small islands close to the shore, often in sheltered waters at the heads of bays. They also return to the same island year after year. This habit is reflected in the Irish names of some of the islands on which they nest - Geabhróg, Oileán na nGeabhróg, Oileán Geabhróg - 'tern island'. These names must be of considerable antiquity, indicating that the terns have nested on them regularly for a very long time. During an all-Ireland tern survey in 1984 Tim Robinson extracted from his vast collection of Connemara place-names all those which included the name geabhróg (tern). All were visited and several previously unknown colonies were discovered.

Three other tern species nest in Connemara. The sandwich tern is the largest species, although it looks short and rather stubby when compared with the others. It has a long black bill with a yellow tip and elongated feathers at the back of its head which give it the appearance of having a crest. It nests in fewer but larger colonies as the figures in Table 13 on p. 157 indicate, usually on islands close to the coast.

The little tern, as its name suggests, is the smallest of the five Connemara terns. It has a yellow bill with a black tip and a distinctive white forehead. Unlike the other species, all of which nest on rocky islands, the little tern nests on sandy beaches on islands and occasionally on the mainland. Whereas the other species often make a nest with local plant material, the little tern just makes a shallow hollow in the sand and lays its two tiny, well-camouflaged eggs directly into this. The eggs are very difficult to see so it advisable that, when we see little terns behaving in an agitated way, we should leave the area in order to avoid accidentally treading on their eggs.

The rarest tern in Connemara, indeed the rarest in Ireland and in Europe generally, is the roseate tern. In many respects it is similar to the arctic and common terns but it has a rosy tinge to its breast feathers, a black bill with some red near the face, pure white tips on its primary (largest) wing feathers and tail streamers which project well beyond the end of its wings when it is perched.

Common terns breed on small islands in sheltered bays.

In 1984, only six pairs were located in Connemara. Since 1985 there has been no further attempt to locate the species so it is not known whether this number has changed or even whether the roseate tern still nests in the region. In the 1960s over 2,000 pairs nested in Ireland, but by 1984 the population had declined to 268 pairs. Since then the population had risen to 456 pairs in 1992 (plus any which might be nesting on the west coast), primarily as a result of intensive conservation action at its two main colonies, Rockabill off the coast of Dublin and Lady's Island Lake on the coast of Wexford. However, this is still a dangerously small number, because it represents such a large proportion of the north-west European population. So conservation work at its breeding colonies in Ireland, Britain and the Azores and in its wintering area off Ghana will have to continue for many years to come.

Nearly one fifth of all the terns in Ireland in 1984 nested in Connemara, making it one of the most important breeding areas in Ireland. The arctic tern population was particularly significant with over a quarter of the national population nesting on Connemara offshore islands. It will be interesting to see how the population has changed since then if, as is hoped, a repeat survey is carried out in 1994.

Map 11: Tern colonies in Connemara.

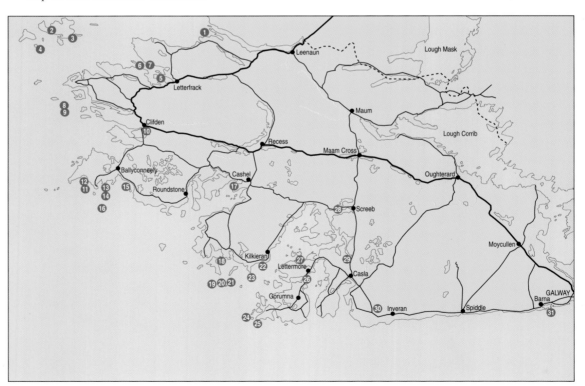

Table 13
Breeding terns in Connemara in 1984.
(from Whilde 1984)

| COLONY | NUMBER OF PAIRS | | | | |
	COMMON	ARCTIC	ROSEATE	SANDWICH	LITTLE
1. Illaunmore		7			
2. Lough Bofin (Inishbofin)	10				
3. Carricknamoyla		5			
4. Inishgort		20			
5. Lamb's Island	4			80	
6. Islet SE of Freaghillaun	2				
7. Carrigeen		4			
8. Eashal Island (a)	12	68			
9. Eashal Island (b)		32			
10. Salt Lake	38	1			
11. Horse Island		}39			4
12. Horse Island north				150	
13. Fox Island		11			6
14. Wherune Island		23			2
15. Islets NW of Inishdawros				34	
16. Hen Island		75			
17. Green Island	45			30	
18. Crumpaun		1			
19. Duck Island (a)	24	234	5	120	
20. Duck Island (b)	6	40			
21. Inishmuskerry					11
22. Carra Rocks	4	42			
23. Maan		1			
24. Eagle Rock		30			2
25. Dog Island		4			
26. Geabhróg	210	10	1		
27. Oileán Geabhróg	60	4			
28. Oileán na nGeabhróg	71				
29. Lough Carrafinla	17	1			
30. Lough Naskanniva	60				
31. Grey Rock	21	4			
TOTAL	584	656	6	414	25
Percentage of all-Ireland total	21	27	2	12	9

All the terns are summer visitors from Africa. The sandwich tern is the first to return, often as early as mid-March, while the others start to appear in April and May. They all feed on small fish such as sand eels in the shallow waters around the coast and so are very vulnerable to the fluctuations in fish stocks which occur naturally or are caused by commercial overfishing. Terns also nest in very vulnerable locations - four species on low, wave-swept islands and the little tern on exposed beaches. It is sometimes surprising that they produce any young at all. However, they are long-lived birds and, as long as each pair produces two chicks which survive to breeding age during their lifetime, the population level can be maintained.

The terns often nest in association with gulls, usually black-headed and common gulls on the sheltered inshore islands and small numbers of herring and great black-backed gulls on the offshore islands. The herring gulls, the great black-backed gulls and indeed the common rats which live on some of the larger islands will take tern eggs and chicks. On the beaches little terns and ringed plovers nest close together.

Birds of woodlands and forestry plantations

Little is known in detail about the birds of Connemara's deciduous woodlands and coniferous plantations. The oak woodlands are very small and, like small islands, have relatively few species. The plantations cover a much larger area but their tree species composition and structure do not at present attract many bird species.

Robins, wrens, goldcrests, blue tits and chaffinches are by far the commonest species in coniferous plantations, while redpolls and siskins nest in small numbers. Perhaps the most

interesting species in many of the more mature plantations is the crossbill. This is a large finch with the upper and lower parts of its bill actually crossed. This modification enables it to open conifer cones and extract the seeds. The crossbill was rare in Ireland before the maturation of the conifer plantations, but is now widespread, though not numerous. Because it nests during the winter it is usually missed by most people studying breeding birds. After the breeding season the crossbills seem to disperse away from the plantations. Some have been seen in gardens and others on the coast near Spiddle. It would appear that the breeding output of the local birds does not sustain the population.

The robin - one of Connemara's most common hedgerow birds.

After a short period at a high level the population declines until it is again supplemented by an immigration of birds from the continent, where an overproduction of young has caused an irruption and mass migration of birds to less suitable habitats at the edge of the crossbill's range. Kevin Blehein, a forestry official in Oughterard, is undertaking a long-term study of the crossbill and would welcome any information about the species from elsewhere in the region. He reports that the population of 100-150 birds in Cloosh Valley Forest, near Oughterard, in the early 1980s, has declined to perhaps only 30-40 birds.

The grasshopper warbler is a summer visitor now heard more frequently in coniferous plantations, especially in areas which have been clear-felled and where new scrubby vegetation is appearing. These little birds are difficult to see but easy to recognise by their grasshopper-like churring calls, which can be heard at any time of the day. Sometimes they are mistakenly reported as nightjars but it seems that nightjars are now extinct in the region. Their call differs from the call of the grasshopper warbler and is usually uttered only for a short period at dusk.

Among the birds of prey, the sparrowhawk is a woodland inhabitant which is seen regularly in Connemara, often in open country as well. The long-eared owl may be present in some plantations but is a secretive bird rarely encountered. The merlin is adapting to nesting in coniferous plantations and may well be feeding increasingly along the wide forest roads. Finally, hope springs eternal that the hen harrier will eventually breed in Connemara. This, the largest and most impressive of Ireland's birds of prey, is seen regularly during the winter and occasionally during the breeding season. But there is no evidence as yet that it is breeding in the region. Although there may be suitable moorland and open plantation habitat for it, it seems unlikely that there is sufficient food to sustain a breeding pair, which needs a good supply of rabbits and woodpigeons.

Birds of the hedgerows

Hedgerows are important habitats, particularly in areas where woodland is scarce. They provide nesting habitat for many common birds such as robins, goldcrests, dunnocks, song thrushes and blackbirds. In the winter they are a source of berries and seeds for visitors from the north, including redwings, fieldfares, continental blackbirds and chaffinches. It is therefore deplorable that hedgerows are being so savagely trimmed by the local authorities, often during the nesting season. Not only is the value of the hedges for shelter being diminished, but young trees are being hacked down in their prime (at a time when others are trying to re-tree Ireland) and, of course, nesting habitat and winter food supplies are being destroyed. Certainly, roadside hedges need to be trimmed. But trimming could be carried out in a manner which is not detrimental to their functional or biological value. Those with executive responsibility for the work must recognise the true value of these natural resources and hedgerow owners should see them as assets worth caring for.

Birds in towns, villages and other man-made habitats

It is not essential to venture into the countryside to see birds. We are lucky in the west of Ireland to have many birds living in our towns and villages. Gardens and areas of rough grass, scrub and hedgerow are good habitats for many common small birds, although there is now a regrettable tendency to have these 'tidied up' in order to impress neighbours and tourists. Deserted buildings, barns and sheds attract nesting swallows, occasional house martins and swifts, and sometimes kestrels. The open faces of sand quarries provide ideal but unfortunately short-lived habitats for breeding sand martins. Small stands of trees serve the nesting needs of rooks and jackdaws. The provision of nest boxes in the spring and feeding tables in the winter can also greatly add to the ornithological interest of any garden or school yard.

Some concluding comments on Connemara's bird-life

'Altogether Connemara is not in my opinion a tempting place for the ornithologist. Bird-life there is woefully scarce, both in species and numbers. Even the Hooded Crow and Redshank seemed to be absent from Connemara.' So wrote the eminent ornithologist H.F. Witherby after spending a fortnight in the region in May 1895.

The hooded crow is now common and widespread in Connemara.

Nearly a century later, what is our opinion of Connemara's bird-life? Must we agree with Witherby or can we find some redeeming features which will soften his rather harsh opinion?

Certainly, hooded crows are now common, and redshanks are probably breeding in small numbers in the region. And the preceding accounts have, hopefully, indicated that bird-life is not as 'woefully scarce' as Witherby suggests. But what else can we say in defence of Connemara as a bird haunt? Perhaps if we look at the numbers of species found there we can gain some comfort. In Table 14 we can compare the numbers of what we can call the regular species seen in Connemara with the numbers seen in the whole of Ireland. On this basis Connemara does not fare too badly with 79 per cent of the regular species total and over 82 per cent of the breeding species (the total of the 'Present throughout the year' and the 'Summer visitor' figures). These figures are, in fact, exceptionally good when we

Table 14
A comparison of the numbers of bird species in Connemara and Ireland.

	Connemara	Ireland	% in Connemara
Present throughout the year*	78	89	88
Summer visitor	25	36	69
Winter visitor	16	27	59
Passage migrant	7	8	88
Total	26	160	79
Scarce and rare species	50 +	237 +	21
Grand total	**176 +**	**400+**	**44**

*Includes resident species and species which occur during the breeding and wintering seasons, though some individuals may not be present during both of these seasons, e.g., ringed plover.

consider that Connemara occupies less than 3 per cent of the land area of Ireland. Admittedly, it has a disproportionate length of shoreline compared with most other coastal regions and this undoubtedly helps to increase the totals, but probably not to any great extent.

Where Connemara loses out, however, is in the number of scarce and rare species reported. This is partly a result of the lack of bird-watchers in the region, but mostly because of its distance from Britain and the Continent. Many more rarities turn up in the east and south of Ireland than in the west. The former point is highlighted by the fact that a growing number of rarities is now being reported from Connemara as the number of active bird-watchers in the region increases. It is quite likely, therefore, that the Connemara total will reach 50 per cent of the national figure by the end of the century. Some of the most recently reported rarities are listed in Table 15.

As to the total numbers of birds, we will have to agree with Witherby. The 1986 winter wetland count showed that the number of water birds in Connemara is very small, especially when we take into account the large number of lakes and the considerable length of coastline. The same is true for the landbirds and most of the seabirds, although we do not have detailed figures for these.

In conclusion, it seems we must, to some extent, agree with Witherby's opinion. Yet there are rare and interesting birds to be seen in the region and with greater bird-watching efforts many more will be reported in the coming years. Moreover, the rarity of species or the abundance of birds are not the only criteria by which we should judge our bird-life. There is still much to be learned about our common species and endless enjoyment to be gained from watching them.

Table 15
Some rare birds recorded in Connemara since 1984.

SPECIES	DATE	LOCATION	NUMBER	USUAL RANGE
Little egret	October/November 1988	Kilkieran	1	S. Europe, S.W. Asia and
	November 1992	Barna	1	Africa
Spoonbill	October 1990	Cleggan and Carna	2	the Netherlands, S.E.Europe, S. Asia and N. Africa
Red-footed falcon	April 1992	Doonloughan	5	Asia
Gyr falcon	April 1991	Ballyconneely	1	Greenland, Iceland and Scandinavia eastwards
Marsh harrier	March 1993	Tully	1	E. England, Europe and Asia
Spotted crake	September 1991	Aughrus	1	Continental Europe, Asia, Africa and India
Dotterel	June 1992	Inish	1	N. Eurasia, N. Africa, Middle East
Black-winged stilt	March 1990	Aughrus Point	1	S. Europe, S. Asia and Africa
Avocet	December 1986	Carna	1	E. England, coast Norway to Belgium, S.Europe and S.Asia
Grey phalarope	August 1989	Ballynahown	1	Breeds in Arctic, winters in subtropical areas
Sabine's gull	October 1992	Omey Island	1	Breeds in Arctic and winters over sea to south
Ross's gull	December 1990	Omey Island	1	Breeds in N. Arctic, wintering area not well known
Little auk	January 1988	Spiddle	1	Breeds in Arctic and winters over seas to south
	February 1988	Errislannan	1	
	January 1991	Oughterard	1	
Hoopoe	April 1989	Near Ballynakill Harbour	1	S. Europe, S. Asia and Africa
	March 1990	Casla	1	
	March 1990	Ballyconneely	1	
Water pipit	July 1992	Clifden	1	C. Europe
Yellow-browed warbler	November 1989	Claddaghduff	1	E. Asia
Golden oriole	April 1987	Ballyconneely	2	S. Europe, C., W. and S. Asia and Africa
	May 1989	Inishbofin	2	

MAMMALS

Noon approaches on a spring morning and at last the sun brings some heat to the mountain slopes. We clamber through a tangle of heather and loose angular boulders, keeping an eye on the treacherous ground. As we round a massive crag, something on the near horizon catches our attention, a shape out of place, a silhouette smoother in form than the surrounding rocks. At first it is still. Then, while our eyes and thoughts are accommodating to this strange intrusion, a slow, easy movement brings into profile a recognisable long snout and erect, sky-pointing ears - a fox. Like us, it is taking full advantage of this first heat of spring. We watch each other for a few moments. Then, with absolute composure and confidence borne of its mastery of the mountains, the fox stands up, stretches a little and saunters off up the hill, stopping every now and again to look back inquisitively at its audience.

Such encounters are not unusual in Connemara, in the mountains or in the lowlands. But they are infrequent enough to delight any naturalist when they do occur. Foxes are common and widespread throughout the region but generally only evident from their distinctive droppings. These are usually black and contain fur, feathers, bones and sometimes seeds. The droppings are often deposited on prominent objects such as stones or fallen branches, but we can also find them on flat ground along well-worn tracks. In the absence of droppings, the unmistakable scent of a fox is a sure sign that it has recently passed our way. Not everyone is able to smell the sharp, slightly sweet smell but, after their first few experiences, those who can are unlikely to forget it.

Foxes are primarily carnivores, eating small mammals, birds, fish, earthworms, insects and carrion - the remains of dead animals. However, they take fruits, too, and it is not unusual to find droppings full of blackberry seeds during the autumn.

Although there is no specific information on the diet of Connemara foxes, we can be sure they take whatever is available, including rabbits, hares, common rats, woodmice and a wide range of birds and their eggs. The birds are most likely to be ground-nesting species such as ducks, skylarks and pipits. But foxes will also climb onto the lower limbs of trees and add magpies and woodpigeons, for example, to their fare. In Connemara, it is likely that a major part of their diet, on the hills at least, is sheep carrion. As we will see later, sheep flocks have expanded enormously in recent years. With this population growth has come an increase in the numbers of dead lambs and ewes on the hills. Although the occasional rogue fox may kill lambs it is more likely that most foxes now take the easier option of scavenging for dead animals.

As well as eating dead sheep, it is not uncommon to see foxes feeding on badgers and other animals which have been killed on the road. Motor vehicles are increasingly becoming agents of death to our wildlife as roads are straightened and widened to satisfy our desire to pass through the region at the greatest possible speed.

Badger corpses are common on the roads in late winter. Many are lactating females, so the loss of these mothers represents the death of a young family, too. Unfortunately, these are usually the only badgers which most people see because they are largely nocturnal, coming out to forage around dusk and returning to their setts before dawn. But, as with foxes, we can find many signs of badgers in the countryside, both on the hills and in the lowlands. For example, they produce distinctive, rather shapeless, black droppings which often contain large numbers of iridescent beetle wing-cases. The droppings occur singly or en masse in shallow latrines which the badgers dig either close to their setts or on the boundaries of their territories.

Unfortunately, badgers are most often seen like this.

Badgers, like foxes, are opportunists in their feeding habits. They take a wide range of animal and plant foods during the course of a year. Earthworms are the most important element in their diet, although large insects, small mammals (mainly young ones), carrion, cereals, fruit and the underground storage organs of plants are also eaten regularly. In their search for insects and roots badgers make characteristic shallow scrapes in the ground. They may also make quite deep scrapes when digging out wasps' nests from under tree roots.

Badgers live only where the soil is fertile enough to support earthworms and deep enough to excavate their setts. They do not therefore live on the bogs, although they can be found nearby. The setts can be simple tunnels or complex networks occupying considerable areas. The setts are kept meticulously clean, and the presence of used bedding of grass, bracken or moss outside one is clear evidence it is currently being used. Each badger social group, which includes four or five adults, has three or four setts in its territory.

Although we do not know how many badgers there are in Connemara, it has been shown in a recent national survey by Dr Chris Smal of the National Parks and Wildlife Service that they occur at a lower density than in more fertile areas of the country. The average density in the west of Ireland is one social group in every 5 square kilometres (0.5 per square mile). This figure suggests that there are about 300 social groups in the Connemara badger population, giving a total of 1,200-1,500 adult badgers.

The social life of badgers is extremely complex and has been described in detail by Dr Hans

Kruuk in his fascinating book *The Social Badger*. This book is compulsory reading for anyone interested in the controversy surrounding the possible role of the badger in the transmission of tuberculosis in cattle.

Rabbits generally require a reasonable depth of dry soil in which to excavate their burrows. For this reason, they are not common in much of Connemara, where the soils are shallow, wet and often peaty. They occur in small colonies on the lower slopes of the mountains, particularly in the Twelve Bens and the Maumturks where the ancient marbles come to the surface. Here the richer soils have produced good feeding for them and sufficient depth for their burrows. Rabbits are most common, however, on the coast where the sand-dunes and sandy soils of the machair provide ideal habitat. In fact, their burrowing activity and heavy grazing pressure, coupled with intense grazing and trampling by domestic livestock is causing serious erosion in some areas, notably around Dog's Bay and Gorteen Bay.

Irish hares are not constrained by the need to excavate burrows because they spend their lives above ground. We can see them on the mountains, on the coast and, importantly, on the bogs. It is always a surprise to raise a hare from its dry form among the rank purple moor-grass and heather of an otherwise lifeless bog. Although Irish hares are not solitary animals they tend to be seen only in small numbers in Connemara, except perhaps during courtship, between early February and late June, when they come together to participate in their ritual 'madness'.

Hares feed on heather and cotton-grass and to a lesser extent or other moorland plants. Rabbits, however, usually eat grasses. Nevertheless, there is sometimes some confusion between the droppings of the two if the animals themselves are not in view. Those of hares are slightly flattened spheres, 15-20 millimetres (about 0.7 inch) across, pale brown or yellow-brown and composed of course plant material. Rabbit droppings, generally deposited in denser heaps, are smaller (10 millimetres, 0.4 inch), rounder and usually darker in colour.

The Irish hare is a sub-species of the mountain hare and differs in several ways from the mountain hares of Scotland, northern Europe, the Alps, northern Asia, Canada and Greenland. One obvious difference is that, while hares of the other sub-species turn white in winter, the Irish hare rarely, if ever, does so completely - a clear benefit in a country like Ireland which receives little snow.

A species we are less likely to see, although it is probably Ireland's commonest mammal, is the wood mouse. It is mainly nocturnal in its habits and usually lives under cover of vegetation, although it can live on the relatively bare floor of beechwoods. It is slightly larger than the house mouse and has bigger eyes, ears and feet. Its fur is a soft, wood-brown above, mixed with black and yellow. Its underparts are mostly white, but there is almost always a yellow-brown spot at the throat, sometimes lengthened into a stripe. It has relatively little hair on its tail, the skin of which is dark brown above and white beneath. An unusual feature of its tail is that it can break off if it is caught by a predator without causing much harm or suffering to its owner.

The wood mouse probably occurs throughout Connemara from the coast to the mountain-tops. But it tends to avoid built-up areas and permanently damp habitats, so it is scarce in towns and on the bogs. When the bogs are drained, wood mouse numbers increase; more so when they are reclaimed for pasture. The wood mouse is also present on some of the offshore islands such as Inishbofin. Island mice tend to be larger than those on the mainland.

Seeds and insects are the wood mouse's chief foods. Overall, it is a very significant member of the Connemara wildlife community, being an important part of the diet of kestrels, foxes, stoats and domestic cats.

The Irish stoat is not nearly as widespread or common in Connemara as the woodmouse, but its reputation as a voracious killer is legendary. Of course, it only does what all carnivores do, kill other animals in order to eat and feed its young. Yet it is impossible for us not to feel some twinges of sympathy, however irrational, for a screaming baby rabbit as it is dragged along by an animal half its size to a nest in a wall where a hungry family awaits its meal.

The Irish stoat differs in several respects from stoats in Britain. Like the Irish hare, it is a sub-species, found only in Ireland and on the Isle of Man. It is generally smaller and browner than the British stoat and is consequently sometimes mistakenly called a weasel. The real weasel, which does not occur in Ireland at all, is even smaller. Interestingly, Irish stoats increase in size from north to south. Those in the southern counties are nearly as big as their counterparts in Britain. In Connemara the average size of male stoats, from nose-tip to tail-tip, is about 365 millimetres (14.5 inches) while the females are about 300 millimetres (12 inches). By comparison, the weasel is only about 250 millimetres (10 inches) long.

Stoats travel with a characteristic bounding motion and have a sinuous flexibility which gives the impression that they can just flow over the contours of a rock or wall. They live in dry stone walls, in hedgerows and in heather and screes on the mountain slopes. In Connemara, they are probably most common on the coastal sandy habitats where rabbits are plentiful, for example beside Dog's Bay. Here young stoats can sometimes be seen on a summer's day chasing each other across the short turf.

Pine martens are closely related to stoats, but unfortunately are less obliging. We are very unlikely to see these beautiful but secretive creatures. They are animals of the woods and plantations and at present are confined mainly to coniferous plantations in east Connemara and around Ballynahinch in the middle of the region. Though there were reports of them earlier in the century on Doughruagh mountain in the west, none was found in this area in a survey during 1983-4. With the expansion of commercial plantations the pine marten will probably extend its range westwards. Though a carnivore like the stoat, the pine marten has a more varied diet. It eats, among many items, small birds, wood mice, rabbits, hares, pygmy shrews, common frogs, ground beetles, bees, wasps, wax, honey and the berries and nuts of a variety of woodland trees and shrubs.

The pine marten is extending its range as coniferous plantations expand.

Pine martens make their dens in a variety of places, including hollow or fallen trees, rock falls, amongst tree roots, quiet derelict buildings and, in the case of one pair, under the thatched roof of a holiday cottage.

Bats also occupy houses. Consequently, the most frequent question we hear about them is 'How do I get them out of my attic?'. Apart from an unjustified fear of these harmless animals, the only possible reason for wanting to get rid of them is the mess and smell caused by their droppings. But it should be emphasised that all bats are fully protected under the Wildlife Act and any attempt to remove them should be made only with the permission and guidance of the National Parks and Wildlife Service.

Four of Ireland's seven bat species have been recorded in Connemara, but it is most likely that all seven will be found when the region is surveyed fully. These species are listed in Table 16 with details of their size, roosting habitats, feeding habitats and main food.

It is only in the past decade that an interest in bats has developed in Ireland. This has been in response to the decline of many species in Britain and elsewhere in Europe and the realisation that they could also be declining here. Pioneering survey work was carried out during the 1980s by Paddy O'Sullivan of the National Parks and Wildlife Service. Now Dr Kate McAney is continuing and extending that work with the same organisation in partnership with the Vincent Wildlife Trust of the United Kingdom.

Although her survey is not yet complete, Dr McAney says: 'Connemara is as rich an area for bats as anywhere else in the country. All seven species are likely to be present and there is no doubt that there are plenty more roosts that we do not know about. There are many old houses that have not been modernised that could contain two or three species. Even the new houses, including bungalows, contain bats and the more exposed hills have houses tucked in tree-sheltered valleys which provide homes to bats. Bridges are also very important haunts for bats. The many lakes are a rich source of insect food for the bats.' This is good news and it is to be hoped that a sufficient appreciation of the importance of bats can be generated before too many old buildings and other bat haunts are renovated or destroyed.

The pipistrelle is the commonest of the bats in Connemara. It lives in a wide variety of buildings and is the species most likely to enter houses during the summer. Pipistrelle roosts located so far contain on average over 100 bats.

The brown long-eared bat ranks second in the region, often sharing roosts with other species such as the pipistrelle and Natterer's bat. The roosts of 10-50 bats are often found in churches, castles and large attics in old houses. The brown long-eared bat is the easiest species to recognise because of its very long ears. However, when hanging upside down in its roost, it tucks its ears under its wings, so these diagnostic characters might be difficult to see.

It was only in 1976 that Natterer's bats were discovered in Connemara. But by the end of 1992, several roosts had been recorded in old buildings, including the Gothic church at Kylemore. The average roost size is 143. The whiskered bat has so far been found at only three locations in Connemara, but is likely to be more widespread. It is easily overlooked, even by experts, because it often roosts with pipistrelles. Because of their scarcity throughout Ireland both Natterer's and the whiskered bat have been included in the *Irish Vertebrate Red Data Book*.

The lesser horseshoe bat, identified by its distinctive horseshoe-shaped nose-leaf, has been found in several caves and a mine shaft at the eastern edge of Connemara but not yet in the heart of the region. Unlike the other species it hangs free from the ceilings of caves, rather than on the walls. Elsewhere in Ireland it is restricted to western counties from south Mayo to Cork. This is the north-western edge of its Eurasian range.

Leisler's and Daubenton's bats have not yet been recorded in Connemara, but Dr McAney is confident that they will be found. Leisler's, the largest of Ireland's bats, lives in a variety of buildings, old and modern, especially in the large spaces around fascia boards. Daubenton's bat, however, roosts almost exclusively in crevices under stone buildings. It is the second most widely distributed bat in Ireland after the pipistrelle.

Bats are endangered by several modern human activities. One of the most serious is the treatment of building timbers with chemicals to kill boring insects and control wood-rotting fungi. These pesticides are often highly toxic to bats, so anyone planning to undertake such treatments, should ensure they will not harm bats.

Filling cracks and crevices in bridges with liquid cement is a hazard to many bats, in particular to Daubenton's bat which roosts almost exclusively under bridges. Dr McAney has produced an advisory leaflet on this matter which can be obtained from the National Parks and Wildlife Service. This attractively produced and informative document should be read by all engineers before they embark on bridge maintenance or restoration programmes.

The felling of woodlands, hedgerows and scrub is a threat to several species which rely on catching insects in these sheltered habitats. Water pollution is also a potential hazard for the species which catch emerging aquatic insects like caddis flies. In this respect, the acidification of lakes, rivers and streams in south Connemara could reduce the potential insect supplies of some species.

Table 16
Four species* of bats recorded in Connemara and three species likely to occur in the region.

SPECIES	AVERAGE LENGTH mm (inches)		AVERAGE WING SPAN mm (inches)		MAIN ROOSTING HABITATS	FEEDING HABITAT	MAIN FOOD
Pipistrelle*	40	(1.6)	220	(8.7)	Confined spaces in buildings	Hedgerows, woodland edge and over water	Insects, e.g. caddis flies and mosquitoes
Brown long-eared*	43	(1.7)	260	(10.2)	Large, open attics	Hedgerows, woodland edge	Moths, butterflies, beetles, earwigs, caddis flies, spiders
Natterer's*	45	(1.8)	275	(10.8)	Buildings, caves and tunnels	Woodland edge, open country	Small insects, moths, caddis flies
Whiskered*	42	(1.7)	225	(8.8)	Houses - between rafters and felt	Wooded and open country	Insects and spiders
Lesser horseshoe	37	(1.5)	238	(9.4)	Caves, mines, tunnels and cellars	Woodland and scrub	Butterflies, caddis flies and flies
Leisler's	59	(2.3)	310	(12.2)	Buildings	Woodland and scrub	Insects
Daubenton's	50	(2.0)	258	(10.2)	Mainly bridges, caves and houses	Over water	Insects emerging from the water

Because bats are sensitive and protected animals we should never disturb roosts in order to identify or count them. Nowadays, we can, with some training and practice, identify bats in flight with electronic bat detectors which register their squeaks in a form we can hear. Although some people can hear the communication squeaks of bats, their navigation pulses are inaudible to the human ear. Each species produces sounds at different frequencies so even if we cannot identify a species immediately, we can at least judge if there is more than one species in the vicinity. With the aid of a detector we can even hear a bat catching an insect, by a tell-tale buzz which interrupts the normal flow of sound.

One muffled splash breaks the silence of the bog. We advance along the stream bank quietly, but are only just in time to see the last fading ripples breaking into the waterside vegetation. We wait several minutes, but the cause of the splash does not appear. So we must look for signs to identify the solitary animal which has vanished so quietly and completely.

Further downstream we come across an area of flattened grass a little distance from the bank. The grass is still warm from its recent occupation. Not far away, a short, well-worn track, about 15 centimetres (6 inches) across, runs diagonally down the bank to the edge of the water. Just a few metres farther downstream, at a junction with an incoming stream, there is a bright green mound of grass. When we look closely we see that it is topped by a smudge of mucilage which gives off quite a strong, musky smell. Beside it are some tiny bleached fragments which, on closer examination, turn out to be the bones of a fish, most likely an eel.

We have all the clues we need now to say that our mystery animal is an otter which had been lying up for the day in its couch when we disturbed it.

In areas where there is a lot of human disturbance otters tend to be nocturnal. But in the peace and quiet of Connemara, it is not unusual to see them during the day. On the bogs their signs are widespread but not numerous. Otter paths link the many lakes and streams, and sprainting sites (otter droppings are called spraints) are widely distributed at stream junctions and on prominent boulders in or beside lakes. But fish life is not plentiful in these waters, except perhaps when the trout come upstream to spawn in winter. So our best chance of seeing otters is on the coast. We should look for sprainting sites where rivers meet the sea; they will often be under bridges which carry the roads running parallel to the sea. On the coast, the otters often lie-up in their holts, secure retreats under the rocks just above the high-water level. Nearby may be a regular sprainting site with piles of crumbling fish bones.

Though their preference is for fish, otters are opportunists when it come to feeding. They eat a wide range of items including birds and their eggs, crabs, snails and frogs. They will concentrate on frogs if these are found in large numbers in their breeding ponds in late winter. If trout are easily catchable in shallow streams during the spawning season otters will feed on them. On the coast they will eat conger eels, pipefish, rocklings, wrasses, gobies, blennies, butterfish, sea scorpions, sea sticklebacks, three-spined sticklebacks and flatfish.

An otter sleeping on a sunny shore.

Although otters are common in Ireland they are scarce throughout much of Britain and now extremely rare on the continent. Ireland is the last stronghold of the species in western Europe, which puts the onus on us to ensure that otters and their freshwater and coastal habitats are properly protected and maintained. From two major surveys in 1980-1 and 1990, based on the occurrence of spraints, we know that otters are widely distributed. We also know a lot about their food from numerous studies carried out around inland waters and along the coast. However, we have no idea how many otters there are in Ireland or how their numbers might be changing. For, although spraint surveys indicate that they are widespread, it is possible that the similar densities of sprainting sites recorded in the two surveys were produced by different numbers of otters. So until we devise some way of estimating the actual numbers (perhaps based on the approach taken in a recent national badger survey) we will not be able truly to fulfil our international obligation to conserve the species.

An animal closely related to the otter, which does not yet occur in Connemara, is the mink. This American species was brought into Ireland in 1951 for the commercial production of fur in captivity. Inevitably, several animals escaped and established populations in the wild. These have grown steadily and expanded their range. Now the species can be found throughout most of the country east of the River Shannon. It has also crossed the Shannon into Clare, east Galway and north Mayo. It would seem to be just a matter of time before it reaches Connemara.

At one time it was feared the mink would oust the otter. This has proved not to be the case, primarily because the two species have different food preferences. Although the mink eats fish, it ventures onto land more and includes a large proportion of birds, small mammals, frogs and invertebrates in its diet.

When the mink does arrive in Connemara the main concern will be about its impact on ground-nesting birds such as ducks, gulls, terns, waders and grouse. Since otters take the eggs and chicks of these birds from time to time, as do large gulls, foxes, badgers and common rats, the impact of an additional predator is hard to predict. It would be useful if we could assess the populations of all the potential victims before the mink arrives so that we can respond to its impact in a rational manner, rather than in the emotional and sometimes hysterical way seen at times elsewhere.

The common rat (currently the official name of what we used to call the brown rat) is a well-known but unloved species, abundant where habitat and food supplies permit. It prefers areas with dense ground cover close to water, where the soil structure is suitable for the excavation of burrows. It is not, therefore, an animal of the bogs or mountains. But even in Connemara, that still leaves it plenty of scope! It is very much associated with human habitations and cultivated ground. To experience a seething throng of common rats we need only visit a rubbish dump with a flashlight at night. A visit during the day will be less exciting, but we will still see a few daytime adventurers foraging through our waste.

Common rats cause considerable damage around farms, eating and fouling grain, killing young animals, polluting water and transmitting the very unpleasant and occasionally fatal Weil's disease. They can cause the total breeding failure of terns, gulls and ducks nesting on lake and coastal islands. They can swim (and dive) so lake islands and nearby coastal islands are well within their reach. They can climb trees and walls, travel considerable distances over land and eat a great variety of foods, including cereals, meat, fish, bones, earthworms, crabs and much more. They are gregarious and highly adaptable and they reproduce rapidly. One female can produce a total of 20-30 young annually in three litters. They are, in short, extraordinary animals which would deserve our admiration if they were not such a nuisance. That they have achieved such widespread distribution and notoriety since first arriving in Dublin in 1722, is remarkable.

The pygmy shrew is Ireland's smallest mammal, weighing about 3.5 grammes (about 0.1 ounce). It is so light that we would barely notice the weight if we held one in our hand. Small and light it may be, but in its own world it is aggressive, pugnacious and intolerant of others of the same species. It is noisy, too. We are likely to become aware of its existence only when we hear its chittering squeaks coming from beneath the ground vegetation at the base of a roadside hedge. Of course, if we have cats, pygmy shrews will be delivered regularly to the doorstep, where they will be left uneaten because they are so distasteful to our domestic predators.

Beetles are an important part of the pygmy shrew's diet, but it also feeds on a wide range of other invertebrates including woodlice, adult flies, insect larvae, spiders, bugs and the occasional snail and slug, though they seem to find the latter, along with millipedes, somewhat unpalatable. It needs a continuous supply of food and must eat throughout the twenty four hours of the day in order to survive. A couple of hours without food means almost certain death. In captivity, pygmy shrews have been shown to consume well over their own weight of food every day.

The pygmy shrew is widespread in Ireland and abundant on every sort of terrain where there is sufficient ground-cover of vegetation. Although we know nothing in detail of its distribution in Connemara, the fact that it is one of the commonest mammals in other upland and moorland areas of Ireland suggests that the same is probably true for this area.

The hedgehog is the last of the small mammals we may meet in Connemara. It is very rarely seen, however, partly because it is nocturnal and partly because it is probably rare in the region. Hedgehogs are most abundant where grassland is found close to woodland, scrub or hedgerow, a combination of habitats not common in Connemara. Like pygmy shrews, they are primarily insectivores, but eat a wide range of ground-living invertebrates, bird eggs, chicks and carrion as well.

Although the hedgehog is widespread in Ireland, we know little about its current distribution, status and ecology. So any new information about it would be welcome.

For more details about this species, and all the other Irish mammals, Professor James Fairley's illuminating and entertaining offering, *An Irish Beast Book*, is thoroughly recommended.

Some captive and domestic mammals

Red deer once roamed free in the hills of Connemara, but were hunted to extinction in the nineteenth century. After a long absence, we can now see them again within the fenced confines erected in an area of the Connemara National Park. These animals were taken from the herd of native red deer in the Killarney National Park in County Kerry. They have settled well in their new surroundings and are breeding successfully. Hopefully, we will see them ranging more widely in the Park in the not too distant future. The Connemara National Park also has a herd of Connemara ponies and is breeding these as part of a conservation programme for this popular and well-known breed.

Connemara ponies.

Ranging freely, however, is an unknown number of feral goats - the largest of Connemara's free-living land mammals. These are descendants of domestic stock which, after a short time in the wild, have reverted to the shaggy, unkempt appearance of wild goats. In the past there were several small herds in the hills of north Connemara but there is little recent information available on their numbers or whereabouts at present.

Dogs and cats are rarely included in accounts of regional wildlife, although they can have a significant effect on the behaviour and numbers of certain wild species. Dogs undoubtedly keep many wild animals away from their own territories and do harm to sheep which is wrongly blamed on the fox. Cats have a more direct affect on the local birds and mammals - they kill and eat them.

If we think for a moment how many domestic cats there must be in the country (hundreds of thousands at least) we will realise that this species is perhaps our most numerous mammalian predator. It is worth having a look at what it kills and eats.

The results of a small study carried out on the eastern fringe of Connemara are presented in Table 17. Over a period of 41 months two cats brought in 488 identifiable small mammals and birds.

The majority of the specimens were wood mice, reflecting, presumably, their abundance, availability and the dietary preferences of the cats. Birds were much less common than we might have expected from the protests of bird-lovers. Overall, mammals made up 70 per cent of the prey and birds 30 per cent, a ratio similar to that found in another study in Britain.

The proportions of the bird species taken by the cats reflected closely the make-up of the local bird community. The predatory activities of the cats did not seem to have any adverse effects on the size or make up of that community. Woodmice were delivered in every month of the year, the greatest numbers appearing in the May-September period when they were breeding and the young were dispersing - leaving home.

Seals, porpoises, dolphins and whales

A close encounter with a seal is a bonus for any visit to the Connemara coast. A common seal will swim close to the shore and return the stare of the inquisitive naturalist, then gently slip under the water, appearing again perhaps hundreds of metres distant. Grey seals will be just as curious, but we have to put in more effort to see them as they live in the waters off the exposed Atlantic headlands.

Common seals are the smaller of the two species (see Table 18). It is difficult to judge sizes when the seals are at a distance, with only their heads showing above the water. In this situation it is the smaller, dog-like head which distinguishes the common seal from the grey seal which has a flat forehead, giving the impression of a large Roman nose. The habitat in which we see the seals is also a good indicator of the species. Common seals are usually found in the sheltered waters at the heads of bays where they haul out on low islands or sand banks. Grey seals prefer the more turbulent waters on the exposed coasts and around offshore islands where they haul out on remote pebbly beaches and in caves.

Bertraghboy, Mweenish, Kilkieran, Ballyconneely and Mannin Bays, and Ballynakill and Killary Harbours are regular hauling out and breeding haunts for common seals. Here they can be seen,

Table 17
The number of prey items brought home by two domestic cats - August 1989 to December 1992.
(from Whilde 1992)

MAMMALS		BIRDS	
Wood mouse	191	Robin	32
Pygmy shrew	93	Chaffinch	19
Common rat	58	Wren	14
		Dunnock	14
		Great tit	8
		Woodpigeon	*7
		Bullfinch	7
		Song thrush	5
		Blackbird	4
		Reed bunting	4
		Greenfinch	3
		Goldfinch	3
		Pied wagtail	2
		Starling	2
		Willow warbler	2
		Blue tit	2
		Unidentified remains	18

* including a single brood of 6 chicks.

with some difficulty against the camouflaging background of seaweed and rocks, lying almost motionless, waiting for the next high tide to lift them off and carry them away on the first stage of the journey to their feeding grounds. There may be up to one hundred common seals living around the Connemara coast, with that number or more inhabiting inner Galway Bay.

Grey seals may be slightly more numerous, breeding in colonies in the vicinity of Golam Head, and on islands such as High Island, Inishbofin and Inishshark, well away from the mainland coast. Nationally, the two species occur in about equal numbers during their respective breeding seasons. Outside the breeding season, though, the Irish grey seal population is joined by seals from the very large colonies in the north of Scotland.

A grey seal pup on an island shore.

During the late 1980s the common seal population of the North Sea was greatly reduced by an epidemic of phocine distemper. Although the disease was reported on the north-east coast of Ireland, none of the west coast populations seem to have been affected by it. This suggests that, unlike some grey seals, the west coast common seals are sedentary and do not mix with other populations to any great extent.

Sailing around the coast of Connemara, or from the mainland to an offshore island during the summer, presents us with the chance to see dolphins and porpoises (cetaceans). The pleasure and excitement of watching these large, streamlined mammals breaching (breaking through the surface of the water) just a few metres from the boat is beyond words. If we imagine the migrations of these great beasts, we are transported for a few moments to another world, the world of the open ocean, stretching endlessly around the earth.

Our most frequent encounters are likely to be with harbour porpoises. These are the smallest cetaceans (whales, dolphins and porpoises), measuring no more than about 1.7 metres (5.5 feet) in length. They have a short, blunt head, no beak, and a small, triangular fin situated in the centre of the dark grey back. Harbour porpoises rarely leap clear of the water like dolphins. In Connemara

Table 18
Connemara seals - some vital statistics.

	COMMON SEAL	GREY SEAL
LENGTH	Up to 1.7 metres (5.5 feet)	Up to 2.4 metres (8 feet)
SPOTS	Small and numerous	Large and few
HEAD	Small, crown rounded, concave 'bridge' between nose and forehead	Large crown, rather flat, no 'bridge'
NOSTRILS	Form V, touching below	Parallel and separated below
HABITAT	Shallow, sheltered waters	Exposed rocky coast
FOOD	Mainly fish with some shrimps and whelks	Mainly fish, probably larger than those taken by the common seal
BREEDING	Single pup produced in June-July; pup can swim immediately at birth	Single pup produced in September-October; pup requires period on land
MAXIMUM KNOWN LENGTH OF LIFE	Male 20 years Female 30 years	Male 26 years Female 38 years
IRISH POPULATION (in the late 1980s)	2,000	2,000+
EUROPEAN POPULATION (in the late 1980s)	70,000	110,000 (of which 90,000 in Britain)

waters they are probably feeding on herring, mackerel, whiting, sprats and sand eels.

The common dolphin is small and swift, has a long, slender beak and can measure up to 2.4 metres (8 feet) in length. It travels in groups of 10-20 individuals which frequently leap clear of the water revealing their distinctive 'hourglass' patterns of yellow intersecting patches on their sides. The back is dark grey to brown or bluish grey with a slender, sickle-shaped centrally-placed fin. They feed on the same fish species as the harbour porpoises.

The striped dolphin is very similar to the common dolphin and can easily be mistaken for it. The striped dolphin lacks the yellow markings on the side, but otherwise is difficult to distinguish from the common dolphin in the water.

Another species we might see is the bottle-nosed dolphin, even if only on postcards depicting one leaping in Ballynakill Harbour in the mid-1970s. White-beaked and Risso's dolphins also venture close to the Connemara coast. Bottle-nosed dolphins have a short but distinct beak, brown or dark grey backs and a moderately tall, slender sickle-shaped fin in the centre of the back. White-beaked dolphins are named for the colour of their beaks. Their backs are black in front of the often erect sickle-shaped fin and grey to white behind. Risso's dolphin is distinguished by its blunt, rounded head and absence of a beak. It is greyish above, often with numerous white scars on its sides. It has a tall, sickle-shaped fin in the centre of the back. It is up to 3.8 metres (12.5 feet) in length, and appreciably longer than the other two species which are both up to 2.7 metres (9 feet) long.

The western seaboard of Ireland is particularly important for cetaceans because it is near the edge of the continental shelf where rich water rises to the surface and generates a high level of plant and animal production. When fish shoals move inshore from the edge of the shelf, some 240-320 kilometres (150-200 miles) away, many of the cetaceans follow, increasing the possibility of sightings from the west coast or even of strandings on our shores.

The movement of cetaceans close to the west coast has long been known and exploited. As recently as the beginning of this century, there was a whaling industry based on the west coast of Mayo. The story of the whales and the industry is admirably told by Professor James Fairley in his book *Irish Whales and Whaling*. In more recent times, the importance of Ireland's west-coast waters to the conservation of this fast-dwindling group of animals has been recognised. All Irish territorial waters have now been declared a whale and dolphin sanctuary, the first of its kind in European waters.

Common dolphins in a Connemara bay.

Table 19
Records of cetacean corpses stranded on the Connemara coast - 1960-93.

SPECIES		DATE	LOCATION
Minke whale		23 July 1981	Salruck
		14 February 1990	Doonloughan
		14 December 1990	Doonloughan
Sperm whale		1967	Inishnee
Pygmy sperm whale		6 October 1985	Silver Strand, Barna
Cuvier's beaked whale		2 November 1964	Slyne Head
		1969	Mace Head
		14 January 1989	Dolan Pier, Ballyconneely
Common dolphin		26 January 1982	Mweenish Island
		13 March 1989	Spiddle
		22 May 1991	Rinvyle
Striped dolphin		24 January 1990	Mweenish Island
		31 January 1990	Finish Island
Atlantic white-sided dolphin		15 March 1990	Spiddle
		21 March 1990	Mweenish
	(3 males)	22 March 1990	Claddaghduff
	(2 males)	24/25 March 1990	Ballyconneely
	(2)	24/25 March 1990	Omey Island
Long-finned pilot whale		7 August 1960	Freaghillaun, Rosmuck
		1971	Claddaghduff
		29 December 1974	Inishnee
		20 November 1978	Barna
		26 February 1982	Clynagh, near Casla
		26 January 1982	Mweenish Island
		4 November 1986	Cloghmore, Ballynahown
		7 November 1988	Little Killary Harbour
		13 February 1990	Furbo
		21 March 1990	Mweenish
		12 January 1993	Ballyconneely
Risso's dolphin		14 July 1978	Illaunanownin, south of Gorumna Island

The closest any of us is likely to get to a cetacean is when one is stranded or a corpse is washed up on the shore. This is not a frequent occurrence, but when it happens it arouses a lot of public and media attention. The corpse of one of these magnificent animals stranded on a beach is a pathetic sight, especially when we recall its graceful demeanour in its rightful medium, the sea. Table 19 lists the stranded corpses found and reported on the Connemara coast since 1960. The numbers of each species probably reflect reasonably well the proportions occurring in Irish west-coast waters. Strikingly, most of the strandings occur during winter months when few cetaceans are likely to be present. At this time of year the seas are rough and perhaps the strong and persistent south-westerly winds drive the corpses from more southerly offshore locations.

The growing interest in cetaceans has led to the recent formation of an Irish Whale and Dolphin Group which would welcome further support and records of sightings of cetaceans at sea and notification of stranded corpses. The representative for Galway and Mayo is Professor James Fairley, Department of Zoology, University College, Galway, to whom records for these counties should be sent.

AMPHIBIANS

The common frog

The night is black; the windscreen wipers are hardly able to clear away the sheets of rain lashing our bleak moorland route. It is mid-February, cold, and wildlife watching is the last thing on our minds. Suddenly we become aware of unexpected reflections in our headlights. We brake quickly and come to an abrupt halt, but keep the wipers working at full speed. Crossing the road in front of us, oblivious to the danger, is an army of common frogs, purposefully hopping from left to right across the rain-drenched tarmac. They are heading for their breeding pond somewhere in the darkness of the bog to our right. If we return in a few days time, in better weather, a search should reveal the result of this annual gathering - masses and masses of frog spawn, not only in the pond but also in many of the drains and ditches in the surrounding area.

Common frogs are widespread in Connemara and are found in a wide range of habitats from mountain-top pools such as occur on Doughruagh down to the edge of the sea. During the early winter they hibernate in ponds and drains. Then, in February, and sometimes earlier, they emerge and make their way to their traditional breeding ponds. The tadpoles develop through the late winter and spring. Those which survive predation by otters and herons, waterlevel changes and other hazards, emerge as tiny froglets which disperse over the countryside, even to areas which we might think are too dry for them, such as hayfields.

Frogs eat a wide range of small invertebrate animals including earthworms, slugs, snails, woodlice, spiders, beetles and many other types of insect. They are unselective in their feeding. On blanket bogs, where food is not abundant, they tend to remain still and wait for prey to come within range, thereby conserving energy. Their diet, on the uplands and moorlands at least, overlaps with that of the pygmy shrew, particularly in the latter part of the year, but the shrew is more selective in its daily fare. Although we rarely see them, these two small animals are probably the commonest vertebrate animals on the bogs and uplands and, as such, must play a significant role in the ecology of these habitats.

The common frog, like all amphibians worldwide, is becoming scarce throughout its range, probably because of the general deterioration in water quality, the drainage of wetlands and the widespread use of inorganic fertilisers and insecticides. In Ireland, although it still seems to be common and widespread, it faces the same hazards, as do the only other Irish amphibians, the natterjack toad, which is restricted to a few locations in a small area in County Kerry, and the smooth newt. Unfortunately, we do not really have many details about the current distribution and status of the common frog. This situation will, hopefully, be rectified for Connemara and neighbouring areas during the coming years by Dr David McGrath and his students at Galway Regional Technical College, who are undertaking a population survey and ecological study of the species and would welcome information about the breeding sites of frogs in the region from local and visiting naturalists.

The common frog is widespread in Connemara.

The smooth newt

Even less is known about the smooth newt, either in Connemara or nationwide. Anecdotal information suggests that it is quite widespread but the reality of its status is largely unknown. There are a few records of the species in Connemara but already some of its known breeding pools have been destroyed. Smooth newts seem to be more selective than common frogs about the habitats in which they live. They usually breed in ponds with abundant aquatic vegetation and appear to have a preference for hard water (see box) and waters which have relatively high concentrations of metals - three features which are probably quite scarce in Connemara. So it would seem that the region does not offer a wealth of habitat for smooth newts, although only intensive field studies will provide us with a true account of their status.

HARD AND SOFT WATER

Hard water is water which is high in bicarbonates of calcium or magnesium or, for example, sulphates of iron. It is alkaline and does not form an immediate lather with soap. Soft water is acidic and forms an immediate lather with soap. Most Connemara freshwaters are soft.

Smooth newts probably breed a little later than common frogs, but by the early summer it is possible to find tadpoles of both species in the same pond, the newt tadpoles being substantially larger than those of the frog. Outside the breeding season they spend much of their life on land in a variety of damp habitats where they can often be found under stones or logs or by searching in crevices and under leaf litter. The adults eat slugs and snails, worms, insects, aquatic invertebrates and also frogspawn and tadpoles of both frogs and newts.

IRELAND'S ONLY NATIVE REPTILE

The viviparous lizard is Ireland's only native reptile. It is frequently seen scuttling across rocks or over walls on warm, sunny days from early spring through summer. It is generally an animal of humid but not wet conditions such as we find under rocks and in stone walls in Connemara.

Viviparous lizards are brown, green or olive with bodies up to 6.5 centimetres (2.5 inches) long and tails ranging from 8 to 13 centimetres (3-5 inches). Like frogs, newts and fishes, lizards are cold-blooded; their level of activity depends very much on the temperature of the surrounding environment. This is why it is common to find them basking motionless on rocks, letting the sun heat them up to 30°C, a temperature at which they can become active and hunt their prey of insects, centipedes and spiders.

This species, unlike most reptiles, produces live young, hence its scientific name *Lacerta vivipara*. The young are produced in litters of 3-15 any time from late June to September, but usually in July. Those which survive will go into hibernation in the burrow of another species or one which they have dug themselves. Younger lizards may hibernate later than adults because of

The viviparous lizard - Ireland's only native reptile.

their greater capacity to utilise the weakening heat of the sun. This arises because the ratio of the area of the heat-absorbing skin to the volume of the smaller bodies of the young lizards is greater than that of the adults. This means, too, that young lizards will be able to come out of hibernation earlier in the spring than adults.

Lizards can be found throughout Connemara from sea-level to considerable heights on the mountains, the highest record so far being for a party seen on the top of Errisbeg. According to the late Dr Arthur Went, one of Ireland's foremost fisheries scientists, they have the potential to reach lake islands, too. In August 1941 he saw a lizard sitting on a rock in Loughaunierin, near Maam Cross. It later went into the water and swam to cover under nearby rocks. Clearly it could only have reached the rock in the first place by swimming the 2 metres (6.5 feet) from the margin of the lake.

INSECTS AND OTHER TERRESTRIAL INVERTEBRATES

Connemara is a potential treasure trove for the naturalist who is interested in insects and other invertebrates. This point is amply made by Dr Martin Speight, one of Ireland's leading entomologists, when he described a cranefly new to Ireland which he found in Connemara. The cranefly *Ctenophora atrata* 'is one of the largest, most noticeable and extravagantly ornate flies found in the British Isles, difficult to mistake for any other species. In flight, the male of this species is quite daunting: making an audible rattling buzz it zig-zags drunkenly and at speed through woodland clearings, flying at about 5-7 feet from the ground, with its long legs trailing beneath it. Since it has a wing-span of nearly two inches and a highly polished, bright orange abdomen it is altogether a most conspicuous animal. The female is even more disconcerting, being larger and with the same bright colours, but armed with a massive black spike of an ovipositor, some 1/4 inch long, with which it lays eggs in rotten logs. It seems inconceivable that such an insect could remain unnoticed here for so long if it were widely distributed, so it is probably local in Ireland, even though it is found throughout Great Britain.'

In this account, Dr Speight captures some of the atmosphere and excitement which awaits the entomologist in Connemara. Along with this colourful cranefly he also discovered two other two-winged fly species (Diptera) new to Ireland during a short May foray in Derryclare Wood. These were *Conops vesicularis*, the largest conopid fly in Ireland and Britain, and *Epistrophe nitidicollis*, a large black and yellow hoverfly. The adults of the former frequent woodland clearings and may be found on the blossoms of male willow bushes or on the flowers of hawthorn or blackthorn. *Epistrophe* is a species of the edges of oakwoods with scrub and hazel thickets. In subsequent visits he collected further interesting flies such as *Hernia frondescentiae*, a widespread species found, for example, near streams in deciduous woods. He also noted a weevil, *Rhynchaenus quercus*, a species which is, as its name suggests, strongly associated with oakwoods. The *Rhynchaenus quercus* was one of over twenty species of weevils recorded in Connemara up to the early 1970s. Weevils are small to medium-sized beetles with a characteristically pointed extension (rostrum) on the front of the head.

From the ease with which Dr Speight discovered species new to Ireland, and the dearth of published work on Connemara insects and other invertebrates we can be certain that there is much rewarding field research still to be done in the region. Entomologists *do* visit Connemara from time to time, but they are rather like birds on passage migration. They stay for a short while, sample the fauna in the most productive areas and then move on, taking with them their findings - which may never be published in readily accessible form. This is a shame, because we all need to be better informed about invertebrates. After all, on the one hand they are the most numerous creatures on earth, but on the other, they are the ones suffering the greatest rates of extinction, even in Europe. In fairness to entomologists, it should be said that they are not the only naturalists who disappear with their information. Undoubtedly, there are many records hidden away in notebooks around the world which could usefully add to our knowledge and understanding of the Connemara flora and fauna. For those whose consciences might be pricked, it is never too late to submit records!

Butterflies

Butterflies, understandably, are the insects which have received most attention in Connemara. Of the twenty-eight residents and three regular migrants recorded in Ireland, we can find twenty-four residents and three migrants in Connemara and these are listed in Table 20. The four 'missing' species are the brown hairstreak, confined mainly to the Burren and neighbouring limestone areas; the purple hairstreak widely but thinly distributed, mainly in southern coastal counties; the pearl-bordered fritillary, occuring only in the Burren; and the gatekeeper largely restricted to the south coast of Ireland. The clouded yellow is a very infrequent migrant to Connemara.

The distribution and abundance of butterflies is closely dependent on the food plants of their caterpillars (larvae) and in Table 20 we can see how these differ among the Connemara species. Those species which are widespread are generally dependent on common plant species such as bird's-foot-trefoil, vetches, clovers, common nettles, gorse, members of the cabbage family and various grasses and sedges. The 'odd man out' appears to be the brimstone which has been recorded throughout much of central Connemara in spite of the absence of its food plant, buckthorn. The question of whether the available distribution map reflects the presence of just a few brimstones, perhaps blown westwards from their more usual limestone habitats, or whether these butterflies occur regularly and in good numbers in that region deserves some attention. The brimstone spends the winter hibernating as an adult and this enables it to appear on the first calm sunny days in spring, its yellow wings bringing the first splash of colour to the hedgerows. It is noteworthy that the brimstone is the original 'butter fly', so named because of the colour of the male.

The small tortoiseshell also overwinters as an adult, often in houses. Individuals can appear at almost any time during the winter and early spring if the weather is suitable. This familiar butterfly, along with the 'four-eyed' peacock, relies almost entirely on common nettles for egg laying and the development of its caterpillars. It is in our interest, if we want to see plenty of them around, to avoid 'tidying up' our nettle patches. We should also plant species like the butterfly-bush (one of the few plants better known by its scientific name *Buddleja*) to attract the feeding adults to our gardens. On the other hand, we do not need to put a lot of effort into attracting large and small white butterflies. They are too well able to look after themselves when it comes to feeding on cabbages in our gardens! Although large whites are seen regularly it is not generally realised that many of these are migrants to the region, their earlier stages having developed in more favourable conditions to the east.

The orange tip appears in the middle of the spring along with the cuckoo and the cuckoo flower (lady's smock) on which it feeds and lays its eggs. Cuckoo flower is widespread in wet habitats throughout Connemara so it is surprising that the orange tip is not more common than current records suggest.

The small copper has been reported only in fairly small areas in northern Connemara, on the

Table 20
The butterflies of Connemara.

RESIDENTS	MAIN WILD FOOD PLANTS OF CATERPILLARS	DISTRIBUTION (L = local; W = widespread*)
Dingy skipper	Common bird's-foot-trefoil	L (east)
Wood white	Common bird's-foot-trefoil, tufted vetch	L (east)
Brimstone	Buckthorn	W (centre)
Large white	Cabbage family	L (north and west)
Small white	Cabbage family	L (north and west)
Green-veined white	Cabbage family	W (throughout)
Orange tip	Cuckoo flower, hedge mustard	L (north and south-east)
Green hairstreak	Broom, gorse, common bird's-foot-trefoil, bilberry, bramble	W (western half)
Small copper	Daisy family, docks, sorrel, knotgrass, common fleabane	L (south-east, north and south-west)
Small blue	Pea family including kidney vetch	L (south-east)
Common blue	Common bird's-foot-trefoil, vetches, clovers	L (east)
Holly blue	Ivy, holly, buckthorn	L (centre and west)
Small tortoiseshell	Common nettle	W (throughout)
Peacock	Common nettle	W (west and south-east)
Dark green fritillary	Common dog-violet	L (centre and west)
Silver-washed fritillary	Violets, raspberry	L (north and west)
Marsh fritillary	Devil's-bit scabious, plantain	L (south and west)
Speckled wood	Grasses including common couch, cock's foot	W (east and west)
Wall brown	Grasses including meadow-grasses, cock's foot	L (north and west)
Grayling	Grasses including hair-grass, couch	W (throughout)
Meadow brown	Grasses including meadow-grasses	W (throughout)
Ringlet	Grasses including meadow-grasses, sedges	W (throughout)
Small heath	Grasses including meadow-grasses, mat-grass	L (north)
Large heath	Common cottongrass, white-beak sedge	L (north and west)

MIGRANTS

Clouded yellow
Red admiral
Painted lady

*   Residents recorded in 12 or more 10-kilometre squares.

western peninsulas and occasionally elsewhere. Its presence on the Slyne Head peninsula coincides nicely with that of one of its important food plants, the common fleabane, which is scarce elsewhere in Connemara.

The small blue has been reported from the dunes near Dog's Bay and at the eastern edge of Connemara where, undoubtedly, it is more closely associated with the nearby limestone habitats than the true Connemara habitats. The holly blue, which relies on widely dispersed plants such as ivy, holly and buckthorn, is restricted mainly to a band running east-west through central Connemara.

The northern distribution of the silver-washed fritillary matches the range of the raspberry, but in the west, where this does not occur, it is more likely to utilise violets as food plants. In contrast, the very local distribution of the marsh fritillary does not match the widespread occurrence of its food plants, indicating that it requires more in its breeding habitat than just the correct plant species. Here is scope for yet another local ecological study.

The small and large heath butterflies are closely associated with the mountains and bogs of north-west Connemara, although their food plants are much more widespread. The large heath is very local in its distribution and probably quite rare. Further records of its distribution would be welcome.

The arrivals in the region of migrants such as the red admiral and the painted lady are always noteworthy because Connemara is so far from their centres of origin. Red admirals tend to occur more frequently, usually arriving from continental Europe in late spring and

The small copper - locally distributed in Connemara.

early summer, although individuals can sometimes be seen well into the autumn. Painted ladies are generally less common but, on occasions when there is a movement of large numbers from northern Africa and southern Europe, we will see them in Connemara. Painted ladies which arrive in May and June may produce an Irish generation later in the year, but none of these butterflies survive through the following winter.

There is much more to be learned about butterflies in Connemara and anyone who wishes to become familiar with these delightful animals could do no better than obtain a copy of *The Butterflies of Ireland: A Field Guide* by the late Dr Norman Hickin. Published in 1992 it is a very useful introduction to an absorbing subject. The book was edited and is introduced by Tim Lavery, one of Ireland's butterfly experts.

Moths

Moths are as attractive as butterflies in many ways and certainly more numerous in terms of both species and individuals. Yet, because most moths appear only at night and are difficult to identify, we do not pay as much attention to them as they deserve. Let us look at just a handful of species which can be found in Connemara.

The northern eggar is a moth we encounter on the bogs and mountainsides, usually as a large, brown and black tufted caterpillar on or near heather or bilberry. The adult male is dark brown with vertical yellow bands on its wings and can be seen flying during the day - usually as a brown blur at a distance too great to permit identification. The female is a rich orange-brown, larger than the male and flies only at night. The northern eggar is a form of oak eggar, but differs from the latter in having a two-year, rather than a one-year life cycle. This is probably due to the less hospitable conditions in which the northern eggar lives. The oak eggar lives in open woodland, heaths, grassland and hedges.

The large yellow underwing is a moth of the lowlands. Its forewings are dark brown, its hindwings a rich golden yellow with broad dark bands near the margins. In Connemara we might find it on agricultural land, moorland, coastal machair and gardens where its food plants include dandelions, common chickweed, docks and a wide range of wild and cultivated herbaceous plants. Its caterpillars often attack plants from underground and the large yellow underwing is one of the main species involved when farmers talk about 'cutworms' attacking the roots of grasses and other plants.

The six-spot burnet is an attractive and easily recognised species. It has six distinct red spots on each of its otherwise blackish forewings. When these are spread the almost completely red upper surfaces of the hind wings are revealed. It flies during the day and can be abundant in dry grassy habitats such as the coastal machair where there are plenty of flowers to feed on. It lays its eggs on the ever-popular common bird's-foot-trefoil.

A very localised moth, discovered near Dog's Bay in the 1960s, is the belted beauty. This is a small rather unimpressive species, the female of which is wingless. Its food plants include common bird's-foot-trefoil, plantain, clover and creeping willow. Outside Connemara it occurs only in Mayo and at a small number of locations in Britain. In 1991 Dr Don Cotton found thousands of belted beauty moths in the dunes at Annagh, on the Mullet peninsula in north-west Mayo. So although it is local in its distribution it may be more abundant than current records suggest. Another rare species reported for the first time in the 1960s is the yellow horned moth. It was discovered on an island in Lough Fadda where, characteristically, it was breeding on birch trees.

It will be clear from these few accounts that moths, like butterflies, are often associated with and dependent on particular plant species. So to conserve their diversity and numbers, we must first of all ensure that their food plants are protected.

Very occasionally some migrant moths reach Connemara. In 1953, for example, an oleander hawk-moth, from North Africa, was seen near Cashla Bay. This was a lucky sighting, because, although it was a bumper year for the species in Ireland and Britain, the total number recorded was only thirteen. In 1962 a death's head hawk-moth from southern Europe, Africa or the Middle East turned up at Moyard. Both these species are very large with wing spans of 120-135 millimetres (4.75-5.5 inches). They could hardly have been mistaken for any local species, the largest of which would be only just over half their size. The death's head is especially spectacular with dark forewings, yellow hindwings with dark bars, an orange striped abdomen and a 'face' on its body just behind the head. With such a low frequency of occurences, we should not hold our breath in anticipation of the arrival of the next giant moth.

Six-spot burnets - abundant in dry grassy habitats such as coastal machair. Here they are feeding on wild thyme.

Damselflies and dragonflies

Damselflies and dragonflies are active, colourful and highly visible insects. They undergo their early development underwater in lakes, streams and bog pools but emerge in the summer as beautiful adults. Most will live for only 1-3 weeks out of the three months during which the species can be seen flying, although adults of the brown hawker can live for two months. The damselflies are small, slender-bodied species; the dragonflies are large and robust. It is the dragonflies, like the common hawker, which we see patrolling hedgerows near water and hear crunching on flies caught in mid-air. Thirteen species of damselfly and dragonfly have been recorded in Connemara so far and these are listed in Table 21.

The large red damselfly is one of the most widespread species. It is usually the first to appear, late in spring. We can find it near most slow-flowing or still waters. The emerald damselfly is, as its name suggests, basically green but the male has light blue eyes and light blue bands at both the front and end of its abdomen. Its flight period is from about mid-June to the end of September and it can be seen in similar habitats to the red damselfly. The blue-tailed damselfly has a dark body and in both sexes a distinctive blue band near the end of the abdomen. It appears towards the end of May and can be seen up to the beginning of September. In the common blue damselfly the male is mainly light blue, while the female is dark and generally lacking any blue bands. If the female does sport any blue it is in narrow bands around the front of each abdominal segment. It flies from mid-May to early October.

The variable damselfly is similar in appearance to the common blue damselfly, but has a larger wing span and the male has a greater proportion of black on its abdomen. It also has a shorter flight period, from mid-May to early August. This damselfly seems to be restricted to the south-west coastal region. Why this should be remains to be discovered. The beautiful demoiselle is by far the scarcest damselfly in the region, having been recorded so far only in the Maam Cross-Maum area and the upper reaches of the Owenboliska River. In contrast to the other damselflies it is a species of fast-flowing streams with pebble beds. It has a dark green abdomen and brown wings, a fluttery, butterfly-like flight. Its flight period is from mid-May to early September. Elsewhere in Ireland it is found only south of a line between Galway and Dublin, so its Connemara locations are at the northern limit of its range.

The common darter is by far the most widespread of the dragonflies. The young stages develop mainly in stagnant waters, lakes, bogs and brackish waters. The adults, with a wing span of 58 millimetres (2.3 inches), are notably fast darters. A dark form of this brown species, sometimes considered to be a species in its own right, was seen near Roundstone in 1967. This form, or species, is called the Highland darter and has been recorded in abundance only in the north-west of Scotland and southern Norway. The black darter is much darker and has a shorter wing span. It is more typical of marshy areas and bogs, especially where there is heather in which it can rest during bad weather. In Connemara we are likely to see the black darter in the coastal fringe from Inveran to Killary Harbour.

The four-spotted chaser - found around boggy pools in west Connemara.

Table 21
Damselflies and dragonflies recorded in Connemara since 1961.
(L = local distribution; W = widespread*)

DAMSELFLIES

Variable damselfly	*Coenagrion pulchellum*	L (west only)
Common blue damselfly	*Enallagma cyathigerum*	W (throughout)
Large red damselfly	*Pyrrhosoma nymphula*	W (centre, west)
Blue-tailed damselfly	*Ischnura elegans*	W (throughout)
Emerald damselfly	*Lestes sponsa*	W (centre, west)
Beautiful demoiselle	*Calopteryx virgo*	L (north-east)

DRAGONFLIES

Brown hawker	*Aeshna grandis*	L (west only)
Common hawker	*Aeshna juncea*	L (south-west
Downy emerald	*Cordulia aenea*	L (south-west)
Keeled skimmer	*Orthetrum coerulescens*	L (north-west)
Four-spotted chaser	*Libellula quadrimaculata*	L (west and north)
Black darter	*Sympetrum danae*	W (south, west)
Common darter	*Sympetrum striolatum*	W (throughout)

* Recorded in 12 or more 10-kilometre squares.

The keeled skimmer - apparently restricted to the north-west of the region.

The common hawker is the largest of the common dragonflies with a wing span of 95 millimetres (3.75 inches). Only the rare brown hawker, which has been recorded so far in just one area in west Connemara, is larger, with a wingspan of 102 millimetres (4 inches). The male common hawker has blue eyes and blue and yellow markings on a dark brown body. In the female green replaces the blue. This is the species we meet patrolling streams and hedgerows from late June through to October. The four-spotted chaser is a brown, wide-bodied dragonfly with yellow patches along the side of its abdomen. We see it mainly around boggy pools in the western half of Connemara from about mid-May to mid-August. The keeled skimmer is a species we encounter mainly in the north-west of the region between Roundstone and Killary Harbour. The male has a distinctive blue-grey, fairly broad abdomen, the female a narrower, pale brown body. It is associated particularly with bogs and uplands, and elsewhere in Ireland it is only widespread in the mountainous areas of Kerry, Cork, Wicklow and Down. Finally, the downy emerald, a species with a downy thorax and green head, is the latest addition to the Connemara list. It was recorded for the first time in June 1992 north of Roundstone. It is a rare species and its only other known station in Ireland is in Kerry.

Grasshoppers, cockroaches and earwigs

Several grasshoppers and related species have been reported in the area. These include the common green, the mottled, the large marsh grasshopper and the common groundhopper. The large marsh grasshopper has been found in purple moor-grass on south-facing slopes around the shore of Lough Inagh and also in the nearby Derryclare Wood. The common groundhopper, which was found in the same area and at several locations in south Connemara, differs from the grasshoppers in that the upper casing of the first segment of its body (*pronotum*) extends back over the body to the end of its abdomen. Both its front and hind wings are reduced and it is, therefore, unable to fly. The groundhoppers have a diet of mosses and algae, while the grasshoppers feed on flowering plants.

Insects which do not evoke a warm response from the human inhabitants of Connemara are the common and German cockroaches. These two species, which belong to a mainly tropical insect group, seek the warmth of houses, schools and many other types of building. They are nocturnal and during the day hide in such out-of-the-way places as ventilation ducts, behind skirting boards and under floors. This means that they can live unnoticed for quite some time, building up their numbers all the while. The harm they do is not so much in what they eat, which is mainly scraps, but in the characteristic smell with which they contaminate all around them.

Mention should also be made of earwigs, the thought of which brings shudders to many people on account of the superstition that the insects enter human ears and bite through the eardrum. There is no truth in this idea, although earwigs will investigate ears if they chance upon

---

CONNEMARA'S OWN BUG

One day in the early 1980s the late Dr Gerald 'Doc' Walton, a well-known zoologist at University College, Cork, was trout fishing on Ballynakill Lough near Cleggan. He noticed some bugs on the large, smooth, black boulders at the eastern end of the lake. He was the right man in the right place at the right time. For, with a lifetime's study of these insects behind him, he was quickly able to see that there was something unusual about these animals. They were stouter than a similar bug which he knew well, *Saldula saltatoria*. Closer examination of one of them indicated that they belonged to a species which had never been reported before. It was a species not just new to Connemara or to Ireland, but to the world - a species new to science. It was to be called *Saldula connemarae*. Later he discovered more of these bugs on the shore of Derrylea Lough near Clifden and specimens of these, along with two slides, were deposited in the National Museum of Ireland, as is the convention with any new species found in the country.

---

them, treating them like any other small hole worthy of exploration as a site for daytime rest. There is one widespread species of earwig in Ireland and one rare species. The latter looks quite different from the common earwig, lives in compost heaps and probably does not occur in Connemara.

Bees and wasps

Bumblebees are colourful and easily recognised, although some species are difficult to identify. Out of a total of nineteen species for the whole of Ireland thirteen have been recorded in Connemara. Within this group ten species are called bumblebees (*Bombus*) while the rest are known as cuckoo bees (*Psithyrus*) because they lay their eggs in the nests of other species. The cuckoo bees are very similar in appearance to their hosts and often difficult to distinguish from them without very close examination. Most records for the bumblebees and cuckoo bees are for the western fringe of Connemara suggesting, like so many invertebrate distributions, that they represent the distribution of the observers rather than of the insects.

Bees, wasps and their look-alikes, hoverflies, are common in the region, although we have no details about their numbers. Hover-flies, though often mistaken for bees or wasps, belong to a different group of insects, the two-winged flies, and do not sting.

Beetles

Beetles are the largest group of insects on earth. They outnumber all known species of higher plants and there are six or seven described beetle species for every one of the vertebrates. It is therefore perhaps surprising that we know so little about beetles in Connemara. Four click beetles have been recorded in a provisional atlas for that group prepared by the British Biological Records Centre and nineteen terrestrial wetland species have been listed by D.A. Lott and D.T. Bilton, two visiting naturalists from England. Among their collection was one specimen of *Hydrosmecta delicatula* collected from an unvegetated shingle bank at the edge of the Failmore River near Maum. This species is said to be scarce throughout its range, and in Britain it is found only in northern England and Scotland. Six further species have recently been reported from Derryclare Wood and the neighbouring moorland and another four species from the Hill of Doon at the head of Lough Corrib.

Other insects

Among the other insect groups to receive some attention are the scuttle flies of which twelve or fourteen species were recorded on Inishbofin in the late 1970s. These are small, grey-black or brownish flies with a curious humped appearance. They often lack wings, but run energetically over the ground. Their larvae live in decaying or putrefying material. An inventory of midges (Chironomidae) in the Connemara National Park in the mid-1980s yielded forty species, of which two, *Bryophaenocladius aestivus* and *Metriocnemus atratulus*, were new to Ireland.

Many other groups of insects have not been considered in any detail in this brief survey. There are several inconspicuous groups living in the soil, in decaying plant material or in water, for example, all worthy of our attention. Much is still to be learned about insects of Connemara. Indeed there must be species new to the region or to Ireland waiting to be recorded and, quite possibly, species new to science to be discovered and described.

Spiders and their relations

To travel through the bogs of Connemara early on a September morning after the cool night has spread a delicate mantle of dew is entrancing, more so because countless spiders' webs are highlighted in silver against the darkness of the vegetation. This spectacle reminds us how common spiders are on the bogs and what an important role they must play in the ecology of the bog community.

One impressive species, a raft spider, was collected recently near the shore of Lough Bofin, to the west of Oughterard. This is a large spider, the female being up to 22 millimetres (nearly 1 inch) long and the male about 12 millimetres (0.5 inch). It is dark brown and has two very distinctive yellow bands running along each side of its body. It lives in swampy areas and appears in early summer. The adults eat flies, damselflies and even small fishes which the spiders attract to the surface by vibrating the water with their front legs. Young spiders are pale brown at first, getting darker as they grow, taking up to four years to reach maturity. They sometimes leave the habitat of the adults and climb into nearby trees and bushes.

Beyond this brief account there is very little more that can be said at present about spiders in Connemara, because of the total lack of published records and information.

A spider's web - one of many highlighted on the bog by an autumn morning mist.

Ticks, which are parasitic mites, are close relations of spiders and are generally unwelcome members of the Connemara fauna. The six-legged larvae lie in wait on a plant until a warm-blooded animal brushes past. Then they transfer to the new host, be it a naturalist or a sheep, and proceed to an area of tender skin which they pierce with barbed mouth parts through which they suck the host's blood. After dining in this manner for several days they achieve the shape of a small balloon and, fully satisfied, drop off their host, return to the ground, digest their meal and moult into eight-legged nymphs. These repeat the cycle and then moult into the adult form. As naturalists are not very common in Connemara (and sheep are also scarce in some areas) it is an advantage to ticks that they can survive for over a year without a meal.

Two tick species have been recorded in Connemara; the sheep tick and the Blyborough tick. The former is undoubtedly the most widespread and its nymphs can be particularly abundant on bracken during late summer. The Blyborough tick is named after a Lincolnshire village in which it was first found in abundance. It is parasitic on bats, especially pipistrelles and, although attacks on humans have been recorded elsewhere, it is doubtful whether we will come into close contact with it in Connemara.

Free-living mites can often be found infesting mammals and birds. For example, a pygmy shrew brought home by a cat, on examination under a microscope, was found to be crawling with mites, *Labidophorus soricis*. Likewise, a brown long-eared bat caught in east Connemara had a mass of tiny orange mites at the base of one of its ears. A little auk, blown inland in a storm and picked up thin and exhausted near Oughterard, was similarly infested with mites.

Spiders, ticks and mites, as much as some of us may dislike them, are part of Connemara's natural history and deserve mention, if not close scrutiny, for they play a significant part in the lives of many species for which we have greater affection.

Animals with many legs

Centipedes and millipedes are long slender animals with many body segments and numerous legs. They belong to two distinct groups within the Myriopoda - the 'many-footed' animals. Although superficially similar, centipedes and millipedes differ in many ways, the most obvious being that centipedes have one pair of legs on each body segment while the millipedes have two pairs on nearly every segment. Centipedes have a tough outer case, but this is not waterproof, so we will only find them in moist places where there is no danger of them drying out. Many live in the soil and amongst the dead leaves on the soil surface where they prey on other small animals. Those that hunt freely on the ground are strictly nocturnal and spend the day hiding under logs and stones where they can keep moist. Only four species have been recorded in Connemara, three of these before 1940. This is perhaps not surprising as centipedes are basically a tropical group of animals. However, some more up-to-date information about them would be welcome.

Millipedes are more common and eleven species have been recorded in Connemara since 1971. If we turn over stones and logs, we can often find them coiled up like black, shiny watchsprings. Their tough coating is rich in calcium so they are likely to be most abundant where the soils are rich in lime and, like the centipedes, they need moist conditions. In contrast to the centipedes, they feed mainly on the soft decaying tissues of fungi, leaves and dead animals. The pill millipede is a species which we will encounter quite frequently. It is rather uncharacteristic of the group, being short and more like a woodlouse than a millipede. But its 17-19 pairs of legs and shiny black coat readily distinguish it from a woodlouse which has just seven pairs of legs. It is rather more tolerant of dry conditions than other millipedes and ventures out into the open more often, for example along forest roads.

Woodlice and a terrestrial sandhopper

We can find woodlice under decaying logs, amongst dead leaves, under rocks, in bark crevices on tree trunks and in damp, shady corners in buildings of all kinds. They are widespread and numerous - and harmless, contrary to some widely held beliefs. In fact, they benefit many natural communities by eating dead leaves and other decaying material, thereby cycling minerals and nutrients through the environment.

Like the pill millipede, some species can roll up in a protective ball. In some areas these species were once thought to have medicinal value and were swallowed alive in attempts to cure digestive ailments - hence the name pill-bug, by which they are sometimes known.

Woodlice belong to a large class of animals known as crustaceans, which includes such familiar aquatic species as crabs, lobsters and waterfleas. They make up one of the few groups of crustaceans which have colonised the land successfully. Nevertheless, they still require damp, shady conditions and if we expose them to drying sunlight they will soon scuttle for cover. They are protected from predation to some extent by the repellant fluids they produce, but they still fall prey to a wide range of animals such as pygmy shrews, common frogs, centipedes, spiders and ground beetles.

Out of twenty-eight species so far recorded in Ireland, only six have been found in Connemara, including the largest species, the sea slater, which we will find only on rocky shores and harbour walls at the edge of the sea. The most widespread species inland are *Oniscus asellus* and *Porcellio scaber. Oniscus* is probably the most conspicuous Irish woodlouse which can live in all but the driest areas. It can tolerate life in lime-deficient habitats and is often the only species found in areas of blanket bog. *Porcellio* occurs in habitats as diverse as seashore, deciduous woodland, moorland and heath and is also quite tolerant of dry conditions. It is often found in very large numbers under the bark of dead trees. *Trichoniscus pusillus* occurs in similar habitats but is less often seen than *Oniscus* or *Porcellio* and, to date, it has been reported only from three locations in Connemara. *Philoscia mucorum* is more closely associated with sand-dunes and coastal grasslands, although it occurs inland as well. Finally, *Metoponorthus cingendus* has been recorded on the coast near Inveran at two of its most northerly stations in Ireland. It has its main centre of distribution in Kerry and Cork, which suggests that it may be sensitive to low winter temperatures or frosts.

Sand-hoppers are crustaceans which have not generally been successful in colonising the land, at least in northern latitudes. So it was a great surprise when a large sand-hopper was found on land near Kylemore Lough in 1936. This unusual animal is called *Arcitalitrus dorrieni* and it has an interesting history. It was described as a species new to science when it was first found in Britain in the 1920s. But it was subsequently found to live naturally in New South Wales and Southern Queensland in Australia. It had obviously been introduced to Britain, where it managed to establish small colonies in about ninety localities. Although it can move quite rapidly (up to 30-40 metres, 100-130 feet per night) it did not spread as quickly or as far as might have been expected. This is probably because, being a species of warmer conditions, it could not survive some of the colder winters in Britain. Its populaton is now concentrated in the warmer parts of Britain, in Devon and Cornwall and on the Scilly Isles. However, there is also one colony near London and there are two colonies on the island of Colonsay off the west coast of Scotland.

From the time it was first discovered in Ireland at Kylemore, *Arcitalitrus* was not seen again until Dr J.P. O'Connor of the National Museum of Ireland found it in the Connemara National Park in 1982. It was rediscovered in April 1987 by Dr Don Cotton, who, not knowing of its existence, was astonished to find this sand-hopper under a slab of stone in the same area. A follow-up survey by Dr Mark Costello in July 1987 showed that it was abundant in the Connemara National Park and environs.

How did *Arcitalitrus* get to Connemara? How did it get to Britain in the first place? Nobody knows. Many of the colonies are in ornamental gardens and nurseries, so perhaps it arrived from Australia with some exotic plants. However it got here, we should at least be thankful that it has not turned into a pest as have so many intentional and accidental animal introductions in the past.

Land snails and slugs

Snails and slugs are not attention-grabbing animals, except, of course, when they eat our vegetables. They are dull, slow moving and generally hide themselves from view. But, as Table 22 shows, there is a strikingly large number of species in Connemara: forty-seven snails and seventeen slugs. These numbers represent 80 per cent of all the snails and 71 per cent of all the slugs reported in Ireland since 1950. These are remarkably high proportions considering, for example, the general lack of woodlands, habitats which are favoured by many snails.

We will find about two thirds of the Connemara snail species in woodland, hedgerow and scrubby habitats and the remainder in dunes, grasslands or wet non-woodland habitats. Well over half the species can be considered widespread but this does not tell us whether they are

Table 22
Connemara land snails and slugs since 1950.
(L = local; W = widespread*)

SNAILS

Acicula fusca	L	(west)	*Discus rotundatus*	W	(throughout)
Carychium minimum	W	(throughout)	*Vitrea crystallina*	W	(throughout)
Carychium tridentatum	W	(throughout)	*Vitrea contracta*	W	(throughout)
Succinea putris	L	(east, north, west)	*Nesovitrea hammonis*	W	(throughout)
Oxyloma pfeifferi	W	(east and west)	*Aegopinella pura*	W	(throughout)
Cochlicopa lubrica	W	(throughout)	*Aegopinella nitidula*	W	(throughout)
Cochlicopa lubricella	W	(north and west)	*Oxychilus draparnaudi*	L	(north-east and south-west)
Pyramidula rupestris	W	(east, north, west)	*Oxychilus cellarius*	W	(throughout)
Columella edentula	W	(east, north, west)	*Oxychilus alliarius*	W	(throughout)
Columella aspera	L	(north)	*Zonitoides excavatus*	L	(west)
Vertigo antivertigo	W	(throughout)	*Zonitoides nitidus*	W	(throughout)
Vertigo substriata	L	(east, north, west)	*Euconulus fulvus*	W	(throughout)
Vertigo pygmaea	W	(east, north, west)	*Cecilioides acicula*	L	(south-east)
Vertigo lilljeborgi	L	(south-west)	*Clausilia bidentata*	W	(east and west)
Vertigo angustior	L	(west)	*Balea perversa*	L	(west)
Pupilla muscorum	L	(Inishbofin)	*Candidula intersecta*	L	(west)
Leiostyla anglica	W	(throughout)	*Cernuella virgata*	L	(west)
Lauria cylindracea	W	(throughout)	*Helicella itala*	W	(east, north, west)
Vallonia costata	L	(centre and west)	*Cochlicella acuta*	L	(centre and west)
Vallonia pulchella	L	(east and west)	*Trichia striolata*	W	(throughout)
Vallonia excentrica	L	(north and west)	*Trichia hispida*	W	(east and west)
Acanthinula aculeata	L	(throughout)	*Cepea nemoralis*	W	(east and west)
Spermodea lamellata	L	(east and west)	*Helix aspera*	W	(east and west)
Punctum pygmaeum	W	(throughout)			

SLUGS

Arion ater	W	(throughout)	*Milax budapestensis*	L	(east and west)
Arion subfuscus	W	(throughout)	*Limax maximus*	L	(throughout)
Arion circumscriptus	W	(throughout)	*Limax flavus*	L	(throughout)
Arion silvaticus	L	(west)	*Limax pseudoflavus*	L	(south)
Arion hortensis	W	(throughout)	*Limax marginatus*	W	(throughout)
Arion intermedius	W	(throughout)	*Deroceros laeve*	W	(throughout)
Vitrina pellucida	W	(east, north, west)	*Deroceros reticulatum*	W	(throughout)
Milax gagates	L	(west)	*Deroceros caruanae*	L	(north and south-west)
Milax sowerbyi	L	(east and west)			

* Recorded in 12 or more 10-kilometre squares.

abundant or easily located. The rest appear to be quite local in their distribution, some, like *Vertigo lilljeborgi* and *Vertigo angustior*, being found in recent years at only single locations in south-west Connemara.

The snails occur in a variety of shell forms ranging from fairly flat discs, as in *Oxychilus* species, to relatively tall spires, as in *Cecilioides acicula*. In some, such as the well-known *Cepea nemoralis*, the shells may be circled by alternate light and dark bands. But most are a rather uniform shade of brown which, of course, helps them to blend in well with their background of leaves, tree bark, sandy soil or mud.

The dividing line between snails and slugs is hard to draw because slugs are basically snails which have lost all or part of their external shells. *Vitrina pellucida*, which we can find in a wide variety of habitats, has a smooth, glossy, very thin and translucent, usually pale green shell. However, the shell is not big enough for the animal to retreat into completely, so it is listed as a slug. In contrast, the common, big, black garden slug *Arion ater* has no visible external shell and is clearly a slug. But it does have a vestige of a shell inside its body and this confirms that it is closely related to the more obviously shelled snails.

Snails and slugs are restricted in their habits by the need to avoid drying up. As a consequence, they are most active in the open at night and during very wet days. Snails can further avoid drying out by withdrawing into their shells but during dry weather slugs have to burrow deep into the soil or retreat into cracks and crevices in rocks and logs to find moist conditions. Slugs can burrow more than a metre (over 3 feet) into the soil in dry weather, which makes them very hard to find. Being nocturnal has another advantage. They avoid being consumed by predators such as birds which hunt by sight.

Most slugs and snails feed on rotting vegetation, fungi, algae and lichens, all but a few generally leaving healthy green plants alone. A few species, like *Zonitoides* and *Vitrina*, are carnivorous and will eat other species of snails and their eggs.

Among the rarer species recorded in Connemara, *Vertigo lilljeborgi* is worthy of mention. This is a tiny, ovoid snail, about 2 millimetres (less than 0.1 inch) high. It lives in saturated, decaying vegetation. It has also been found in Cork, Kerry and Mayo since 1950, and in Clare and Sligo before that. Otherwise, it occurs only locally in the upland areas of Britain and in Scandinavia. It clearly is a northern species and its west of Ireland stations are at the southern edge of its range. However, in the years following the end of the Ice Age it was more widespread in Ireland, as recent studies of some sediments in Dublin City have shown. At this time, 10,000-9,400 years ago, it lived in a snail community which included several other present-day Connemara species such as *Cochliocopa lubrica*, *Cochliocopa lubricella*, *Columella edentula*, *Columella aspera*, *Vertigo pygmaea*, *Pupilla muscorum* and *Euconulus fulvus*. In more recent times species such as *Carychium minimum*, *Vertigo substriata* and *Leiostyla anglica* have appeared in the community. *Discus rotundatus* and *Vertigo angustior* were amongst the later arrivals, appearing 8,100-7,100 years ago. There have been no studies of snails in Connemara sediments, but it is probably safe to assume that most of the species listed above would have been present in the region by about 10,000 years ago.

Vertigo angustior, another tiny snail of very wet habitats, is very rare in Ireland and Britain. Since 1950 it has been recorded elsewhere only at single sites in Kerry, Mayo and Norfolk, and in two places in Co. Dublin. However, it has been found in post-glacial fossil forms at several sites around the Irish coast and at inland locations in Britain. *Leiostyla anglica*, a snail of damp woods and marshes, is an Atlantic species. In Europe it is found only in western Britain and Ireland, with its main population concentration north of a line from Galway to the Mountains of Mourne on the north-east coast. *Spermodea lamellata*, a snail found in leaf litter and under logs in old deciduous woods, has a similar distribution, with some outlying populations in Denmark and the southern margins of Norway and Sweden.

In Connemara several species occur close to the northern limit of their south-west European ranges. These include the snails *Candidula intersecta*, *Cernuella virgata*, *Helicella itala* and the slugs *Arion lusitanica* and *Limax pseudoflavus*. The snail *Cochlicella acuta* is notably restricted to the coasts and midlands of Ireland and the western coasts of Britain and France.

Finally, it is interesting to note that the small, top-shaped *Pyramidula rupestris*, a species generally associated with dry limestone rocks, occurs in west Connemara. So too does *Zonitoides excavatus*, a snail which has the contrasting requirements of a largely lime-free habitat. A study of the distributions and specific habitats of these two snails could be most informative.

LIFE IN LAKES AND RIVERS

Early freshwater life

At the end of the Ice Age Connemara was a cold and watery place, but not without life. We have seen how arctic-alpine plants followed the glaciers and colonised new ground soon after it was freed of its ice burden. We have noted, too, how some of those plants, such as alpine clubmoss, have survived on the exposed summits and ridges of the highest Connemara mountains. But the plants were not alone. Animals arrived, too, some, such as the insects, flying to the newly available habitats, others, like the fish, swimming up from the sea. And some of these early colonising animals have survived the improving climate in the cold, infertile lakes on the mountain-tops and in the deep lowland lakes.

It was the late Dr Gerald Walton, the Cork zoologist, who, in the mid-1960s, first alerted us to the presence of some of these glacial relicts in Connemara. He trudged to the summit of Doughruagh, pond net and sample jars on his back, and searched the dark, cold waters of some of the highest lakes in the region. In his own words, 'If local hearsay may be depended on this mountain is unique in being the only peak in Connemara with a cluster of small lakes at such an altitude' (529 metres, 1,736 feet). Although these are not the only lakes at such a height, local hearsay certainly guided him to some interesting discoveries.

In the most westerly lake, about 21 metres (70 feet) across, he found a few stems of pondweed and the occasional freshwater shrimp when he swept his net through the water. But when he turned over stones at the edge of the lake he discovered a large water beetle. This proved to be

Facing page: An upland stream.

Dytiscus lapponicus, the smallest of the great diving beetles, a northern species recorded only once previously in Ireland from a pool in west Donegal. Otherwise it is confined to lakes at considerable altitudes in the Scottish Highlands and to small lakes at sea-level on some of the western islands of Scotland. The great diving beetles are well known for their large size and yellow markings, and for the predatory habits of their larvae. *Dytiscus lapponicus* spends a long period hibernating in mud at the bottom of its lake during the extended mountain-top winter.

Moving on to the second lake, which was richer in plant life, including water lobelia, Dr Walton first found swarms of tadpoles and unmistakeable tracks of a pine marten - two observations which would be sufficiently satisfying in themselves for most naturalists venturing into that bleak environment. But when he searched through some moss, *Scorpidium scorpioides*, at the edge of the lake, he found a second northern beetle, *Agabus arcticus*. This species had been recorded previously only high on the Wicklow Mountains and at more than 300 metres (1,000 feet) in Antrim at the beginning of the century.

The third lake is deep and clear and it yielded yet another glacial relic, a waterboatman called *Glaenocorisa propinqua*. This species had been recorded only three times before, in the uplands of Donegal and Kerry and in Lough Enask in the Roundstone bogs. *Glaenocorisa propinqua*, unlike many waterboatmen, is a carnivore and feeds on small invertebrates living in the open water.

The fourth lake was a disappointment. It was too big to sample from the shore. Anyone with the energy and motivation to sample it will have to carry a collapsible rubber dinghy up the steep, rough slopes of Doughruagh.

Lake five was not an anti-climax for amongst the numerous waterboatmen was another high-level species, *Callicorixa wollastoni.* All in all Dr Walton had had a very good day's fieldwork.

Since that short, pioneering expedition several other arctic-alpine or high-altitude species have been discovered in Connemara. Another waterboatman, *Arctocorisa carinata*, was discovered in the early 1970s in a lake at 485 metres (1,600 feet) near the summit of Lugnabrick, in the hills overlooking the village of Maum. A stonefly, *Capnia atra*, was found in Lough Nadirkmore, in the Partry Mountains just to the north of our rather artificial Connemara boundary. Interestingly, too, this species has been caught on the western shore of upper Lough Corrib, a deep body of water in which we will find other relics of colder times like arctic charr and the tiny shrimp *Mysis relicta*.

Stoneflies and waterboatmen of the upland streams and lakes

The rain falling on the mountains quickly finds its way to the lowlands in countless steep, rocky streams. One moment water is gently flowing over and between angular, mossy boulders, the idyllic image of a mountain stream. The next moment the boulders are submerged by a frightening torrent of peaty water sweeping down from a rain-washed summit. All but the smallest and most specialised animals find it impossible to live in such violently changeable habitats. It is only when we reach the lower slopes, where the gradient is less, that we will find insects and other

A summit pool.

invertebrates in any quantities, living in the protective mantle of moss or in the shelter of immovable stones.

Stoneflies are important members of the upland stream communities. As adults, these delicate insects live for only a few days. They are rarely found far from water because even those which can fly do so weakly. So we will give our attention to the young stages, the nymphs, which live underwater. In most species the nymphs take one year to develop from egg to emergent adult. The time of emergence, and therefore of egg-laying which occurs soon after, varies between species. In some species it is early in the year, in others it can, for example, be late in the summer. This means that it is necessary to visit a stream or lake several times in a season to ensure that we find the nymphs of all species. For once a species has emerged, there will be no nymphs present in the stream for several weeks, until the newly laid eggs hatch to produce a new generation.

Stonefly nymphs have two long tails, a characteristic which distinguishes them immediately from those of three-tailed mayflies. Some mayflies also live in the upland streams, but generally they are more common in lowland rivers and lakes where the stoneflies are less prominent members of the aquatic community.

In the east Connemara streams which eventually flow into Lough Corrib, Drs Mark Costello, Martin Farrell and Kieran McCarthy recorded twelve species of stoneflies out of the nineteen or so which are known to live in Ireland. They found the most widespread species to be *Siphonoperla torrentium*, a carnivorous species of soft waters, which inhabits stony rivers and lakeshores. *Amphinemura sulcicollis, Protonemura meyeri, Leuctra hippopus* and *Leuctra inermis* are also quite common but these live only in streams. *Isoperla grammatica* is another species found just in rivers, but in the east Connemara streams it occurs only below an altitude of 60 metres (200 feet). *Nemoura cinerea, Leuctra fusca* and *Chloroperla tripunctata* are uncommon river species, while *Nemurella pictetii* has been found only in the river flowing into Coolin Lough on the northern flanks of Benlevy and *Nemoura avicularis* only in the River Kip near Moycullen. The latter species has been recorded at just three other sites in Ireland, in Wicklow, Cavan and Westmeath. *Diura bicaudata* is apparently restricted to Lough Nafooey and a river flowing into that deep, infertile lake, suggesting that it may be another arctic-alpine relic.

It is notable that, in contrast to its abundance in the soft waters of Connemara, *Siphonoperla torrentium* is completely absent from the hard waters of the limestone lowlands to the east. Some stonefly species seem to occur together regularly. It has been noted, for example, that *Amphinemura sulcicollis* and *Protonemura meyeri* are often associated, though it is thought that they are not competing for resources because there are differences between the sizes of their nymphs and the times at which they emerge. *Amphinemura, Leuctra inermis* and *Leuctra hippopus* also frequently occur together but possibly avoid competition by living on different types of riverbed within the same habitat. Likewise, *Protonemura meyeri* and *Isoperla grammatica* can live together because they have different diets.

Only *Siphonoperla torrentium* and *Diura bicaudata* have been found in lakes in east Connemara, the remaining species being restricted to streams. Up to eight of the twelve species can occur in any one river system although, as we have seen, they are often segregated by their diets, habitats or life-cycles. The number of species grows with an increase in the gradients of the streams and a decline in their alkalinity. So we can predict that the higher we go into the mountains (within obvious limits) and the less alkaline the water becomes, the more stonefly species we will encounter.

In a constantly moving habitat like a stream there is always a danger that small animals such as stonefly nymphs will be washed away. This happens particularly at the end of the development period when the nymphs are ready to emerge. At this time many are washed downstream and become easy prey for young brown trout and Atlantic salmon.

Fewer species of waterboatmen occur in the upland and soft waters of Connemara, although where they do occur there might be large numbers of an individual species. *Hesperocorixa sahlbergi, Hesperocorixa castanea* and *Sigara scotti* are the species most likely to be found in the foothills in infertile lakes and pools, the latter species probably most in evidence because it can live in exposed conditions where there is little vegetation. *Sigara fossarum* and *Sigara distincta* also live in soft waters but only in the lowlands. All these species have a mixed diet of algae and detritus (animal and plant remains).

Waterboatmen, or back-swimmers as they are sometimes called, are familiar insects in ponds and ditches. We often see them floating at the surface, upside down, with the tip of the abdomen tilted to touch the surface film, taking air. This air supply is held by long rows of bristles on the abdomen. According to records dating back to the mid-1950s, *Sigara scotti* is the most common waterboatman species in some of the small lakes in the Roundstone bogs. *Hesperocorixa castanea* occurs frequently but in small numbers while species more frequently associated with hard waters can also be found. These include *Arctocorisa germari, Corixa dentipes, Corixa punctata* and *Cymatia bonsdorffii*, a carnivorous species.

Waterboatmen are heavily preyed upon by fish. In Sweden, where fish populations have been reduced by acidification, species like *Glaenocorisa propinqua* have become more widespread in lakes as a result of the reduced predation pressure. This is the sort of ecological change which we should be looking out for in the west of Ireland, particularly in areas where there is a threat of acidification to our lakes and rivers.

Like many of the waterboatman species, some of the closely related pond skaters favour temporary pools as breeding habitats. One such pond skater is *Gerris costai*, a small species which appears to glide across the surface of the water. It has been observed on large puddles in a forestry plantation in east Connemara at an altitude of about 150 metres (500 feet). When disturbed, all the pond skaters scatter to the edge of the puddles, sometimes taking to dry land, and disappear under the nearby vegetation. Also living in the puddles are the waterboatman *Sigara nigrolineata* and the water cricket *Velia caprai*.

Velia caprai is a distinctive water bug (the collective name for the waterboatmen, pond skaters, water crickets and several other related groups), being black with rows of crimson spots running along the edges of its back. Underneath it is orange-yellow. It is common and widespread, and can often be found in large gatherings in drains, peaty pools and slow-flowing stretches of streams within upland forestry plantations.

Diversity in a lake

Maumwee Lough (see Map 12), about 1.5 kilometres (1 mile) north of Maam Cross, is a rather unimpressive lake, rectangular in outline and overshadowed to east and west by mountains. It is about 1 by 0.6 kilometres (0.6 x 0.4 miles) and has a maximum depth of 8 metres (26 feet) near the south-eastern shore. Its still, black surface, reflecting just the clouds above, will not raise much enthusiasm in the passing naturalist. But that blank surface belies the richness of the life below - not in weight or volume of life, but in species of tiny suspended plants and animals known collectively as phytoplankton and zooplankton.

Our knowledge of this diversity comes from a detailed study carried out in the mid-1980s by Dr Jim Bowman and his colleagues in the Environmental Research Unit of the Department of the Environment and a number of other researchers from University College, Dublin, and elsewhere. The purpose of the survey was to assess whether several lakes in Ireland had been affected chemically and biologically by acidification resulting from the discharge of acidic gases from Moneypoint Power Station on the Shannon Estuary and to provide a baseline against which any future changes can be judged. Before we proceed any further, we should set our minds at rest by noting that, up to the mid-1980s, Maumwee Lough had not been adversely affected by acid precipitation. However, Connemara is not entirely free from acidification problems, as we will see later.

It is not possible to give a comprehensive account of the ecology of Maumwee Lough here. But Tables 23, 24 and 25 will give an idea of the plankton and invertebrate communities living in the lake and its inflowing streams and serve as a guide to what we could expect to find in some of Connemara's other large lakes.

Phytoplankton

The phytoplankton of Maumwee Lough is composed of over 200 species of microscopic plants and blue-green bacteria. Some occur in abundance but most only in small numbers and infrequently through the year. Overall, the quantity of phytoplankton in the lough at any one time is very small, somewhere between 4 and 80 cubic millimetres in each cubic metre of water. This compares with over 10,000 cubic millimetres per cubic metre in one of the richer lakes in the Department of Environment study. However, that lake had less than 150 phytoplankton species. We can liken this comparison to one between an unfertilised meadow and a fertilised one. In the former we will find a wide variety of flowers and low-yielding grasses; in the latter we will find few flowers and perhaps only one dominant grass which is adapted to producing a high yield in very fertile conditions. In an infertile water such as Maumwee Lough there is insufficient food to allow any one species to grow at the expense of others. This is a very important lesson for conservation. Too much fertility (pollution!) can lead to a huge loss in species diversity. We must therefore aim at not over-enriching our environment, particularly with inorganic nitrogen, phosphorus and potassium, if we want to retain a rich variety of plants and animals around us.

The planktonic green algae, as their name indicates, are typically green. They may be single-celled like *Chlamydomonas* or linked in chains like *Spirogyra* - two species which will bring back memories of school biology. The desmids are also green algae but are basically single-celled and made up of two distinct halves. The cells may be solitary, with ornate spines, like *Xanthidium armatum*, or they may form irregular or filamentous colonies. They are generally confined to soft waters, so Connemara is an ideal place for them, and a Mecca for naturalists who wish to study them.

Table 23
The phytoplankton of Maumwee Lough.
(based on Bowman 1991)

GROUP	NUMBER * OF SPECIES	SPECIES OCCURRING MOST FREQUENTLY **
Green algae (exc. Desmids) (Chlorophyceae)	24	*Spirogyra* spp., *Mougeotia* spp., *Botryococcus braunii*, *Chlamydomonas* spp.
Desmids (Chlorophyceae)	152	*Xanthidium armatum, Micrasterias fimbriata, Micrasterias truncata,* *Staurastrum anatinum*
Diatoms (Bacillariophyceae)	33	*Tabellaria* spp., *Navicula* spp., *Asterionella formosa*
Cryptomonads (Cryptophyceae)	1	*Cryptomonas* spp.
Golden-brown algae (Crysophyceae)	5	*Mallomonas* spp., *Dinobryon bavaricum*
Dinophyceae	8	*Peridinium inconspicuum, Glenodinium* spp., *Ceratium comutum*
Blue-green bacteria *** (Myxophyceae)	14	*Merismopedia glauca*, and other *Merismopedia* spp.

*	These are minimum numbers because many specimens were not identified to species level.
**	Species which occurred in a large proportion of samples, but not necessarily in large numbers.
***	Formerly known as blue-green algae.

The diatoms are single-celled but have a characteristic wall of overlapping halves which are composed of silica. They come in many attractive shapes. *Tabellaria* forms flat zig-zag filaments of rectangular cells, *Navicula* is long and spindle-shaped while *Asterionella* forms star-shaped floating colonies.

Cryptomonas is one of a small group of single-celled brown to olive-green algae with kidney- or pear-shaped cells and two whip-like flagella. The golden-brown algae, like *Mallomonas*, are single-celled, oval and covered all over with glossy scales of silica, like overlapping roof tiles. *Peridinium*, a member of a small group called the Dinophyceae, is a round, armoured, helmet-like, single-celled alga with two flagella. The blue-green bacteria, formerly known as blue-green algae, take on many forms. Some, such as *Merismopedia* are made up of round cells, linked in flat colonies like rafts. Some form chains of cells sometimes enveloped in jelly, others form branched chains, and so on.

Words cannot do justice to these beautiful living structures, or to the planktonic animals we are about to discuss. They must be seen live through a microscope to be fully appreciated. In this day and age any serious naturalist should have access to a microscope. Reasonable models, particularly if they are second hand, are no more expensive than many items of sports equipment which are readily affordable by many.

Phytoplankton studies were also carried out in the 1940s and 1950s in several other Connemara lakes. These were Loughs Bofin, Loughaunierin, Ardderry, Oorid, Derryclare, Inagh, Ballynahinch, Kylemore, Doo, Rinvyle and several in the Roundstone bogs. Although the phytoplankton communities differed in detail, they were broadly similar to the one in the more recent study of Maumwee Lough. This suggests that it is unlikely that there has been any serious environmental deterioration in most of these waters during the intervening thirty or forty years. Nevertheless, it would be unwise to be complacent and repeat surveys of the phytoplankton of these lakes should be undertaken in the near future to establish for certain their current state of health.

Zooplankton

The plant plankton serves as food for the larger species of animal plankton - the wheel animalcules (or rotifers, a less attractive but more economical name), water fleas and copepods.

The rotifers are small, ranging in size from 0.04 to 2 millimetres, and are so named because the ciliated crown on many species gives the appearance, when it beats, of a rotating wheel. The rhythmic beating of the cilia serves the dual purpose of propelling the animal through the water and bringing food particles to the mouth. Some feed on suspended matter, others prey on planktonic algae, protozoa (single-celled animals) or other rotifers. Most rotifers seen are females and in some species the males have never been observed. But, when the males do occur they are incapable of feeding and soon die. The females can produce two kinds of eggs without fertilisation. Small ones develop into males and large ones into females. A resting egg can also be produced, which can survive through unfavourable conditions and develop later when conditions have returned to normal. Two species of rotifer are common in Maumwee Lough. *Kellicottia longispina* is the most abundant, peaking in numbers in June or July. The *Conochilus unicornis* population tends to peak in September, although large numbers can also occur in June and July.

The water flea, *Daphnia*, is the most familiar of all freshwater planktonic animals. It can occur in immense numbers in still waters, and provide abundant food for many of the larger animals. *Daphnia* has a one-piece shell, which is folded over the back and open at the front, rather like a mussel. It can be up to 5 millimetres (0.2 inch) long. Through its transparent shell, with the aid of a microscope, we can see its beating limbs, food passing along the food canal and eggs in the female's brood chamber. In Maumwee Lough *Daphnia* is most abundant in May, June and July and again in October, November and December. These peaks typically follow peaks in the phytoplankton on which the *Daphnia* feed. The successive peaks and troughs in the abundance of phytoplankton and zooplankton follow well-established and predictable cycles in the commoner species. But the size and timing of the cycles may vary somewhat between species and from year to year.

Although *Daphnia* is common in Maumwee, another water flea, *Bosmina* is much more numerous at certain times of the year. Whereas the *Daphnia* population peaks in early summer and autumn, *Bosmina* numbers are at their highest from October through to February and sometimes in April and May. *Bosmina* is smaller (0.5-1 millimetre long) than *Daphnia* and somewhat circular in side view. It has a characteristic pair of slightly down-curved immovable antennae which project from the front of the head like a beak.

Daphnia and *Bosmina* are present in the plankton throughout the year, but most water flea species, including *Diaphanosoma brachyurum*, *Holopedium gibberum* and *Sida crystallina*, appear intermittently and peak in much smaller numbers. One species which occurs in small numbers only in the summer months is *Leptodora kindtii*. This is the largest water flea known to science and can attain a body length of 10 millimetres (0.4 inch). It is also unusual in being totally transparent, except for its single large eye. Its presence in a plankton sample can often be detected only by the movement of water it generates. *Leptodora* is a carnivore and preys on smaller water fleas and copepods.

The only copepod water flea recorded in Maumwee Lough is *Cyclops* (there may be several species involved, but these are difficult to distinguish). Its body is pear-shaped, 0.5-1 millimitres or more in length, with two long tail appendages, on each side of which the female may be carrying prominent egg-sacs. On its head there is a single eye, from which the name *Cyclops* has been given, in reference to the giants of Greek mythology. *Cyclops* is present throughout the year and can be abundant in any month.

Zooplankton studies in lakes in the Roundstone bogs, in the vicinity of Carna and in east Connemara indicate that the communities in these lakes are generally similar to that found in

Table 24
The zooplankton of Maumwee Lough.
(based on Bowman 1991)

GROUP	NUMBER OF SPECIES	SPECIES OCCURRING MOST FREQUENTLY
Wheel animalcules (Rotifera)	24	*Conochilus unicornis, Kellicottia longispina*
Water fleas (Cladocera)	20	*Daphnia hyalina, Bosmina* spp., *Diaphanosoma brachyurum, Holopedium gibberum , Sida crystallina*
Water fleas (Copepoda)	12	*Cyclops* spp.

Maumwee Lough. The only major difference seems to be in the absence of the copepod *Diaptomus gracilis* from Maumwee Lough. Elsewhere, in the larger Connemara lakes, this species is a regular and abundant member of the zooplankton community. In appearance it differs from *Cyclops* in having a longer (1-2.5 millimetres), thinner body, a shorter tail appendage with a single egg-sac in the female, and two antennae which are as long as the body.

Invertebrates of Maumwee Lough

The Maumwee Lough shore has a rich invertebrate community but the streams flowing into the lake are less well endowed with species, as Table 25 shows. Mayfly nymphs are the most numerous shore insects, *Caenis luctuosa* being particularly common. This is an encouraging sign because this is an acid-sensitive species. It lives in silt between gravel and stones and is described as a sprawler because of the manner in which it lies in the surface film of silt. It feeds on fine particles of detritus which it gathers from the surrounding silt. In contrast, *Paraleptophlebia werneri* is a burrower and lives deeper in the lakeshore silt than *Caenis luctuosa*. Stoneflies and caddis flies are not common in the shore community but freshwater shrimps and several of the snails and orb mussels are present in good numbers.

Adult caddis flies, or sedge flies as they are also known, are rather dull insects. They have two pairs of wings that are characteristically covered with fine hairs and held roof-like over the body when at rest. They have antennae which are often longer than their bodies and most species are some shade of brown or black. Since their mouthparts are poorly developed the adults can feed only on nectar and plant juices. They come out mainly at dusk and spend their brief lives beside the waters in which they lived as larvae.

Caddis fly larvae are much more impressive, primarily because of the variety of distinctive cases and nets which many species construct to protect their soft bodies and catch food. They are by far the most diverse group of the larger and better-known aquatic insects, with well over 100 species known in Ireland, compared with fewer than thirty mayflies and only nineteen stoneflies. But, with no more than about 12 per cent of Irish species, Maumwee Lough is poorly endowed with caddis flies, as presumably are most Connemara lakes. Furthermore, the species which are present occur infrequently and in small numbers. *Sericostoma personatum* is the most common caddis fly on the lakeshore. Its case, which curves and tapers towards the hind end, is made of sand grains. *Polycentropus flavomaculatus* is a species of running water and lakeshores exposed to wave action. Neither it nor the *Holocentropus* species build cases. Instead they live under protective stones to which they attach silk nets which trap food carried to them in the water currents. The larvae of *Hydropsyche instabilis* occur only in fast-flowing water where they live in flimsy, trumpet-shaped nets attached to plants or stones. As far as is known all these species are omnivorous, feeding on plant material, detritus and any small animals which come their way.

The small shrimp *Gammarus duebeni* is widespread and common throughout Ireland, living in shallow, clean, well oxygenated water. It is 25-30 millimetres (1-1.2 inches) long, flattened from side to side, and has eyes shaped like an elongated kidney. Its habit of lying and moving on its side enables it to squeeze under stones and survive in fast-flowing streams, such as the western stream flowing into Maumwee Lough. In spring and summer two shrimps will often be seen swimming in tandem, the larger male holding onto the female beneath. They remain like this for about a week before mating, after which they separate. The female then carries with her the fertilised eggs until they hatch and mature into tiny shrimps. *Gammarus* feeds mainly on detritus and is eaten by fish, especially young trout and salmon.

The mayflies, stoneflies and midges are the most abundant groups in the two streams flowing into Maumwee Lough, one from the north and the other from the west. *Baetis rhodani* and *Leptophlebia vespertina* are the commonest mayflies in these running water habitats, while the widespread stonefly *Siphonoperla torrentium* is also present along with several of the species already discussed.

Most of the other groups are represented mainly or only on the lakeshore. The beetles include great diving beetles (*Dytiscus*) and whirligig beetles (*Gyrinus*). The latter gather on sheltered patches of water during the day, literally whirling across the surface in a manner which demands that they collide - but they never do.

Leeches are significant predators in the lakeshore community. *Erpobdella octoculata*, with eight eyes arranged in four pairs around the top of its head, is brown and up to 40 millimetres (1.6 inches) long when at rest. It feeds on midge larvae, caddis fly larvae, worms and a variety of crustaceans. *Glossiphonia complanata* is smaller (15 millimetres, 0.6 inch) but more colourful. It is green-brown with two black and yellow stripes running along the length of its back. It has six eyes set in pairs in the centre of its head. It sometimes sucks the body fluids of worms and insect larvae, but chiefly it preys on snails such as *Lymnaea* and orb mussels, *Sphaerium*.

Another species which is found from time to time on the shore of Connemara lakes is the horse leech (*Haemopsis sanguisuga*), named thus either because it frequents places where horses and cattle drink or merely because it is large - up to 60 millimetres (2.4 inches) in length. It is a formidable predator, devouring earthworms, snails, insects, tadpoles, small or wounded fish, frogs, leeaches of its own and other species and carrion of any sort.

Finally, mention needs to be made of the midges, which are also known as plumed gnats in reference to the feathery antennae of the adult males. Their worm-like larvae are important members of the lake community. The presence of haemoglobin-like pigment in their blood gives many species a red colour, hence their common name, bloodworm. They feed on detritus and small animals and serve as a very important food supply for other species in the lake.

In bog lakes midge larvae play an important role in cycling the peat which gets into the water. According to research carried out in England, by the time loose peat particles have settled to the lake bed their nutrient value has increased substantially, presumably because of the micro-

Table 25
The invertebrates of Maumwee Lough.
(based on Bowman 1991)

GROUP	NUMBER OF SPECIES			MOST ABUNDANT SPECIES		
	Lake-shore	Stream west	Stream north	Lakeshore	Stream west	Stream north
Stoneflies (Plecoptera)	5	7+	5+	*Siphonoperla torrentium*	*Leuctra hippopus* *Siphonoperla torrentium*	*L. hippopus* *Nemoura cinerea*
Mayflies (Ephemeroptera)	11	7+	5+	*Caenis luctuosa, Paraleptophlebia werneri*	*Baetis rhodani*	*Leptophlebia vespertina*
Caddis flies (Trichoptera)	16	6	5+	*Holocentropus* spp., *Polycentropus flavomaculatus* *Sericostoma personatum*	*Hydropsyche instabilis*	*Hydropsyche instabilis* Polycentropidae
Dragon flies (Odonata)	+	0	0			
Midges (Diptera)	15	4	6	*Paratanytarsus* spp., *Procladius* spp.		*Cricotopus* spp.
Flies (exc. midges) (Diptera)	+	+	1++	*Tipula* spp.	*Simulium* spp.	
Waterboatmen (Corixidae)	1	0	+	*Sigara scotti*		
Snails / orb mussels / pea mussels (Mollusca)	6	1	0	*Lymnaea peregra* *Sphaerium* spp.		
Shrimps (Crustacea)	1	1	0	*Gammarus duebeni*		
Worms (Oligochaeta)	6	1	1	Limbriculidae		
Beetles (Coleoptera)	4+	2	1	Dytiscidae *Limnius volckmari*	*Limnius volckmari*	
Leeches (Hirudinea)	3	1	0	*Erpobdella octoculata* *Glossiphonia complanata*	*Erpobdella octoculata*	

organisms which have colonised them. The midge larvae eat these enriched particles and subsequently produce faecal pellets which are eaten by small water fleas. During their feeding activities the water fleas break down the pellets to a size which the midge larvae can also eat. This breakdown of pellets is accompanied by a further increase in nutritional value as the bacterial content of the faecal pellets increases by over 300 per cent. So both species benefit from this relationship which is based on just tiny fragments of peat!

Midge larvae emerge as flies in dense, buzzing swarms in spring. At this time they are sometimes called duck-flies, because they are important food for mallard ducklings. They are significant irritants for human beings, but at least we can be thankful that most of them do not bite.

Freshwater molluscs

The distributions of Connemara's freshwater snails and mussels have been comprehensively mapped, like those of the land snails which were discussed earlier. The list of species reported since 1950 is presented in Table 26. It is perhaps surprising to find so many species in a region which is generally considered to be lime deficient. Out of the twenty-four freshwater snail species recorded in Ireland, twenty-one have been seen in Connemara since 1950. The three missing species are *Myxas glutinosa*, *Lymnaea auricularia* and *Planorbis laevis*. The last two were recorded before 1950, so it is possible that they are still present, bringing the Connemara total up to 96 per cent of that for the whole of Ireland.

One Connemara snail with a strange history and unusual breeding habits is the tiny Jenkins' spire shell, *Potamopyrgus jenkinsi*. This dark-shelled species, which is rarely taller than 5 millimetres (0.2 inch), is sometimes extremely abundant in running water and still water habitats, including wells and water troughs. It was known in British brackish coastal waters in the nineteenth century, although its origin was, and still is, controversial. Some naturalists suggest that it had been introduced from New Zealand. In 1893 it first appeared in freshwater and has since spread throughout England, parts of Wales and Scotland and through much of Ireland, even as far as islands such as Inishbofin. How it reached the offshore islands is open to debate. The vast majority of these snails are females (the first male was found only in 1958 and few have been reported since then) and they produce, without fertilisation, fully formed young snails. In technical terms they are both parthenogenetic and viviparous.

Of the three freshwater mussels in Ireland only the pearl mussel, *Margaritifera margaritifera* lives in Connemara. It lives in relatively infertile, soft waters and is known from four locations in the region. In the past it was exploited for the pearls it produces on the inner surface of its shell. And it is said that one of the pearls in Queen Victoria's coronation crown came from Galway. It is now an extremely uncommon species in Ireland and Britain and rare in mainland Europe. Its remaining populations need to be carefully conserved. The swan mussel, *Anodonta cygnea*, occurs in Lough Corrib and was recorded in south-east Connemara prior to 1950 so the only species without any

Connemara connections is the duck mussel, *Anodonta anatina*. All these species are large, 100-150 millimetres (4-6 inches) long, and live buried in the sand, gravel or mud of rivers or lake beds.

The orb and pea mussels are, in contrast, tiny. The orb mussels are up to about 10 millimetres (0.4 inch) across while the pea mussels are just 2-7 millimetres (0.1-0.3 inch). Of the two Irish species of orb mussel, only *Sphaerium corneum* has been recorded in Connemara since 1950. *Sphaerium lacustre* was recorded in the south-east corner of the region only before 1950 and has been excluded from the list. The orb mussels are whitish or yellowish in colour and are common in many habitats where they burrow into the sediment.

Table 26
Connemara freshwater molluscs recorded since 1950.
(L = local; W = widespread)

SNAILS

Theodoxus fluviatilis	L	(east)	*Planorbis planorbis*	L	(east)
Valvata cristata	L	(east)	*Planorbis carinatus*	L	(south)
Valvata piscinalis	L	(east and west)	*Planorbis leucostoma*	L	(south)
Potamopyrgus jenkinsi	L	(east and west)	*Planorbis vortex*	L	(west)
Bithynia tentaculata	L	(east)	*Planorbis contortus*	L	(east and west)
Aplexa hypnorum	L	(west)	*Planorbis albus*	L	(east and west)
Physa fontinalis	W	(throughout)	*Planorbis crista*	L	(west)
Lymnaea trucatula	W	(throughout)	*Segmentia complanatus*	L	(east)
Lymnaea palustris	W	(throughout)	*Ancylus fluviatilis*	W	(east and west)
Lymnaea stagnalis	L	(east)	*Acroloxus lacustris*	L	(north)
Lymnaea peregra	W	(throughout)			

MUSSELS

Margaritifera margaritifera	L	(central)

ORB MUSSELS

Sphaerium corneum	L	(east and west)

PEA MUSSEL

Pisidium casertanum	W	(central and west)	*Pisidium lilljeborgii*	L	(east and west)
Pisidium personatum	W	(north and west)	*Pisidium hibernicum*	L	(east and west)
Pisidium obtusale	W	(central and west)	*Pisidium nitidum*	W	(east and west)
Pisidium milium	W	(east and west)	*Pisidium pulchellum*	L	(east)
Pisidium subtruncatum	L	(east and west)			

Nine out of Ireland's eleven pea mussels have been found in Connemara, the missing species being *Pisidium amnicum* and *Pisidium henslowanum*. The pea mussels are yellowish or buff and extremely difficult to identify. They occur in a wide range of habitats including isolated spring pools and water troughs. Like *Sphaerium* they can also be found climbing on plants on a ladder of mucus.

The orb and pea mussels are detritus feeders. They are hermaphrodites and produce fully developed offspring. In contrast, the larger species, such as the swan mussel, produce immature forms which, on release from the parent, become parasitic on fish for about three months during which time the adult form develops.

Fish

The relative infertility of Maumwee Lough, which favours a diverse community of planktonic plants, has the opposite effect on the fish community, which is composed of just four species, Atlantic salmon, brown trout, European eel and minnow. This is because the low production of plant material leads to similarly poor production in the zooplankton and invertebrates which, in turn, are the staple diet of the fish. This is the situation throughout Connemara where only five of the thirty or so species which occur in Irish freshwaters are widespread or common. Even this figure is an exaggeration because, in addition to European eel, Atlantic salmon and arctic charr, it includes both brown and sea trout which are in fact the same species.

Fish like the pike, minnow and stone loach occur on the fringe of the region in tributaries of Lough Mask and Lough Corrib, but they are not found in the heart of Connemara as far as can be determined from existing records. The pike is restricted to Lough Nafooey which is linked to Lough Mask by the Finny River. Minnows can be seen in shoals in several of the lakes bordering the north-western arm of Lough Corrib, from which they are likely to have travelled in the first place via the connecting streams. The minnows make a pleasant sight, shoaling among the water lobelia in the shallows of Loughaunierin on a bright summer morning. The stone loach has been recorded in only one Connemara tributary of Lough Corrib. However, this small (10 centimetres, 4 inches) fish, with six sensory barbels (fleshy finger-like projections) on its upper jaw, is nocturnal in its habits and may have been overlooked in other Corrib tributaries. But it is unlikely to be found in any waters in the heart of Connemara.

Although there seem to be no published records for sticklebacks in Connemara, it is known that they are widespread. Most of the fish in the region are likely to be three-spined sticklebacks, though the generally less common nine-spined stickleback may also be present. In the literature this species is also referred to as the ten-spined stickleback. But neither description is satisfactory because the fish may have anything from eight to twelve spines. Both species occur in freshwater and in estuarine and coastal waters. Three-spined sticklebacks have, for example, been found stranded from time to time in pools high on the seashore near Carna.

Several fish species may leave the sea and enter Connemara estuaries and rivers to spawn, but at present there is no documented information for any of these. Sea lampreys, eel-like fish which as adults are parasitic on a variety of sea fish and occasionally on harbour porpoises, are said to breed in south Connemara rivers, although their numbers are apparently declining. River lampreys might also enter Connemara estuaries and rivers, but to say more would be pure conjecture. The non-migratory brook lamprey breeds in the lower reaches of the Drimneen River which flows into Lough Corrib near Oughterard, but it would be stretching a point to claim it as a Connemara species.

The twaite shad, a member of the herring family, is represented in Ireland by two sub-species: a migratory form which lives most of its life in the sea and spawns in freshwater and a non-migratory form, the Killarney shad or goureen, which occurs only in Lough Leane in Kerry. The migratory form has been recorded in the past in north Connemara but there is no recent information to establish whether it still breeds in the region. Nor is there evidence that the closely related Allis shad enters Connemara rivers, although it has been recorded in the River Corrib.

The flounder is a flatfish which, unlike the others of its kind, spends a lot of time in freshwater. Like the eel, it spawns in the sea, but then the young fish move into estuaries and sometimes swim considerable distances up rivers and into lakes. The flounder is widespread around the Connemara coast and many of the estuaries and lower river pools offer it ideal habitat.

From this it is clear that very little indeed is known about most of our fish, be they entirely freshwater species or fish which move between the sea and freshwater at some stage in their lives. In fact, it is safe to say that, apart from the commerical and recreational species, less is known about our fish than any other group of vertebrate animals in Ireland, and probably less than is known about many groups of invertebrates as well. This is an extraordinary state of affairs which needs to be rectified soon if we are not to lose some of the rare and endangered species such as the lampreys, shads and the arctic charr.

The scarcity of fish species in Connemara does not just reflect the infertility of the environment. It also mirrors the situation in Ireland as a whole, which has only about thirty fish species compared with nearly twice that number in Britain and a north-west European total of 130. If we recall the period after the Ice Age we will find a clue to this scarcity. As the glaciers melted, sea-levels rose, and within 1,500 years of the end of the Ice Age Ireland became an island - about 8,500 years ago. Another 1,500 years passed before Britain was finally cut off from continental Europe. During this 3,000-year period freshwater fish which had, during the Ice Age, retreated southward to refuges in southern Europe, most notably the Danube basin, moved northwards again. But no species which are restricted entirely to freshwater reached Ireland before the Irish sea formed, and only a few reached Britain before it was isolated by the sea. This explains why all of Ireland's native fish are species which can live in the sea as well as in freshwater; only species with this capacity could have reached the country. It also means that all of Ireland's coarse fish (species not belonging to the salmon family), including, for example, the pike, roach and minnow, must have been introduced. And, indeed, historical records confirm that this is the case. For instance, the minnow first appeared in the Dublin region in the seventeenth century and was subsequently introduced to many waters around the country. The roach was introduced to Aughrusbeg Lough within the last ten years.

European eels

European eels are widespread and probably present in most of the Connemara river systems, although they are relatively scarce and usually quite small, presumably because there is little food available for them. This is certainly the case in the Ballynahinch River system where fishing trials in the late 1970s and early 1980s produced disappointing results in terms of numbers and size of fish.

By the time young eels arrive at the mouths of the Connemara rivers they will already have spent the best part of two and a half years swimming across the Atlantic from their birthplace in the warm Sargasso Sea, east of Bermuda. When they reach our coast in the winter the eels are only about 6.5 centimetres (2.5 inches) long, transparent and called glass-eels. They live under stones along the shore where they provide a bountiful harvest for turnstones and other wading birds during the late winter months.

Once the rivers have warmed up to about 9° C., usually in April or May, the glass-eels start to move upstream, changing colour to the more familiar grey-black of the adults. At this stage they are called elvers. These sometimes have to surmount considerable obstacles on their way up the rivers. For example, at the head of Killary Harbour their way into the River Erriff is impeded by the Aasleagh Falls. And, although three small side streams enter the Erriff between the falls and the tidal water, the elvers select the main river and reach it by leaving the water and ascending through damp moss where water trickles down beside the falls.

The European eels of Maumwee Lough will have reached that lake via Lough Corrib, having travelled more than 50 kilometres (30 miles) from the mouth of the River Corrib in Galway City. Their northward journey probably takes several years, lower Lough Corrib serving as a nursery prior to the movement of the eels into upper Lough Corrib and its tributary streams and lakes. During their years in freshwater, the smaller eels (up to 50 centimetres, 20 inches in length) feed mainly on insects, snails and crustaceans, while the larger ones include a variety of fish in their diet. Their growth rates are very variable and depend on the amount of food available. So it is likely that they grow slowly in Maumwee Lough where food is not abundant.

Most European eels stay in freshwater until they are at least twelve years old, but some until they are more than forty. Then, in autumn, they move downstream, becoming silver eels in preparation for their return to salt water and migration back to their spawning area in the Sargasso Sea. This time their journey across the Atlantic takes only about three months.

European eel populations have been declining throughout Europe since the mid-1970s for reasons which are not yet apparent. Pollution and other adverse factors could be blamed in some countries, but they are unlikely to apply in the west of Ireland where the population decline seems to be just as serious. Whether the decline stems from a lower return of adults from Europe to their breeding area, a drop in the production of young European eels due to unknown factors in the Sargasso Sea or adverse conditions in the open Atlantic remains to be determined. We could, of course, just be witnessing the 'downside' of a natural population cycle.

The European eel is a fascinating fish and plays an important role in the ecology of our rivers and lakes. It feeds on a wide variety of invertebrates and fish and in turn is eaten by other fish, cormorants, herons and otters. However, it tends to be overshadowed by salmon and trout in the minds and actions of anglers and naturalists. This is a shame because it is a species worthy of our attention.

Arctic charr

Before we turn to Atlantic salmon and trout let us look at the 'forgotten' member of the salmon family which lives in some of Connemara's larger lakes. This is the arctic charr, mentioned in Chapter 1 in the context of Connemara's post-glacial history. In Connemara, and elsewhere in western Ireland, the arctic charr is non-migratory and lives in deep, cool and infertile lakes. The fish are generally small. A sample netted at depths ranging from 9 to 35 metres (30-115 feet) in Lough Nafooey were 17.5-22.5 centimetres (7-9 inches) long and weighed around 100 grammes (4 ounces), suggesting that they were 3-4 years old. Arctic charr feed on a wide range of planktonic animals such as *Daphnia, Cyclops* and even the transparent *Leptodora*. At certain times in the spring they may concentrate on midge larvae and during their spawning season in the winter months they will feed on the eggs of other arctic charr.

At one time it was considered that there were six 'species' in Ireland, but recent sophisticated biochemical analysis has shown that all the Irish arctic charr, and those which live in Windermere in the Lake District of north-west England, belong to one species and that all the now-separate populations descended from a common ancestor within the past 50,000 years, possibly in the immediate post-glacial period.

In Connemara, arctic charr live in Ballynahinch Lake and Loughs Nafooey, Inagh, Kylemore, Muck, Fee, Shannakeela, Shindilla and Glenicmurrin. In the past they were reported to be in Derryclare Lough and Loughs Oorid, Derryneen and Glendollagh but there is no recent information to indicate that they are still there.

The arctic charr is an arctic-alpine species. A few populations, such as occur in Ireland, Britain, the Alps, northern Russia and northern North America, are non-migratory and live only in freshwater. But most of the world population, which is distributed at high northern latitudes all around the globe, breeds in freshwater and then moves to the sea to feed, like Atlantic salmon and sea trout. The migratory arctic charr can attain a length of 1 metre (3.3 feet) and a weight of over 12

The Ballynahinch River with Benlettery in the background.

kilogrammes (27 pounds) and are veritable monsters compared with their non-migratory cousins.

Connemara is of considerable conservation significance for arctic charr because it holds nearly 50 per cent of the Irish populations. In turn, the Irish populations are very important in a European context because many populations in Britain and on the continent have become extinct in recent decades and others are in imminent danger of dying out. The species is very sensitive to any deterioration in water quality, and to acidification in particular. So we must be greatly concerned for those populations living in lakes which are being surrounded or even bordered by coniferous plantations, particularly in south Connemara, because they are especially susceptible to acidification. Arctic charr can suffer predation by and competition with brown trout, so in the interest of charr conservation, it would seem unwise to stock their lakes artificially with brown trout. It would also be unwise to establish fish farms in charr lakes until their long-term effects are thoroughly understood. Finally, being a cold-water species, arctic charr (and other members of the salmon family) could be adversely affected by climatic warming, should it occur in the west of Ireland.

The arctic charr is an *Irish Vertebrate Red Data Book* species and as such requires immediate research and conservation action.

Trout and Atlantic salmon

Like the arctic charr, the trout has non-migratory and migratory forms. But, in contrast to the arctic charr, both forms live together in the same waters. We call the non-migratory form brown trout and the migratory form sea trout, or white trout as they are often known in Ireland.

Since all our native fish arrived originally from the sea it would seem that it was the sea trout which changed in behaviour and appearance when improving environmental conditions enabled it to feed all year round and to reproduce in freshwater. According to some biologists, this development reflects the way freshwater trout (and other members of the salmon family) might have evolved from totally marine ancestors in the distant past. However, it is suggested by other scientists that, rather than being a sea fish which adapted to life in freshwater, the trout and all the other members of the salmon family originally evolved in freshwater. They base their argument on the fact that most salmonid species live entirely in freshwater and that no species in the salmon family needs to go to sea to complete its life-cycle. Migration into salt water is considered to have been a later development in fish which presumably could no longer thrive in deteriorating environmental conditions. The situation in Connemara would seem to support this idea because it is only in relatively infertile waters with poor food supplies that some trout seem to be compelled to migrate to the sea to feed outside the breeding season. And even in these waters it is often only the females which are migratory, possibly because they need to build up reserves for egg production and the strength required to excavate their redds (nests).

A young Atlantic salmon.

The question of whether all Connemara trout became brown trout during the post-glacial times when Connemara was undoubtedly a richer habitat, and only later reverted to the migratory habit as environmental conditions deteriorated is open to speculation. Only if archaeologists find some sea trout scales of, say, Mesolithic age, might it be possible to answer this question.

There is little observational information about the migratory habits of trout or of their life in salt water off the Connemara coast, although much has been inferred from studies of their scales. Evidence from patterns on scales suggests that some fish spend only short periods in salt water in some years, perhaps migrating no further than the estuary of their home river. In other years the same trout may go further out to sea. The main downstream movement to the sea of young trout is in the spring but there is also a lesser exodus in the autumn. The fish descending in the spring are silvery, adapted to living in salt water and called smolts. Those going downstream in autumn are younger, smaller, still 'brown' and not fully adapted for their movement into salt water, where many perish. The reason for this almost suicidal descent to the sea is not clear. It may be that these fish are forced downstream by existing territory holders in the rivers (trout are aggressively territorial). They may also be escaping the predatory attention of mature sea trout and brown trout which are moving upstream to their spawning beds. Whatever the reason for this autumn movement, it is obvious that the lives

---

BROWN TROUT AND SEA TROUT

Brown trout and sea trout can be difficult to distinguish in their freshwater habitats. This is illustrated by a case of a fish caught in 1992 in Doolough on the north side of Killary Harbour. It was large, 3 kilogrammes (6 pounds 9 ounces), with the appearance of a ferox brown trout (one which feeds almost exclusively on fish). But when its scales were examined it turned out to be a sea trout that had been to sea no fewer than five times. However, after returning to freshwater to spawn in 1991, it apparently remained and 'reverted' to being a brown trout, feeding on the plentiful supply of small fish in Doolough.

---

of these young trout are fraught with danger - from their own kind, other predators and hostile environmental conditions. Of the small numbers which survive, some become estuarine or 'slob' trout while others develop into true sea trout.

To describe the brown trout as non-migratory, is not entirely correct. For within the freshwater system, many brown trout migrate between their feeding grounds in lakes and their spawning beds in rivers and streams. Brown trout spawn from late October to mid-November, a little earlier than sea trout and about a month earlier than Atlantic salmon. Eggs are laid in redds in the gravel bed of a river or stream and develop through the winter, hatching two or three months later, depending on the water temperature. Development takes about two months at 8°C and three months at 5°C. Among the newly hatched fish, the stronger ones may hold territories in the streams but the remainder will move downstream, mainly at night, into the lakes. Many fish die during these early stages and only a very small percentage survives to adulthood.

Brown trout are more widespread than sea trout or Atlantic salmon and are found in most streams, rivers and lakes throughout Connemara. Those confined to infertile upland or bog lakes are generally small and stunted.

Sea trout numbers, as illustrated by angling returns, fluctuate considerably as

---

**THE FISHERY STATUS
OF 73 CONNEMARA LAKES
(based on Bowman 1991)**

SPECIES	NUMBER OF LAKES
Brown trout	31
Brown trout / sea trout	11
Atlantic salmon	4
Atlantic salmon / brown trout	3
Atlantic salmon / brown trout / sea trout	4
Atlantic salmon / sea trout	20

indicated in Figure 10. Here the catches in the Connemara Fishery District, which includes all the south Connemara catchment areas between Inveran and the head of Roundstone Bay (see Map 12), are plotted for the period from 1968 to 1992. Disappointing as the overall figures for the region are, the stocks in some individual fisheries have reached critically low levels. In 1992, for example, only two sea trout were trapped in the Gowla fishery and just twenty-five in the Invermore system. In the past, these fisheries yielded 1,000-2,000 sea trout each year to rod anglers.

While the fluctuations between 1968 and 1988 might be considered normal, the drop in landings in 1989 and the low returns in subsequent years indicate that something unusual is happening to the stocks. This is not the place to go into detail about the sea trout problem. Suffice it to say that there are some very complex issues involved in the attempts to explain the decline. These have included a range of environmental conditions in the rivers and in the sea, disease, predation, overfishing, afforestation, pesticides, acidification and the proliferaton of sea lice (*Lepeophtheirus salmonis*) which has been related to the intensive rearing of salmon in the sea. Work at the Salmon Research Agency near Newport in Co. Mayo suggests that the sea trout stock collapse in Connemara can not be explained by most of these factors. The cause of the collapse would seem to lie with the proliferation of sea lice, operating in combination with natural factors which have normally regulated sea trout survival. Nevertheless, research and debate on the issue continue and it is to be hoped the problem will be resolved in the near future.

It has been possible to give only a brief and sketchy description of the life history of the sea trout. A more detailed account of this intriguing fish is presented by Dr Edward Fahy in his authoritative book *Child of the Tides - A Sea Trout Handbook*. In addition to the biology and ecology of the species, he discusses sea trout fisheries and presents a stimulating review of the evolution of the sea trout and its relationships with other species. For a comprehensive account of fish and angling in Connemara and Ireland in general, Dr Ken Whelan's *The Angler in Ireland* is thoroughly recommended.

The life history of Atlantic salmon is essentially the same as that of the trout except that all young fish, after one, two or three years in freshwater, go to sea to feed for one or more years. In the sea they travel considerable distances from the Irish shore, some to the north of Scotland, others as far as waters off the west coast of Greenland. The predictability of their return migrations to Connemara rivers has made them an important resource for coastal fishermen as the histogram in Figure 10 indicates. Prior to 1969 there was no official drift-netting off the Connemara coast. Since its introduction in 1969, however, landings have grown, although, as the diagram shows, catches have fluctuated quite strikingly. Undoubtedly, not all the fish caught off the south Connemara coast are destined to enter rivers in the region. Many are on their way to the Owenboliska, the Corrib and the Kilcolgan Rivers and perhaps to rivers further south. So these figures do not tell us how many Atlantic salmon have been removed from the Connemara rivers. Yet, they do raise the question of what effect the removal of such large quantities from the population

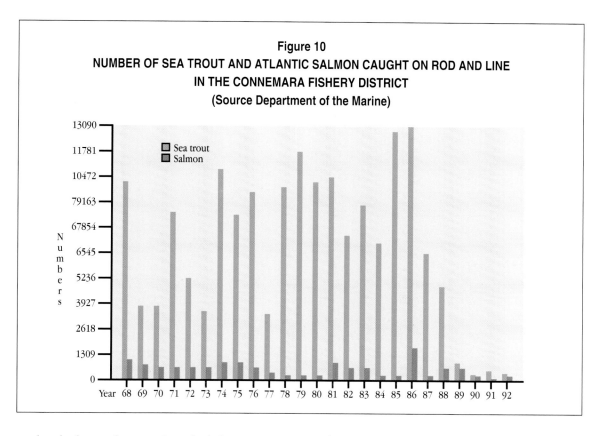

Figure 10
NUMBER OF SEA TROUT AND ATLANTIC SALMON CAUGHT ON ROD AND LINE
IN THE CONNEMARA FISHERY DISTRICT
(Source Department of the Marine)

has had on other species which live in some sort of association with the salmon - their prey, predators and parasites. For whenever people exploit a population of wild animals or plants, they inevitably disrupt their associations and relationships with other plants and animals - a point too rarely considered by people in their rush to profit from nature.

The numbers and total weight of Atlantic salmon caught on rod and line in the rivers declined in parallel with the increase in landings from drift nets at sea. The annual average number of salmon caught on rod and line in the ten year period 1978-87 was 25 per cent less than in the previous decade, 1968-77. The total weight of the salmon hooked was 40 per cent lower in the second decade.

While these figures represent only a very superficial analysis of the catch statistics, they do indicate that we should be concerned about the level of salmon catches in the sea and their impact on the numbers and size of fish which return to the rivers to spawn. Not only are Atlantic salmon populations suffering reductions due to heavy commercial fishing, together with sea trout and brown trout they are facing problems in their spawning rivers in south Connemara as a result of acidification.

Acidification of Connemara's freshwaters

One of the major current conservation concerns in Connemara is the acidification of its freshwaters associated with acid rain and afforestation. But before we can assess whether rivers and lakes are becoming more acidic we need to know whether they have been acidified in the past.

History in the sediments

Let us therefore return briefly to Maumwee Lough, where a recent study has addressed this question. By studying a core of sediment from the lake bed, scientists from University College, London, have shown that Maumwee Lough has not become more acidic in the past 130 years - the period of industrialisation in western Europe. They have drawn this conclusion from the fact that the diatoms preserved in the sediment have changed little in species composition since 1864. At all levels in the sediment *Brachysira vitrea* and *Fragilaria virescens* are the most common species in the diatom community.

Encouraging as this news is, it does not mean that Connemara has avoided all atmospheric pollution. During the late 1800s little carbonaceous material was deposited in the lake. But after 1900 it increased gradually until the late 1960s when there was a sharp increase, followed in the last few years by a slight decline. Maumwee Lough has also been receiving trace metals from a contaminated atmosphere since the late nineteenth century. And radioactive deposits from weapons tests and the Chernobyl nuclear accident have been detected in the sediments, too.

Overall, however, it seems that Maumwee Lough is in a reasonably healthy state and has some reserve capacity to withstand acidification. This seems to be because, despite its quartzite-granite catchment, it receives some alkaline waters from its surroundings, as is indicated by the presence along its shores of the great fen-sedge, a species typical of neutral or alkaline habitats.

The lakes and rivers of south Connemara

The state of lakes and rivers in south Connemara is less satisfactory. These have a low acid-neutralising capacity, so any increase in acid deposition will increase their acidity and cause serious harm to the animal life in them. Lakes tend to be less seriously affected by acidification than rivers, in which acid pulses after heavy rain can be very damaging to aquatic life. This, at least, is fortunate for sea trout which spend most of their freshwater life in lakes rather than rivers.

Acid rain is not always the result of industrial pollution. In Connemara, seaspray carried in on winds from the Atlantic Ocean can increase rainfall acidity. In winter, showers after westerly storms can cause brief but very damaging acidic pulses in streams and rivers. The conversion of sulphur to sulphate and then to sulphuric acid during the decomposition of the peat of the blanket bogs appears to be another important source of acidity. No doubt the cutting and ploughing of peat accelerates this process. The presence of conifer plantations upstream in catchment areas with low acid-neutralising capacity also leads to increased stream acidity, but the mechanisms that underlie

Figure 11
WEIGHT IN KILOGRAMMES* OF ATLANTIC SALMON CAUGHT IN DRIFT NETS AND ON ROD AND LINE IN THE CONNEMARA FISHERY DISTRICT- 1968 to 1992
(Source Department of Marine Annual Reports)

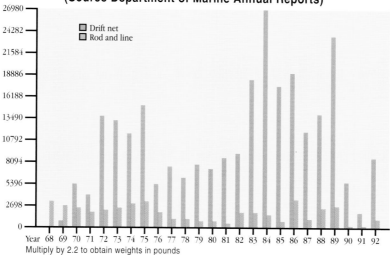

□ Drift net
□ Rod and line

Year 68 69 70 71 72 73 74 75 76 77 78 79 80 81 82 83 84 85 86 87 88 89 90 91 92

* Multiply by 2.2 to obtain weights in pounds

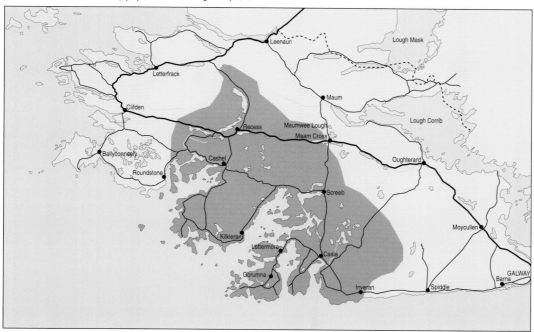

Map 12: Connemara Fishery District.

the relationship between tree cover and stream acidity are unknown at present. It is known, however, that trees 'scavenge' pollutants from the air. The pollutants are deposited on the leaves and are subsequently washed to the ground by rain. Trees, with their greater height and leaf surface area, are much more effective 'scavengers' than the usual, low-growing bog plants such as purple moor-grass and heather, so it is not surprising that commercial forestry plantations are implicated in the acidification of lakes and rivers in Connemara.

Fish and acid waters

The main worry about acidification relates to the damage it causes to fish, aquatic invertebrates and birds such as dippers which rely on stream insects for food.

Salmon and trout populations can be affected by the damage acid water does to their eggs. It will be recalled that they lay these in the winter, when storms and rainfall are likely to be regular and intense and bring increased acidity to the breeding streams. If the acidity of the water drops below pH4.5, an enzyme within the eggs which dissolves their cases will be deactivited and hatching will be prevented. At later stages in their development fish can tolerate pH levels below

The Ballynahinch River in spate.

4.5, but if a drop in pH is too rapid, their blood becomes viscous, weakening the circulatory system and putting a fatal strain on the heart. Death can occur within a few hours.

The complexities of acidification are legion and barely understood at present. Yet it is clear that certain activities increase acidity and damage fish and wildlife populations. It should be evident at this stage that the development of one natural resource, such as coniferous forestry, at the expense of others is undesirable environmentally, economically and socially. Clearly, if the wild fish populations of Connemara are to be conserved and enhanced there will need to be immediate modifications in land-use practices associated with forestry, agriculture and turf exploitation.

LIFE ON THE SEASHORE

A habitat of change

As the tide ebbs gently down the shore a new world is revealed, at first sight, a quiet, almost lifeless world. But the limp seaweeds draped over the arching rocks, the crusty barnacles crowded on their life-long anchorages and the boulder-hugging limpets which first attract our attention are but a small part of a community of plants and animals which is as rich as many other habitats of similar dimensions. The ribbon of shoreline which constitutes the interface between Connemara and the sea may be narrow, but it is at least 440 kilometres (275 miles) long and occupies an area of at least 33 square kilometres (nearly 13 square miles) - the size of Gorumna Island.

The fascination of the seashore lies in the changes brought twice each day by the tides. Incoming tides flood the shore for a little over six hours, bringing nutrients to seaweeds, food to animals, respite from exposure to the air and the attention of predators such as shorebirds. The receding tide carries away the young stages of seaweeds and animals to colonise new areas. The timing and height of the high and low tides vary from day to day. Over a 24 hour period, corresponding tides are about forty minutes later than the previous one during spring tides and an hour or more later during neap tides. Thus, if high tide is at 1030 hours one day during a neap tide, it will be at about 1130 hours the following day. But over the regular monthly cycle, the time of high water spring tides, for example, will always be the same. In Connemara these occur at about 0500 and 1700 hours Greenwich Mean Time. This means that the daytime low spring tide always occurs at around midday - an ideal time for the seashore naturalist.

Spring tides occur around the periods of full and new moon whilst neap tides occur during

Facing page: Seashore zonation on a cliff at Glassilaun near the mouth of Killary Harbour.

Figure 12

a) gradient of marine to terrestrial conditions from low to high on a shore, based on % emersion time calculated from tide tables

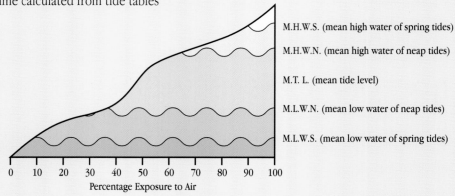

M.H.W.S. (mean high water of spring tides)

M.H.W.N. (mean high water of neap tides)

M.T. L. (mean tide level)

M.L.W.N. (mean low water of neap tides)

M.L.W.S. (mean low water of spring tides)

Percentage Exposure to Air

b) terms used in describing tidal levels and the shape of typical spring and neap tide curves ----- from Marine Field Course Guide 1: Rocky Shores (Immel Publishing).

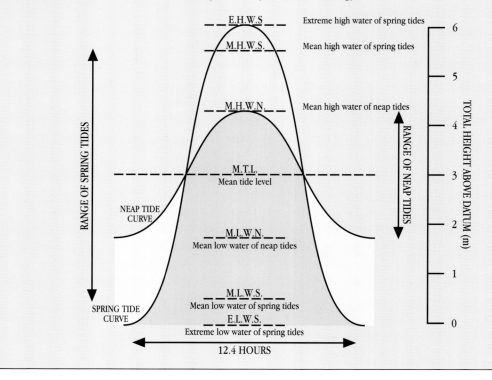

the intervening periods of waxing and waning moons. The gravitational pull of the moon (in conjunction with the sun) is stronger during the full and new phases of the moon and causes the tides to rise higher and fall further during the spring tide periods than during those of the neap tides. During the spring tides the water rushes in faster, reaches the high-water spring tide level on the shore and then almost immediately rushes out again, eventually exposing the shore down to the low-water spring tide level at the end of this cycle. The neap tides come in at a more leisurely pace and the high-water neap tide level is perhaps only three-quarters of the way up the shore. They also recede more gradually and at the turn of the tide there is often a period of slack water when little or no tidal movement is apparent. The low-water neap tide level is about three-quarters of the way down the shore.

The average vertical tidal range on the Connemara coast is about 4.5 metres (15 feet) during spring tides, but as little as 1.9 metres (6.25 feet) during neap tides. The horizontal distance covered by the tides depends on the steepness of the shore. On steep, cliff-like shores it may be as little as 10-15 metres (33-50 feet); on shallow sloping shores the tide may go out 100-200 metres (330-660 feet).

Tide times and ranges for Galway Harbour are given in tide tables which are published by the Galway Harbour Commissioners and in local papers. The times of the tides in Spiddle, Kilkieran, Clifden and Killary Harbour are approximately 0, 10, 5 and 26 minutes respectively later than those at Galway Harbour.

The height of the tides is also affected by the wind. A strong, onshore wind will force a tide higher up the shore than it would go in calm conditions. The same sort of wind would prevent a receding tide from reaching its usual low point. (This is usually the situation which naturalists encounter when they desperately want to examine seashore organisms at the low tide level.) Exposure to wind-driven waves is a very important factor in seashore ecology. On exposed shores, such as we find on the Connemara headlands and islands, the species composition and structure of the communities differ noticeably from those on the sheltered sides of the bays and inlets. Currents also play a role in the formation and maintenance of communities. These may occur, for example, where the tides are squeezed through narrow channels between the south Connemara islands or over shallows such as occur at Keeraunagark on the south-east coast of Cashla Bay.

The area of shore exposed at low tide is called the intertidal zone. Beyond the low water mark is the sublittoral zone and above the highwater mark we meet the supralittoral or splash zone. It is mainly the life in the intertidal zone which will concern us in this chapter.

Seashore plants and animals must be able to tolerate alternate immersion and exposure (not only to the desiccating air but also to freshwater rain) for differing periods of time. They must be able to withstand the pull of currents and the battering of waves. Those communities living in estuaries or close to the mouths of streams and rivers must be able to survive large and abrupt changes in the salinity of the water.

A variety of seashore types

The long Connemara coast comprises a variety of seashore types. These range from rocky shores on the exposed, wave-battered coasts to soft and muddy shores in the sheltered estuaries such as we find at Clifden. In areas of intermediate exposure we find stony or boulder beaches. On sheltered shores where the boulders are large and sufficiently stable they are covered with seaweeds such as knotted or egg wrack, which produces the characteristic golden or greenish-yellow fringe around many Connemara bays. Where there is a source of sand from the nearby seabed or eroding shoreline, and currents and tides permit, sandy beaches have developed. Some, such as those around Omey Island, are composed mainly of quartz sand. Others, such as those at the head of Mannin Bay and in Cashla Bay are 'coral strands', composed of dead fragments of the calcareous algae *Lithothamnion* and *Phymatolithon*. In contrast, the beaches at Dog's Bay and Gorteen Bay are composed of the tiny shells of foraminiferans, single-celled marine animals.

From the naturalist's point of view the 'hard' shores are initially the most interesting because the plants and animals can live only on the surface and are therefore readily visible. It is the flora and fauna of these that most of this chapter will consider. Muddy shores also support a wealth of animals but we would need boots, a spade and a sieve to find them and, in doing so, would unnecessarily disturb their habitat. Because they are relatively unstable, sandy shores support less life. Yet where they contain a reasonable amount of organic matter, there will be clams, cockles, razor-shells and worms living beneath the surface. We can detect the presence of lugworms by the characteristic spiral casts they deposit on the surface of the sand. Near each cast there is a small depression where the worm has drawn in sand. As this passes through its body the worm digests any organic matter and then returns the 'empty' sand to the surface.

The species of snails and bivalves living in a beach, on a nearby rocky shore or in the neighbouring seabed is evident from the shells lying on the surface of the sand. A quick survey of the beach at the south-east corner of Mannin Bay, beside the Clifden-Ballyconneely road, yielded

Table 27
Shells on a Mannin Bay beach.

Common limpet	Cowrie	Great scallop	Norway cockle
Flat or purple top-shell	Wentletrap	Variegated scallop	Carpet shell
Edible periwinkle	Dog-whelk	Rayed artemis	Trough shell
Flat periwinkle	Netted dog-whelk	Warty venus	Large sunset-shell
Auger or screw shell	Common saddle oyster	Striped venus	Razor-shell

the list of species in Table 27. Most of these species come either from nearby rocky shores or from the seabed below the low water mark. With the aid of a lens it is possible to detect the fragments of other animals in the sand. The purple, ridged spines of sea urchins, for example, are a distinctive and colourful component of this and several other beaches.

Life on some rocky shores

The ebb and flow of the tide create great differences in the living conditions between the top and bottom of the seashore. The plants and animals at the top of the shore spend most of their lives exposed to the air. Those at the bottom are covered by water for much of the time. Between these extremes there is a gradation of conditions which is reflected in the zonation of the seashore flora and fauna. The species composition changes in a fairly predictable way as we move down the shore from the splash zone to the low-water spring tide level. (But be warned, you will often find species in the 'wrong' place, no doubt for good ecological reasons which are not apparent to us.)

We will take the rocky seashore to the west of Spiddle Pier as our example and look at some of its common inhabitants - plants and animals which are also common to many similar shores around the Connemara coast. The shore is composed mainly of granite outcrops and boulders interspersed with rock pools and patches of muddy sand. It is quite exposed to the open sea but protected from the worst violence of Atlantic storms by the Aran Islands, to the south-west at the mouth of Galway Bay.

The splash zone

This is the transition zone between the land and the sea. On a calm day it is dry and the colourful, lichen-covered rocks belong to the land. But on a stormy day, particularly during high spring tides, it belongs to the sea. Breaking waves and spray drench the rocks with salt water which most land plants and animals cannot tolerate.

High on the rocks there are patches of yellow *Xanthoria parietina* and reddish-orange *Caloplaca. Xanthoria* is a widespread lichen, common on stone, bark and wood from sea-level to high altitudes. Interspersed with these lichens are the greenish-grey, stiff, upright tufts of *Ramalina siliquosa*, typically coastal species. Below these lichens there is a dark band composed of black, tar-like *Verrucaria maura* and blackish-green, tufted *Lichina pygmaea*. Both these species tolerate immersion in seawater and extend well into the upper middle shore.

Animal life is scarce in the splash zone; only around the high-water spring tide level will we start to find resident periwinkles. Close scrutiny of the rock crevices at this level will reveal the small periwinkle. This is about 5 millimetres (0.2 inch) high and has a black, pointed shell. It feeds on micro-organisms, detritus and lichens and browses over the rock surface during damp conditions. In many respects it is similar to land snails. However, it needs the sea to complete its reproductive cycle. It breeds during winter and spring. At two-weekly intervals, on spring tides, it

Table 28
Some common plants and animals on the Spiddle seashore.

LICHENS
Xanthoria parietina
Caloplaca sp.
Ramalina siliquosa
Verrucaria maura
Lichina pygmaea

ALGAE
Channel wrack
Spiral wrack
Enteromorpha spp.
Pepper dulse
Carrageen (2 species)
Bladder wrack
Toothed or serrated wrack
Lithothamnion spp.
Corallina officinalis
Oarweed

FISH
Blenny
Corkwing wrasse
Two-spot goby
Butterfish

INVERTEBRATES
Small periwinkle
Sea slater
Sand-hopper
Rough periwinkle
Thick top-shell
Acorn barnacles (2 species)
Common limpet
Edible periwinkle
Flat periwinkle
Flat or purple top-shell
Dog-whelk
Common mussel
Common starfish
Shore crab
Common hermit crab
Common prawn
Beadlet anemone
Sabellaria sp.
Pomatoceros triqueter
Spirorbis spp.
Star ascidian
Alcyonidium sp.
Breadcrumb sponge

Channel wrack

Dog whelk

Star ascidian

Common hermit crab

releases egg capsules, each containing one egg. The capsules drift in the water for several days. Then free-swimming larvae emerge and spend about three weeks in the plankton before settling on the shore in cracks, crevices and empty barnacle shells. Small periwinkles can live for five years or more - a long life span for such tiny animals.

The upper shore

Sheltering in crevices and under stones on the upper shore is the common sea slater. Looking like a large woodlouse, the sea slater is grey, with an oval-shaped body and can grow to a length of 30 millimetres (1.2 inches). The sea slater is omnivorous and feeds on detritus, decaying seaweed and diatoms.

During the autumn gales large volumes of seaweed are thrown up onto the upper shore. These strong-smelling piles of rotting algae become host to hoards of flies and sand-hoppers. The latter are greenish-brown, up to 22 millimetres (0.9 inch) long and have black eyes. Unless disturbed they stay in hiding during the day, emerging at night to feed on detritus.

In more open situations on the upper shore we find the rough periwinkle (see box). It is up to 20 millimetres (0.8 inch) high and distinguished by its rough, ridged shell which can be white, yellow, reddish-brown, grey or greenish. The rough periwinkle, like the other periwinkles, top-shells and limpets, feeds on micro-organisms, detritus and seaweeds. It does this by scraping material off the rocks or seaweeds with its rasping, ribbon-like radula, located in its mouth cavity. It breeds mainly in May and June. In contrast to the small periwinkle, the young rough periwinkles develop to the shelled stage within the female and emerge as fully formed snails.

In the vicinity of the rough periwinkles we will meet patches of the channel wrack. It is dark olive-green and its branched fronds (seaweeds do not have leaves) are curled to form a distinctive channel. Some plants spend as much as 90 per cent of their time out of water. During this period they lose up to 65 per cent of their water and turn black and brittle. Channel wrack reproduces during summer and autumn when the reproductive bodies at the tips of its fronds become bright orange, bringing welcome colour to the upper shore.

THE PROBLEMS OF TAXONOMY

There has been muchf confusion about the status and naming of the rough periwinkle but now it seems to have been accepted by biologists that the name covers at least four species, *Littorina nigrolineata*, *Littorina neglecta*, *Littorina saxatilis* and *Littorina arcana*. While this need not concern us in our appreciation of seashore life, the controversy surrounding the status of the rough periwinkle illustrates the difficulties even professional biologists sometimes have in identifying and naming species. Taxonomy, the naming and classifying of organisms, is a difficult, complex and very important subject. It is a vital tool in ecology and conservation but unfortunately is much under-valued as a scientific discipline at the present time.

Spiral wrack, another upper-shore seaweed, is olive-brown and, like channel wrack, a member of the family of brown seaweeds which are common in the intertidal zone. These seaweeds contain a brown pigment called fucoxanthin which largely masks their green, photosynthetic chlorophyll. This pigment helps the seaweeds to absorb blue light at depths where red and orange light have been filtered out by the surface-water layers. The branched fronds of spiral wrack are often twisted. Spiral wrack lacks air bladders and the edges of its fronds are smooth, two characteristics which distinguish the species from bladder wrack and toothed wrack which occur further down the shore.

In places where freshwater accumulates or passes regularly over the shore there are patches of the green alga *Enteromorpha*. Its fronds can grow up to 70 centimetres (28 inches) in length, are tubular, sometimes branched and may be spirally twisted. When they dry out they are bleached white.

Small numbers of thick top-shells live on the upper part of this and other Connemara shores. Their shells are greyish with purple markings, often with the top eroded and silvery. They are large snails with shells up to 30 millimetres (1.2 inches) high. Ageing them by reading the lines on the shells has shown that some individuals live ten years or more. In the summer they produce larvae which spend a few days drifting in the plankton before settling on the upper shore, finding refuge under stones and boulders. These snails belong to a southern species and are confined to western and southern shores in Ireland, with an outlying population around Strangford Lough on the north-east coast. They show their preference for warmer conditions by moving down the shore during the colder months of the year.

Acorn barnacles encrust the rocks on many shores.

We meet the first acorn barnacles on rocks in the upper middle shore (see box). Although they appear lifeless when the tide is out, these greyish-white, conical encrustations soon spring into action when the sea returns. We can simulate the return of the tide by placing a barnacle covered stone in a dish of seawater. Soon after they have been immersed, the barnacles open their opercular plates ('trapdoors' on the top) and project their cirri (modified 'legs'). The whip-like beating of the cirri draws food-carrying water to the barnacles. We can watch this action with the naked eye, but it is much more enthralling through a magnifying lens or a low-powered stereoscopic microscope.

Common limpets live on rocks between the mid-upper shore and the mid-lower shore. They remain firmly attached to the rocks while the tide is out. But when it returns they leave their home scars and move over the rocks, grazing algae as they go. When the tide starts to ebb they return unerringly to their home scars following a chemical trail laid on their outward journey. To ensure a watertight bond with their home rocks, limpets mould their shell to the rock if it is harder than their shell. Alternatively, they mould the rock to their shells if the rock is soft, like limestone. Limpets living high on the shore tend to be taller and narrower than those living at lower levels. In the exposed conditions of the upper shore the shell muscles are contracted for longer to hold the limpets tight against the rock and prevent drying while the tide is out. This is thought to have the effect of pulling in the shell-secreting tissues which, in turn, affects the shape of the shell. Fast-growing limpets live for four or five years but slow-growing individuals can live for 15-17 years.

BARNACLES

Many people think that, because barnacles look superficially like cone-shaped limpets, the two animals must be closely related. That is not the case. Limpets are snails which have adapted to living in very exposed conditions by attaching themselves securely to the rocks. Barnacles have adapted in the same way to living in these difficult conditions. These two very different types of animals have undergone convergent evolution. The mention of the 'modified legs' of the barnacles tells us they are not snails and gives us a clue to the group to which they belong - the crustacea. Also belonging to the crustacea are crabs, lobsters, shrimps, sand-hoppers and sea slaters. Superficially, adult barnacles look like none of these. However, they produce larvae which drift in the plankton before settling and attaching permanently to a rock. These look like crab larvae rather than snail larvae, confirming that barnacles are crustaceans.

Limpets differ from periwinkles in the way they reproduce. They spawn mainly from October to December, stimulated, it is believed, by rough seas and onshore winds. Sperms and eggs are released into the sea where fertilisation occurs. The larvae drift in the plankton for a few days and then, when they are about 0.2 millimetres in size, settle in rock pools or damp areas of the shore. After breeding limpets change sex, in common with several other molluscs such as oysters.

If we search carefully on the upper shore we will find pepper dulse. It is a small, compact, rusty-red seaweed giving off a peppery smell if crushed a little. It grows up to 15 centimetres (6 inches) in length and has alternate, though sometimes opposite, branches. Carrageen (also spelt carragheen and carageen), or Irish moss, appears at the same level and, like pepper dulse, extends down the shore in occasional clumps. The term carrageen covers two similar but variable species, *Chondrus crispus* and *Mastocarpus stellatus*. Both are dark red to purple and grow to about 10 centimetres (4 inches) in length. They have flat fronds which widen from the narrow stipe (stalk).

Pepper dulse and carrageen are amongst the few red seaweeds inhabiting the intertidal zone. Most red seaweeds live below the low-tide level, often at considerable depths. In deep water the red pigment, phycoerythrin, improves their ability to absorb blue and violet light in the absence of red and orange light which has been filtered out in the surface layers of the sea.

The middle shore

Bladder wrack is the most abundant seaweed on the middle shore. It is olive-brown and easily recognised by the usually paired, spherical air bladders on its fronds. The air bladders buoy up the plants and help keep them in the well-lit surface waters when the tide is in. On shores more exposed to strong wave action plants tend to have fewer bladders. This is because the resistance they offer to the rough seas would cause the plants to be torn away from the rocks. On very exposed shores, such as we find on Connemara's western headlands and islands, there are few seaweeds of any kind because they cannot withstand the constant tugging of the waves. In such conditions, the only organisms which can survive on the surface of the rocks are low-growing, firmly attached species like barnacles.

Bladder wrack has separate male and female plants. During the breeding season males can be distinguished by the orange swellings at the tips of their fronds. In the females these swellings are deep green in colour. At high tide the plants shed their gametes (reproductive cells) into the sea where fertilisation takes place. After a period of development the young seaweed attaches to a rock or other suitable hard substrate where it develops from a tiny, club-shaped structure into a new and recognisable bladder wrack.

SEAWEEDS

Unlike many land plants seaweeds do not have roots to absorb nutrients or to anchor them to the ground. Instead, their fronds absorb nutrients directly from the sea and they cling to the rocks by means of structures called holdfasts.

Mingling with bladder wrack is another brown seaweed, toothed wrack. Its fronds are olive-brown, lack air bladders and are characteristically saw-edged. It becomes more common on the lower shore where bladder wrack is absent. In sheltered conditions, toothed wrack often has a rich variety of animals growing on its fronds. These include sponges, sea-firs (hydroids), sea-mats (bryozoans) and tube-living bristle worms like *Spirorbis*. Such epiphytes also grow on other seaweeds, but generally not in the profusion found on toothed wrack.

If we turn over the seaweeds of the middle shore we are bound to find some edible periwinkles. These familiar black or dark grey snails are the largest of the periwinkles, growing to a height of 30 millimetres (1.2 inches). They feed on micro-organisms, detritus and several green algae, but not on some of the brown algae which apparently produce a chemical which they find distasteful. Edible periwinkles breed in the early spring. Their eggs are shed into the sea in gelatinous capsules during spring tides. The larvae hatch after a few days and then drift in the plankton for up to six weeks before settling on the lower shore in June or July.

The edible periwinkle is a valuable resource. In 1989, for example, 55.6 tonnes, valued at Ir£26,000, were harvested commercially in Connemara.

Whereas a limpet must cling tightly to the rocks to avoid drying out during low tide, an edible periwinkle can seal the entrance to its shell with an operculum ('door') when it withdraws from drying conditions or needs to escape a predator. So, too, can the flat periwinkle and the flat or purple top-shell, two other snails which occur under the seaweeds of the middle shore.

We will find flat periwinkles browsing amongst the fronds of bladder wrack and toothed wrack. Lacking spires, their olive-green, yellow, brown or even banded shells grow only to a height of 15 millimetres (0.6 inch). They lay their eggs usually in spring and early summer, though breeding can take place throughout the year. The egg masses are whitish, usually oval or kidney-shaped in outline and contain up to 280 eggs. Young snails emerge from the eggs after about six weeks. Like the rough periwinkle, the flat periwinkle species has recently been 'split', but, so far, only into two species, *Littorina obtusata* and *Littorina mariae*.

The flat or purple top-shells are greyish-green and roughly triangular in outline, being about 16 millimetres (0.6 inch) high and 22

A dense settlement of Spirorbis on oar weed.

millimetres (0.9 inch) broad. As well as their size and shape, the presence of a large hole (umbilicus) at the centre of the underside of their shells distinguishes them from the thick top-shells which live higher up the shore. As with the larger species, the top of their shells become silvery when their outer surface is worn down.

Important members of the middle-shore community are the dog-whelks. They are taller than the other snails and, on the Spiddle shore, usually whitish-grey. The shell is normally up to 30 millimetres (1.2 inches) high, but can grow considerably bigger. The shape and roughness of the shell and the size of the opening vary with the exposure of the shore. In exposed conditions, where waves persistently dash the shore, dog-whelks tend to have short and broad shells with relatively large openings. In sheltered locations their shells are taller and have narrower openings.

In contrast to the periwinkles and top-shells, the dog-whelks are carnivorous. They feed on acorn barnacles and common mussels. In summer we can often see dog-whelks 'grazing' like a flock of sheep on a barnacle-covered rock. An adult dog-whelk can force open the opercular plates of barnacles to reach the flesh using a snout-like proboscis which can be extended to a length roughly equal to that of its own shell. While doing this, it injects a narcotic to relax the barnacle and ease its entry into the shell. To reach the flesh of all but the smallest mussels the dog-whelk must bore a hole through the shell by a combination of mechanical and chemical means. This takes several hours. When it reaches the flesh the whelk secretes digestive enzymes into the mussel and then sucks up a rich 'soup'. This means that the dog-whelk is a liquid feeder and therefore produces little in the way of solid faeces, in contrast to the plant- and detritus-feeding periwinkles. If the latter are kept in an aquarium for any length of time it soon becomes evident that they produce a lot of solid waste.

At higher levels on the shore common mussels crowd into fissures in the granite boulders, but lower down, in the less-exposed conditions, they can grow more freely. In exposed positions they

Common mussels live at high densities.

remain very small, but in the shelter of the rocks and seaweed, in places like Killary Harbour, they grow to a length of 50 millimetres (2 inches) or more. These dark blue molluscs are the only bivalves living on the surface of the Spiddle shore. They secure themselves to the rocks by means of a byssus composed of tough, horny threads. If the byssus is broken, a mussel is capable of renewing it and reattaching to a rock. This makes common mussels ideal subjects for mariculture as we can see in Killary Harbour. Here, young mussels settle out of the plankton on to ropes suspended from rafts, often at densities of up to 1,000 per 25 millimetres (1 inch) of rope. Clearly, they could not grow to maturity at this density so they are thinned out. Those removed from the ropes are then placed in mesh bags which are secured to clean ropes. From here the young mussels creep out onto the ropes and reattach themselves at more modest densities.

The byssus can also serve other functions. For example, a young mussel can drift on a byssal thread which acts as a parachute preventing it from sinking. In dense beds, mussels can immobilise a dog-whelk, one of their main predators, by attaching large numbers of byssal threads to its shell, eventually overturning it. Other enemies of common mussels include the shore crab and the common starfish, of which we will find small specimens on the lower shore at Spiddle and other similar shores around Connemara.

To reach its meal a common starfish must force open the two shells of the mussel. It does this by wrapping itself around the mussel and gripping the valves with the tips of the many tube-feet arranged along the underside of each arm. As soon as a tiny gap, though to be as small as 0.1 millimetres, is created between the valves, the starfish everts its stomach, passes it between the shells and starts digesting the mussel flesh.

Common starfish are yellow-brown to red and sometimes violet. They have five arms, although occasionally we will find individuals with four or six arms. Sometimes one arm is shorter than the rest, indicating that the starfish has probably lost an arm which is now being replaced. On commercial oyster beds, where starfish are considered pests, fishermen used to break off the arms of starfish and return them to the water, assuming that they would die. But, far from dying, they grew new arms, and even additional starfish when the several fragments developed into new animals, thus adding to the problems of the fishermen rather than solving them.

The common starfish preys on mussels, oysters and other bivalves.

Shore crabs are also well-known seashore predators that eat a variety of live animals as well as dead animal material. Mussels, barnacles, dog-whelks, bristle worms, top-shells, limpets, shrimps, sea urchins and many other types of seashore animal make up its diet. When the tide is out, shore crabs retreat under stones and seaweed. But when the water returns they can often be seen scuttling sideways across the seabed in typical crab fashion.

Shore crabs are generally dark green above and green or orange-red below. Young animals are often marked with white patches above. At their largest they can reach 80 millimetres (3 inches) or more across their backs. Crabs of this size have very powerful pincers and should be treated with great caution! In crabs, unlike lobsters and shrimps, the abdomen is folded under the body to form a distinctive, segmented triangle. In the male the abdomen forms a narrow triangle of five segments. In the female the abdomen is broader, almost semi-circular and made up of seven segments, better enabling her to carry eggs.

In the autumn, a female can occasionally be found carrying eggs (up to 185,000 of them) under her abdomen (most egg-carrying females move offshore). The eggs hatch after several months and larvae are released into the sea where they develop in the plankton, before settling on the seabed two to three months later.

Sometimes a crab will be found carrying a yellow-brown mass under its abdomen. This looks superficially like a mass of eggs. But, as males also carry these masses, this cannot be the case. The mass is, in fact, a parasitic barnacle called *Sacculina carcini*. The visible part of the parasite contains just the reproductive organs which are connected with a series of roof-like feeding threads which ramify through the body of the crab. One of the effects it has on male shore crabs is to change their hormonal balance. This leads to the males developing female features at the next moult.

In order to grow, crabs, like lobsters and shrimps, must moult their shells. During the moulting period the new shell takes some time to harden and the crabs must hide from predators while they are in such a vulnerable state. The shell makes up about 40 per cent of the weight of a crab - and presumably of a common lobster, a sobering thought for those who like to dine expensively on the latter!

Unlike most other crabs, the common hermit crab has a soft abdomen. It protects this by living in the shell of a snail such as a periwinkle or a dog-whelk. It is often surprising to see what we thought was an empty periwinkle shell rise up and walk away. As it grows, the hermit crab must move into a bigger shell. When it retreats into a shell the crab partially closes off the entrance with its right pincer which is considerably larger than the left one.

Common hermit crabs are red, yellow or brownish in colour. On the shore they reach about 35 millimetres (1.4 inches) in length but they grow much bigger when they move into deeper water offshore. They breed in the winter and in July large numbers of small hermit crabs in periwinkle shells are present in pools on the lower shore. Hermit crabs are scavengers, feeding on a variety of plant and animal materials as well as filtering small particles from the water.

Closer to the sea

The rock pools of the middle and lower shore are delightful 'gardens' of encrusting calcareous red algae such as *Corallina officinalis* and species of *Lithothamnion*. *Corallina*, a purple-pink branching plant with stiff chalky segments, forms extensive tufts 8-10 centimetres (3-4 inches) high. *Lithothamnion* is a pink or mauve encrustation covering large areas of the rock surface. Both seaweeds are impregnated with chalk (calcium carbonate) which is thought to give them strength and reduce their palatability to grazers.

Interspersed with these algae, and sometimes on sheltered rocks outside the pools, we will find dark-red, soft-bodied beadlet anemones. These relatively simple animals, up to 50 millimetres (2 inches) across, are related to jellyfish. Underwater the stiff jelly-like domes are transformed by the emergence of up to 192 tentacles arranged in six circles around a central mouth. The gentle swaying of these innocent-looking appendages belies the danger they present to passing animals. The tentacles have a battery of stinging cells capable of capturing and paralysing a wide range of animals, including fish which may even be bigger than the sea anemone itself. The distinctive blue spots around the top of the dome also contain stinging cells but how the sea-anemone uses these is not clear.

Occasionally, we will catch a glimpse of a prawn darting across a pool. Its shell is very thin and relatively transparent so we can see its internal organs quite clearly. Prawns breed from November through to June. A single female can carry as many as 4,000 eggs. These are brooded for up to four months, then released into the plankton, young prawns later settling on the shore in July and August.

The terms prawn and shrimp are imprecise but usually relate to the size of the animals. The larger species are referred to as prawns and the smaller ones as shrimps. However, the common prawn can readily be distinguished from the common shrimp by the saw-like rostrum which projects forward beyond its eyes. The common shrimp has no such adornment. Furthermore, we are unlikely to find shrimps in the rock pools as they live buried in sand from the middle shore to considerable depths under the sea.

Occasionally, too, we will find a fish stranded in a pool by the falling tide. It could be a shanny with a long dorsal fin divided into two by a depression, a deep-bodied corkwing wrasse, a two-spot goby, a butterfish with its slender body and distinctive row of black spots at the base of its long dorsal fin or any of a dozen or more species which regularly turn up in pools.

Nestled amongst the boulders and seaweeds near the low-tide level we may come across 'honeycombs' of apparently empty tubes made of consolidated sand and mud. Each tube is about 5 millimetres (0.2 inch) across. Far from being empty, the tubes are the homes of bristle worms called *Sabellaria*. These are reddish-brown in colour and up to 40 millimetres (1.6 inches) long. When the tide is in the worms project their tentacled heads into the water to catch food.

The other worms which are evident on the surface of the Spiddle shore are the tubeworms, *Pomatoceros triqueter* and several species of *Spirorbis*. *Pomatoceros* lives in an elongated, white calcareous tube which is usually firmly cemented to a rock, seaweed or a shell. Tubes can be up to 30 millimetres (1.2 inches) long and 4 millimetres (0.2 inch) wide. Each tube has a characteristic ridge along its length, which extends to a point over its opening. *Spirorbis* worms are no more than a few millimetres long and live in coiled tubes about 3 millimetres (0.1 inch) in diameter. The tubes of the common species are coiled in a clockwise manner. (A less common species which lives

The tubeworm Serpula vermicularis forms small reefs in Salt Lake, near Clifden.

mainly in deeper water has an anti-clockwise coiled tube.) *Spirorbis* lives mainly on seaweeds such as toothed wrack and oarweeds on which it can settle in great densities.

The beautiful star ascidian also lives on the fronds of oarweeds. This is a colonial animal related to the sea-squirts. The tiny individual animals are embedded in a star-like pattern in a transparent, gelatinous case which forms an extensive but thin covering on the oarweed frond. Despite its apparent simplicity, the star ascidian is an advanced species and shares several important physical characteristics with vertebrates in the earlier stages of its life.

The star ascidian should not be confused with the much simpler but somewhat similar-looking

---

Table 29
The range of animals that can be found on the Spiddle seashore.
(based on records of the students and staff of the Zoology Department, University College Swansea)

INVERTEBRATES	Number of species
Sponges (Porifera)	3
Sea anemones, jellyfish and their relations (Cnidaria)	11
Flatworms (Platyhelminthes)	4
Ribbon or proboscis worms (Nemertea)	4
Bristle worms (Annelida; Polychaeta)	23
Barnacles (Crustacea; Cirripedia)	6
Sea-lice and sea slaters (Crustacea; Isopoda)	12
Sand-hoppers (Crustacea; Amphipoda)	6
Prawns and shrimps (Crustacea; Decapoda)	11
Sea spiders (Pycnogonida)	4
Chitons or coat-of-mail shells (Mollusca; Polyplacophora)	4
Snails (Mollusca; Gastropoda)	23
Bivalves (Mollusca; Bivalvia)	5
Sea-mats (Bryozoa)	11
Starfish (Echinodermata; Asteroidea)	3
Brittle-stars (Echinodermata; Ophiuroidea)	2
Sea urchins (Echinodermata; Echinoidea)	2
Sea-cucumbers (Echinodermata; Holothuroidea)	2
Sea-squirts (Ascidiacea)	5
VERTEBRATES	
Bony fishes (Osteichthyes)	12

---

sea-mats or moss animals (bryozoans). These are thin, white, orange or brownish encrustations on seaweeds and rocks. They consist of colonies of very small individuals in thin gelatinous or chalky sheets. A hand-lens is required to determine the shape of the individuals. *Alcyonidium* is a common and widespread species which occurs on toothed wrack, *Chondrus crispus* and *Mastocarpus stellatus.*

As we approach the low-tide level we begin to meet sponges such as the distinctive olive-green breadcrumb sponge. It lives in gullies, under rocky overhangs and among the holdfasts of seaweeds. It can cover extensive areas and will even grow over other encrusting invertebrates. The green colouring is due to the presence of green algae within its tissues. A sponge's simple outward appearance belies its surprisingly complex internal structure and behaviour.

We know we have reached the low-tide level when we meet oarweed, a broad, leathery, brown seaweed with hand-like

> ### THE STORY OF THE CHINAMAN'S HAT
>
> The aptly named Chinaman's hat is a small, limpet-like snail, first reported in west-coast waters in 1963, in Clew Bay, Co. Mayo. In 1975 a single dead shell was discovered in Ballynakill Harbour in Connemara and in 1980 the species was found to be common on small stones around low-water spring tide level in Ballynakill Harbour.
>
> The appearance of this snail in two west-coast bays posed a mystery. It had not been recorded in the region previously, in spite of intensive survey work earlier in the century. It had been reported from the east coast of Ireland, but considerable doubt has been cast on these records.
>
> Essentially, the Chinaman's hat is a southern species, with some outlying populations on the south and west coast of Britain. So how did it get to Ballynakill Harbour? It is suggested that it was introduced with oysters imported from Brittany during the 1950s and 1960s. Such accidental introductions highlight the dangers of moving animals around the globe. Many pests and diseases are spread as a result of ill-considered transfers of commercial species. The inadvertent transportation of species on ships' hulls and in their ballast water is also causing grave concern around the world. The Chinaman's hat does not appear to have caused any damage in Ballynakill Harbour, but it could have done.

fronds. The solid, smooth, flexible stipe, oval in cross-section, is attached to a rock by a strong, branched and slightly dome-shaped holdfast. The latter is worth investigating as it is a habitat for a variety of small animals such as sea slaters and sand-hoppers.

In this brief survey of the Spiddle shore we have noted some of the common and more obvious plants and animals. In doing so we have merely scratched the surface of a fascinating and absorbing subject. As Table 29 indicates, there are many more animals to be found on the shore and undoubtedly many more seaweeds too. Galway Bay is particularly rich in seaweeds, with 350-400 species recorded to date. Many of the plants and animals noted here will be found on rocky shores elsewhere around the Connemara coast, although often in different proportions and sometimes different forms, depending on the environmental conditions. This is what makes seashore ecology so interesting; no two shores are the same.

SOME UNUSUAL VISITORS

Goose barnacles

South-westerly autumn gales bring much flotsam and jetsam to the Connemara coast. Much of it, regrettably, is rubbish dumped from ships. But from time to time we will find lumps of driftwood covered with goose barnacles. These differ from the familiar acorn barnacles in being much larger and having a long-rubbery stalk and a 'head' bearing a number of calcareous plates. Overall, they can reach a length of 20 centimetres (8 inches). Goose barnacles are tropical and subtropical animals and require sea temperatures of 19-25º C to breed succesfully.

Goose barnacles carried on floating timber from the open ocean to the seashore.

The name goose barnacle is said to arise from the myth that barnacle geese hatched from barnacles growing on trees at the water's edge. This belief is not surprising because goose barnacles and barnacle geese appear at the same time. And it is not so long ago that people had no idea that barnacle geese migrate to Ireland in the autumn from their breeding grounds in Greenland.

Another, perhaps more plausible, origin of the name is that the stalk and head of a goose barnacle look like the neck and head of a goose. Hence, they are sometimes called goose-necked barnacles.

Jack sail-by-the-wind

This is a small blue jellyfish, known also as the by-the-wind-sailor. It is also a species from tropical and subtropical waters which is driven northwards onto Connemara shores. It consists of an oval float, 80-100 millimetres (3-4 inches) long, on which there is an erect, triangular sail set diagonally in one of two ways. Some are mounted north-east-south-west and steer the jellyfish to the right as they drift. Others are aligned north-west-south-east and drive them to the left. Both forms occur in the Atlantic but are segregated by the wind as they cross the ocean. Most of those reaching Connemara are left-sailors, the right-sailors presumably having been driven onto the shores further south in Europe and Africa.

Jack sail-by-the-wind jellyfish have been recorded on the Irish coast in all months of the year, although they tend to be reported less frequently in the winter when fewer people are walking the shores. Dr David McGrath, a biologist in the Galway Regional Technical College, has kept records of them since 1976 and would welcome further reports of strandings in Connemara and elsewhere around the Irish coast.

CONSERVATION

'In the end, we will conserve only what we love, we will love only what we understand,
we will understand only what we are taught.'

Baba Dioum, a Senegalese conservationist,
quoted in *The Diversity of Life* by Edward O. Wilson, 1992.

What is nature conservation?

Nature conservation is a practical approach to living in harmony with the natural environment. It derives its principles from the science of ecology. This science tells us how plants and animals relate to each other and to the world around them. The nature conservation approach should underpin all natural resource management and land-use planning. In Connemara, where people's lives and livelihoods depend very directly on nature, conservation is especially important.

To apply the principles of nature conservation we must take three steps. First, we must learn all we can about nature in our region - how the plants, animals, land, water and air behave, and why. Once gathered, this knowledge must be communicated to the people who live in Connemara so that all can take part in an informed debate on the conservation issues. Finally, this knowledge should be used to formulate conservation action programmes and guide the making of new laws. Such laws should help both public bodies and private individuals to take better care of our shared environment.

Knowledge and understanding

The natural history of Connemara is probably better documented than that of any other area of comparable size in Ireland. The 962 references in the Bibliography (which is undoubtedly incomplete) attest to the fact that much has been written about nature in Connemara in the past 150 years. An analysis of the references by subject is presented in the pie chart in Figure 13a. Further analysis of the references to flora and fauna indicates a severe imbalance in the attention given to the groups within these categories. This is clearly indicated in the histogram (Figure 13b

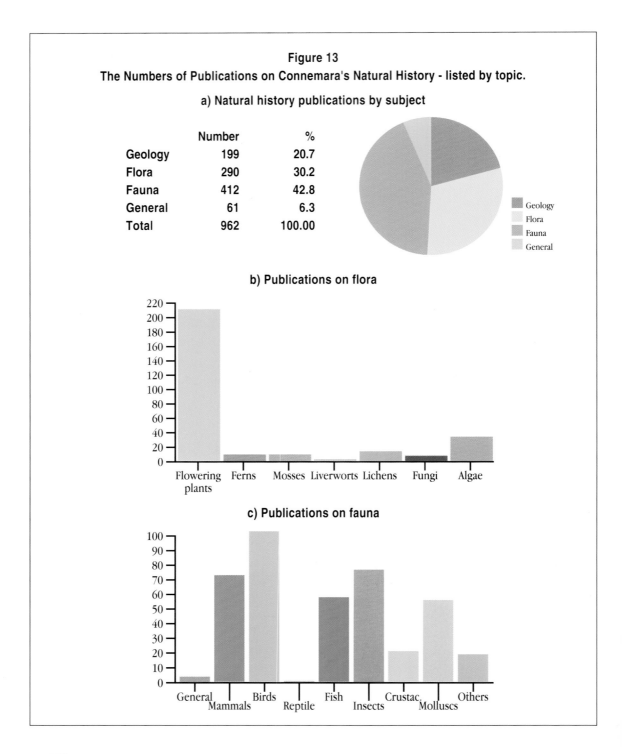

Figure 13
The Numbers of Publications on Connemara's Natural History - listed by topic.

a) Natural history publications by subject

	Number	%
Geology	199	20.7
Flora	290	30.2
Fauna	412	42.8
General	61	6.3
Total	962	100.00

Geology
Flora
Fauna
General

b) Publications on flora

Flowering plants, Ferns, Mosses, Liverworts, Lichens, Fungi, Algae

c) Publications on fauna

General, Mammals, Birds, Reptile, Fish, Insects, Crustac., Molluscs, Others and c) which shows that three quarters of the flora references are about flowering plants and only one quarter about lower plants. Of the 412 animal references, over half refer to vertebrates. Amongst these, the mammals, birds and fish are well represented (although within each of these groups only a fraction of the species receives most of the attention), but amphibians and Ireland's only native reptile, the viviparous lizard, are scarcely mentioned. Most often referred to among the invertebrates are the insects, followed by the molluscs and the crustaceans; only about 5 per cent of the publications relate to the rest of Connemara's invertebrate fauna.

The imbalance of information is neither unusual nor surprising. Worldwide, more is known about flowering plants and vertebrates than about the lower forms of wildlife. Nevertheless, for conservation to function in a comprehensive way it is important that much more information be gathered about lower plants and invertebrates.

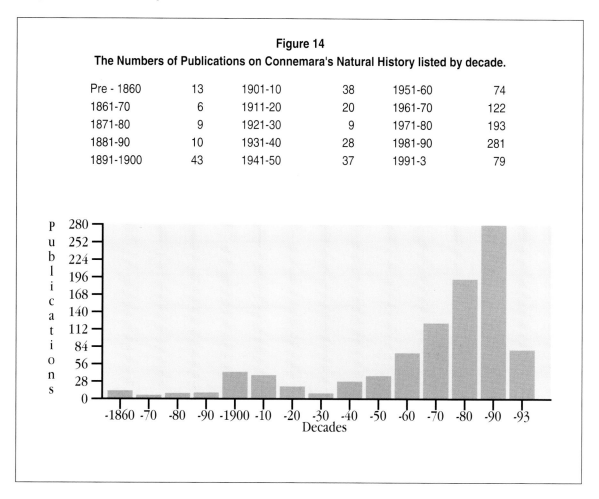

Figure 14
The Numbers of Publications on Connemara's Natural History listed by decade.

Pre - 1860	13	1901-10	38	1951-60	74
1861-70	6	1911-20	20	1961-70	122
1871-80	9	1921-30	9	1971-80	193
1881-90	10	1931-40	28	1981-90	281
1891-1900	43	1941-50	37	1991-3	79

The rate of publication has increased with time (see Figure 14). Of the 962 references, 70 per cent have appeared since 1960, reflecting an upsurge in publishing by university staff and students. Nearly 30 per cent of the total was published in the 1980s alone. Since 1960 geology and flora have each provided about 25 per cent of the publications, mammals, birds and fish 9 per cent each, invertebrates 16 per cent and general natural history papers the balance.

But this deluge of literature must not lead us into the mistaken belief that the natural history of Connemara is well known or clearly understood. The analysis shows that our knowledge is patchy in terms of species and biased towards geology, flowering plants, birds and mammals. Furthermore, much of the information on the invertebrates is out of date. This is not a satisfactory basis for a comprehensive and effective programme of nature conservation.

The scarcity of up-to-date information for some groups may be mitigated to an extent by the existence of unpublished material based on recent research and surveys. But such information can be of little value until it is presented in the public arena. Those who collect data could do a public service by ensuring it is published in scientific journals or popular publications.

Collecting and publishing information

The lack of information on much of Connemara's flora and fauna can be attributed, in part at least, to the dearth of naturalists in the region. This dearth in turn reflects the relatively small population, the absence of a tradition of natural history in education or society as a whole and possibly an understandable turning away from nature in response to the hardship it is perceived to have inflicted on the region in the past.

Encouragingly, in recent years, staff and students in the departments of natural science at University College, Galway, and Galway Regional Technical College have produced several valuable scientific papers and theses relating to the natural history of Connemara. However, much of the natural history research has been and continues to be conducted by visiting naturalists, students and research scientists. Unfortunately, some of these fail to publish their findings or present them in journals not readily available to local naturalists. This is understandable as there is little scope for publishing natural history information locally. There are no regular local or regional natural history journals or magazines, so information collected in Connemara must be submitted to the *Irish Naturalists' Journal, Irish Birds,* the *Bulletin of the Irish Biogeographical Society,* the *Proceedings of the Royal Irish Academy,* the *Journal of Life Sciences of the Royal Dublin Society* or a foreign journal.

Two things could help to overcome these deficiencies. First, a regional natural history journal could benefit conservation in Connemara, feeding information back into the community and stimulating interest and further field research. This journal could cater not only for Connemara but also for neighbouring areas of west Mayo, the Corrib region, the Burren and the Aran Islands - all areas of outstanding natural history interest. Secondly, it would be helpful if visitors to the region were made aware of the local interest in their work and invited to deposit their results in a properly managed data bank, perhaps based at the Connemara National Park, where there is already much information available for consultation. This would ensure that even if some of the information was not published, it would still be available locally for consultation. All relevant university and college theses and reports should also be sent to this data bank.

Education

The gathering of natural history information, as well as serving science, can serve both formal and informal education. It is heartening to see that this is now the case in Connemara where, in the primary sector in particular, increasing numbers of schools are undertaking natural history projects as a matter of routine. Staff of the Connemara National Park, wildlife rangers of the National Parks and Wildlife Service and naturalists from non-governmental institutions and voluntary bodies visit schools. Primary school teachers attend environmental and natural history courses at University College, Galway, the Conamara Environmental Education Centre at Letterfrack, the Corrib Conservation Centre near Oughterard and centres further afield. This encouraging development should be reinforced by giving teachers more time for in-service training.

Natural history is less well catered for in secondary schools where examination pressures tend to concentrate the attention of teachers and pupils on basic subjects and activities most likely to help pupils obtain jobs. Nor is natural history pursued as an extracurricular subject. It would seem that no secondary school in the region has a natural history club.

Students in the departments of natural science at University College, Galway, and Galway Regional Technical College undertake field studies in Connemara, as do participants in adult education courses. In a commendable development, the Geology Department at University College, Galway, has recently restored and opened to the public its James Mitchell Museum. School parties will be particularly welcome to the Museum and their members will no doubt be enthralled by the fine collection of minerals, rocks and fossils on display.

At present, there is little consistent support for non-governmental and voluntary bodies to develop educational programmes for schools. The European Community gives large sums of money to build sophisticated interpretative centres, primarily used by casual visitors. Yet it is difficult to raise money for the environmental education of Ireland's young people. The imbalance between interpretation and education is well illustrated by a recent example. The funding made available by the European Community for the construction of an interpretative centre in Co. Clare could have paid for 2,000 year-round environmental courses of the type recently run in eight primary schools by members of a local voluntary wildlife organisation.

A wide range of informal educational activities is provided at the Connemara National Park at Letterfrack. These include guided walks, talks, guided tours for school parties, special nature-related activities for children in the summer and evening lectures during July and August. The

Connemara National Park has an excellent audio-visual display, an interpretative centre and a laboratory for use by visiting student groups and individual researchers. The staff have produced a wide range of books and leaflets on the natural history of Connemara. They also visit schools and other organisations to give illustrated talks about the region. As well as education, the staff and visiting students undertake ecological research within the Park. The results of this research will guide the Connemara National Park officials in their efforts to restore the degraded landscape of the area to its former natural richness and variety.

The Conamara Environmental Education Centre is also based in Letterfrack. Founded and energetically promoted by Leo Hallissey, the local primary school headmaster, the Centre provides environmental education services for Connemara schools and runs courses for teachers and members of the general public. As well as organising activities on the mainland, it runs summer courses on Inishbofin. Leo Hallissey is an ardent conservationist. He has contributed to national surveys and educational programmes on the state of Ireland's coast and has campaigned vigorously for the conservation of Connemara's blanket bogs.

The Connemara Field Studies Centre, run by David Hogan in Cleggan, offers a variety of services including an educational package for primary schools. This involves talks and the distribution of slide sets with teachers' notes. The Centre also offers adult seminars and lectures on landscape appreciation, weekend courses on flora and guided walks. It supplies maps and brochures describing the ecology and archaeology of walking routes in Connemara.

Roundstone-based author and map-maker Tim Robinson has contributed enormously to our knowledge and appreciation of Connemara with his books and maps. Prepared painstakingly by hand, his maps present a wealth of information about the landscape and archaeology of the region. In a gazetteer accompanying his map of Connemara, he details the meanings and derivations of many of the Irish placenames given on the map. These are more meaningful than the anglicised versions we see on road signs and other maps; conscientious students of Connemara will find much of interest and value in them.

Among the national voluntary bodies engaged in education and conservation activities in Connemara are the Irish Peatland Conservation Council, the Irish Wildbird Conservancy, the Irish Wildlife Federation and An Taisce (the National Trust). A leading member of the latter organisation, Professor Emer Colleran, is particularly noted for her untiring promotion of conservation in Connemara.

Legislation and administration

But an appreciation and understanding of nature are not sufficient to ensure its conservation. Legislation is required to codify and formalise our aspirations and administrative structures are needed to put them into practice.

Galway County Council has immediate responsibility for the administration of Connemara. Its

County Plans, usually revised every five years, increasingly emphasise conservation in their management strategies. However, this emphasis is largely aspirational and the County Plans do not adequately specify means for achieving particular nature conservation objectives. We must turn, therefore, to national and international legislation for site and species conservation.

National legislation

At national level there are several acts which have practical implications for nature conservation (see box).

The Wildlife Act, administered by the National Parks and Wildlife Service, is concerned with the protection of flora, fauna and habitats in Connemara. Two nature reserves have been established under the Act. Derryclare Wood is one of the best remaining examples of semi-natural oakwood in Connemara and Leam West Blanket Bog near Oughterard is an important intact blanket bog. At present there are no Wildfowl Sanctuaries or Refuges for Fauna in Connemara. However, several Wildfowl Sanctuaries have been proposed and it is to be hoped that these will be designated in the near future. Likewise, it is desirable that important wildlife areas, such as the tern breeding islands off the Connemara coast, be officially protected, perhaps as Refuges for Fauna.

The Connemara National Park compensates to some extent for the lack of Nature Reserves, Refuges for Fauna and Wildfowl Sanctuaries. Although generally perceived as a place for recreation and education, its primary function is the conservation of 3,000 hectares (7,400 acres) of the Connemara mountains and blanket bogs. The Connemara National Park is administered by the National Parks and Wildlife Service of the Office of Public Works. The National Parks Service and the Wildlife Service were combined in the late 1980s. Together they offer

---

LEGISLATION AND ADMINISTRATION

National legislation

Several acts have practical implications for nature conservation in Connemara. The Planning and Development Act, Water Pollution Act, Air Pollution Act, Foreshore Act, Fisheries Act and Forestry Act can all be invoked for conservation purposes. But, it is the Wildlife Act which is most relevant to the present discussion. The Wildlife Act, currently (August 1993) under review, is administered by the National Parks and Wildlife Service. Its main provisions include the protection of wild birds, their nests and eggs, some mammals (including dolphins, porpoises and whales), reptiles and amphibians but currently not fish. Further provisions of the Wildlife Act are presented in Appendix II.

International legislation

The European Community has adopted a number of directives and conventions relevant to nature conservation in Connemara. All have been signed and ratified by Ireland. These are: the Directive on the Conservation of Wildbirds - the 'Birds Directive'; the Directive on the Protection of Natural and Semi-Natural Habitats and of Wild Flora and Fauna - the 'Habitats Directive'; the Convention on the Conservation of European Wildlife and Natural Habitats - the 'Berne Convention'; and the Convention on the Conservation of Migratory Species of Wild Animals - the 'Bonn Convention'.

considerable potential for effective nature conservation in Ireland. But the National Parks and Wildlife Service will be able to achieve this potential only in the context of a national nature conservation policy, adequate resources and long-term political support - three important ingredients presently lacking.

An Environmentally Sensitive Area

The designation, by the Department of Agriculture and Food, of the Slyne Head peninsula and neighbouring areas around Ballyconneely and Mannin Bay (townlands of Doonloughan, Errislannan and Bunowen; see Map 13) as an Environmentally Sensitive Area is a recent development which should benefit conservation. Farmers in the area, who are willing to join the scheme, will be subsidised to continue farming in a traditional manner. In this way it is hoped the flower-rich machair and dunes and some of Connemara's few remaining corncrake breeding sites can be conserved. In the long term, the benefit of the farmers and wildlife may best be served by designating the whole of Connemara an Environmentally Sensitive Area.

The Environmentally Sensitive Area scheme is grant-aided by the European Community. It is used extensively in other countries and widely supported by farming communities elsewhere. For

Map 13: Environmentally Sensitive Area.

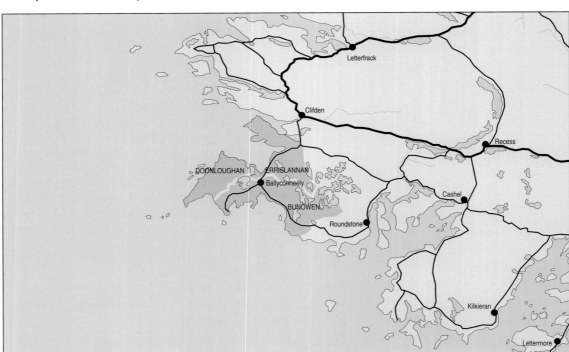

example, in Northern Ireland the Mourne Mountains and the Glens of Antrim are now Environmentally Sensitive Areas. But in the Republic of Ireland, the scheme has not been used to full advantage and the only areas designated by mid-1993 are areas in Connemara and the Slieve Bloom Mountains. It is to be hoped this valuable scheme will be implemented more widely for the benefit of the environment and the farmers in disadvantaged areas.

Areas of Scientific Interest / Natural Heritage Areas

During the 1970s and 1980s more than fifty Areas of Scientific Interest were designated in Connemara. While these had no statutory basis, they were taken into account by the County Council in the preparation of its County Plans and therefore had potential as instruments of nature conservation. However, the status of the Areas of Scientific Interest was challenged in the courts in 1991, following a controversial proposal to build an airport near Clifden on blanket bog which had been designated as an Area of Scientific Interest. As a result of the court decision, the National Parks and Wildlife Service is now obliged to reassess all the Areas of Scientific Interest in the country with a view to redesignating them as Natural Heritage Areas. The new Natural Heritage Areas will be treated as Environmentally Sensitive Areas and their owners will be eligible to apply for financial aid from the Department of Agriculture and Food. This aid will enable the owners to farm in an environmentally friendly manner and help ensure the conservation of the areas.

International legislation

There is an international aspect to conservation. This takes in not only migratory animals such as birds, insects, fish and whales, but also the habitats they use in the countries they visit. Further, as some sedentary species occur in several countries we need to co-ordinate their conservation internationally. To this end the European Community has adopted a number of directives and conventions, several of which are relevant to Connemara. These are listed in the box on p. 255 and described in Appendix II. One of the requirements of the 'Birds Directive' is that member states designate Special Protection Areas (SPAs) for birds. Ireland has designated a small number but has been slow to comply fully with the Directive in this respect. Further designations of SPAs are currently being considered and it is likely that several significant wildlife areas in Connemara will be designated. Among these are the islands off the coast which are important for breeding terns and other seabirds.

The 'Habitats Directive' requires the conservation of natural and semi-natural habitats, flora and fauna in the European Community. Importantly, the Community will provide funds for the implementation of this Directive. It is to be hoped, therefore, that the Irish Government will make a vigorous case for the money required to protect Connemara's important habitats - mountains, blanket bogs, lakes, rivers, machair, dunes and other coastal habitats.

The 'Berne Convention', in one of its provisions, obliges countries to promote national policies for the conservation of nature. But Ireland has not produced a policy on nature conservation, reflecting the low priority it has been given by the Government. Until such a policy is produced and adequately supported financially and politically it will be difficult to implement effective conservation measures. It will also be difficult to counter the piecemeal destruction of the natural environment which is permitted and politically condoned in contravention of both national and international legislation.

Under the 'Bonn Convention', an international Agreement has been reached on the conservation management of the Greenland white-fronted goose population. This is important for Connemara, as a small proportion of the international population winters in the region. In the long term, it is desirable that similar Agreements should be reached for other migratory species such as terns, for which Connemara is an important breeding area.

Each of these pieces of legislation lists species which require conservation action and the animal species are presented in Table 31. Only two plant species, the bog orchid and the slender naiad are listed in the 'Berne Convention'. Clearly, not all the species listed demand the same level of action. In Ireland, for example, common birds like robins and wrens do not require conservation measures at present. So priorities must be set. With respect to rare and endangered plants and animals these priorities have been established in Red Data Books.

Plants

Of the 150 or so flowering plants, ferns and clubmosses in the *Irish Red Data*

**Table 30
Irish Red Data Book plant species
found in Connemara.**

SPECIES	STATUS IN IRELAND	(EUROPE)
Rough poppy	Endangered	
Northern yellow-cress *	Rare	
Spotted rock-rose *	Rare	
Pale dog-violet	Vulnerable	
Purple saxifrage*	Rare	
Small cudweed	Rare	
Heath cudweed	Rare	
Alpine saw-wort *	Rare	
Mackay's heath *	Rare	
Dorset heath	Vulnerable	
Pyramidal bugle *	Rare	
Bog orchid	Rare	(Vulnerable)
Irish lady's-tresses	Rare	(Rare)
Green-winged orchid	Vulnerable	
Small-white orchid	Vulnerable	
Hydrilla	Vulnerable	
Slender naiad	Rare	(Vulnerable)
Slender cottongrass	Rare	(Vulnerable)
Bog hair-grass	Rare	(Vulnerable)
Wood small-reed	Rare	
Pillwort	Rare	(Vulnerable)
Parsley fern	Rare	
Forked spleenwort	Rare	
Holly fern *	Rare	
Marsh clubmoss *	Rare	

* = not protected under the Wildlife Act (at the end of August 1993).

RED DATA BOOKS

Red Data Book species

The concept of a Red Data Book was proposed in 1963 by the late Sir Peter Scott, the doyen of international nature conservation, and later defined as 'a register of threatened wildlife that includes definitions of degrees of threat'. In brief, Red Data Books contain summaries of information about species considered to be rare or endangered in a particular country. Their function is to provide guidelines in the development and execution of conservation programmes for national conservation agencies. Ireland has produced a Red Data Book on vascular plants. Another, on vertebrate animals, is due for publication and one on lower plants is being prepared. International Red Data Books are also produced to highlight those species in danger of extinction worldwide. An important thing to remember about Red Data Books is that they are not set in stone. They are working documents which can and must be modified as circumstances dictate. If the population of a once rare species increases to a safe level, it can be removed from the Red Data Book. If a species declines to a level at which it is considered rare or endangered it must be added. Curlew are a case in point. Their breeding population in Ireland appears to be declining. If this decline continues much longer the species will have to be added to the *Irish Vertebrate Red Data Book* list and breeding curlew will become a priority for conservation action. (Of course, ideally, no species should be allowed to decline to a level requiring its inclusion in a Red Data Book. Action should be taken at an earlier stage to protect it!)

'Red data' plants and animals are classified in a number of categories:

ENDANGERED	species in danger of extinction in Ireland and whose survival is unlikely if the causal factors continue operating.
VULNERABLE	species believed likely to move into the ENDANGERED category in the near future if the causal factors continue operating in Ireland.
RARE	species with small Irish populations which are not at present ENDANGERED or VULNERABLE but are at risk.
INDETERMINATE	species known to be ENDANGERED, VULNERABLE or RARE in Ireland but for which there is not enough information to say which of these three categories is appropriate.
INTERNATIONALLY IMPORTANT.*	species common and/or widespread in Ireland but considered RARE, VULNERABLE or ENDANGERED in the European Community and listed in Annex I of the 'Birds Directive' and/or Appendix II of the 'Berne Convention' and/or Annexes II, IV and V of the 'Habitats Directive'. These are species for which Ireland should take special responsibility in a European context.
SPECIES TO WATCH *	several species which still have relatively large populations in Ireland are declining and could come under pressure from habitat deterioration and contraction, exploitation or illegal control. Although these species do not yet warrant inclusion in the Red Data Book proper, their status needs to be monitored on a continuing basis.

* Additional categories used only in the draft *Irish Vertebrate Red Data Book*.

Table 31
Connemara animals listed for conservation measures in international directives and conventions.

SPECIES	'BIRDS DIRECTIVE'	'BERNE CONVENTION'	'HABITATS DIRECTIVE'	'BONN CONVENTION'
BIRDS				
Storm petrel	x	x		
Mute swan				x
Whooper swan	x	x		x
Greenland white-fronted goose	x	x		x
Barnacle goose	x	x		x
Shelduck		x		
Kestrel		x		
Merlin	x	x		
Peregrine	x	x		
Corncrake	x	x		
Ringed plover		x		
Golden plover	x			
Common sandpiper		x		
Sandwich tern	x	x		
Roseate tern	x	x		
Common tern	x	x		
Arctic tern	x	x		
Little tern	x	x		
Kingfisher	x	x		
Sandmartin		x		
Chough	x	x		

also listed in the 'Berne Convention' are the swallow, house martin, meadow pipit, rock pipit, grey wagtail, pied wagtail, dipper, wren, dunnock, robin, yellowhammer, reed bunting, greenfinch, goldfinch, siskin, linnet and redpoll.

MAMMALS				
Hedgehog		x		
Pygmy shrew		x		
Lesser horseshoe bat		x	x	x
Whiskered bat		x		x
Natterer's bat		x		x
Daubenton's bat		x		x
Leisler's bat		x		x

SPECIES	'BIRDS DIRECTIVE'	'BERNE CONVENTION'	'HABITATS DIRECTIVE'	'BONN CONVENTION'
Pipistrelle				x
Brown long-eared bat		x		x
Irish hare		x	x	
Pine marten		x	x	
Stoat		x		
Badger		x		
Otter		x	x	
Harbour porpoise			x	x
Common dolphin			x	x
Bottle-nosed dolphin		x	x	x
All cetaceans		x	x	
Common seal		x	x	x
Grey seal		x	x	x
REPTILE				
Viviparous lizard		x		
AMPHIBIANS				
Smooth newt		x		
Common frog		x	x	
FISH				
Sea lamprey			x	
River lamprey			x	
Brook lamprey			x	
Atlantic salmon			x	
Allis shad			x	
Twaite shad			x	
INVERTEBRATES				
Vertigo angustior			x	
Pearl mussel			x	

Book of Vascular Plants, twenty-five occur in Connemara (see Table 30). Only the rough poppy, which has been recorded at one location in south-west Connemara, is endangered. Most species are classified as rare, but five are considered vulnerable and could move into the endangered category if their circumstances get worse. Several of the rare species are classified as vulnerable in Europe as a whole, which considerably increases the significance of their presence in Connemara. All but the species marked * are protected under the Wildlife Act (at the end of August 1993). Those not protected are widely distributed or may be found in habitats where they are not threatened.

Of the Red Data Book species not discussed in Chapter 2, most occur at a small number of locations, rarely more than one or two. Some, such as small cudweed and Irish lady's-tresses, are found only on the eastern fringe of the region beside upper Lough Corrib.

Animals

Of the twenty-six endangered, vulnerable or rare species of vertebrates in Ireland, ten are known to occur or possibly occur in Connemara (see Table 32). Eighteen of the nineteen internationally important species occur in Connemara (only the brent goose is omitted from the list, but even this is an irregular visitor to Connemara). All but two (puffin and rudd) of the 'species to watch' can also be found in the region. Although the numbers of any one species occurring in Connemara may not be large, the number and range of Red Data Book animals found in the area indicates that it does have conservation significance in a national context.

The decline of the corncrake has been well documented. It started early in the century but the first full census of the species was carried out only in 1978 when it was estimated that there were 1,200-1,500 pairs nationwide. From 1978 to 1992 the population has declined to fewer than 250 pairs, with very few pairs left in Connemara. While conservationists have long been aware of this decline, it was a great shock to discover in 1991 that the native grey partridge had declined to the same low level. The grey partridge seems to have disappeared from its Connemara breeding haunt around Carraroe. This is part of an international trend which has seen the species' numbers decrease by up to 90 per cent over much of its range in the past thirty years.

At the turn of the century, the corn bunting bred commonly in almost every coastal county in Ireland. Since then it has disappeared from all but a few locations. It was present on Inishbofin, Gorumna Island and near Casla in the 1980s, but its current status is not known. The hen harrier is another species under threat nationally. Although it is not thought to breed in Connemara at present, the occasional sighting of birds in appropriate habitat during the breeding season raises hopes that it might.

The present breeding numbers in Connemara of the roseate tern, little tern and dunlin are unknown. As the last comprehensive surveys of these species were carried out in the mid-1980s, there is an urgent need to determine their current status. The breeding golden plover population was surveyed in the 1980s, but rapid changes in its habitat demand that its small population

Table 32
Irish Red Data Book vertebrates found in Connemara.

	MAMMALS	BIRDS	AMPHIBIAN	FISH
ENDANGERED		Corncrake (B)		Allis shad
		Roseate tern (B)		
		Grey partridge (?B)		
		Hen harrier (?B)		
		Corn bunting (?B)		
VULNERABLE		Golden plover (B)		Twaite shad
		Dunlin (B)		Arctic charr
		Little tern (B)		Smelt
RARE		Gadwall (B)		
		Merlin (B)		
INDETERMINATE	Whiskered bat	Tree sparrow (B)		Sea lamprey
	Natterer's bat	Twite (B)		
INTERNATIONALLY IMPORTANT	Hedgehog	Storm petrel (B)	Common frog	Atlantic salmon
	Pipistrelle	Whooper swan (W)		
	Brown long-eared bat	Greenland white-fronted goose (W)		
	Lesser horse-shoe bat *	Barnacle goose (W)		
	Leisler's bat *	Peregrine (R)		
	Daubenton's bat *	Chough (R)		
	Irish hare			
	Pine marten			
	Badger			
	Otter			
SPECIES TO WATCH		Red grouse (R)		Brown/Sea trout
		Curlew (B)		Nine-spined stickleback
		Ringed plover (B)		
		Redshank (B)		
		Common sandpiper (B)		
		Razorbill (B)		
		Cuckoo (B)		
		Kingfisher (R)		
		Dipper (R)		

B = breeding; W = wintering; R = resident;
* = thought to occur in Connemara, but still to be recorded; ? = presence in Connemara uncertain.

should at least be monitored on a regular basis. The gadwall is a rare breeding duck throughout Ireland. It has only once (in 1991) been reported breeding in Connemara. However, with its secretive nesting habits and the large area of habitat available, it may have been missed in the past. The merlin is the subject of a National Parks and Wildlife Service research project elsewhere in the west of Ireland. The results of this work should benefit the Connemara merlin population.

Of the 'indeterminate' species, surveys are currently being carried out on bats. The tree sparrow used to breed in ruined buildings along the Connemara coast but has been scarce or absent in recent years. A return of the species to some of its former breeding haunts elsewhere in the west of Ireland might herald a return to Connemara. But a comprehensive survey of its likely breeding habitats will be required to determine its status. Nationally, the twite has declined since the early 1970s, and presumably this is also the case in Connemara. Although it is present in some coastal areas during winter, there is no information on its breeding status in the region.

Why have these species become endangered or rare? Some of the answers are reflected in the environmental changes we can see in Connemara. The corncrake, for example, has become endangered because agricultural intensification has destroyed its breeding habitat throughout much of Ireland and elsewhere in its European range. Its preferred nesting habitat is in hay meadows. These have been rendered unsuitable and unsafe for nesting by the introduction of mechanised hay cutting and earlier harvesting. Only on the Shannon callows, in the Midlands, has a reasonably healthy population of corncrakes survived. This is primarily because winter flooding of the meadows has prevented early hay cutting. There have been no such natural safeguards in Connemara. It is now almost certain that we will witness the extinction of the corncrake in Connemara before the end of the present century. It is hard to see how its loss can be avoided at this late stage.

The corn bunting and the grey partridge have also suffered from land-use changes and agricultural intensification. The corn bunting, as its name suggests, is a seed eater. So with the almost total shift from tillage to livestock grazing in Connemara, it comes as no surprise that the corn bunting has nearly, if not completely, disappeared from the region. Only the restoration of traditional farming practices in some areas, including the growing of barley, is likely to save the corn bunting from extinction in Connemara.

The grey partridge has never been widespread in the area. For many years there was a small population living in the fields around Carraroe. Surveys in 1991 and 1992 suggest that this population has died out. In other words, the partridge is now extinct in Connemara. The reasons for its disappearance are not clear. Elsewhere in its range, it has suffered from habitat loss and the poisoning of its food by agricultural herbicides and pesticides. It seems unlikely that these factors affected it in Connemara, although habitat deterioration cannot be ruled out.

The problems of the roseate tern lie outside Connemara. They include breeding habitat loss in Europe and exploitation for food and sport in its wintering area in West Africa. Nevertheless, the south Connemara islands constitute one of the most important tern breeding areas in Ireland. All five tern species (assuming that small numbers of roseate terns still use the islands) nest in the region and, for the most part, feed in Connemara's shallow coastal waters. It is worrying, therefore, that we have no up-to-date information on their breeding numbers. Since the national tern survey of 1984 the breeding population of kittiwakes on Inishmore has declined substantially, mainly, it would seem, as a result of food shortages during critical periods of the breeding season. As terns feed on similar fish stocks in the same area, it is reasonable to ask if they have also been affected by food shortages. And, if so, what has caused the food shortages? Did environmental changes in the sea lead to the decline in their food fish? Did these fish move away from the Connemara coast? Have the fish stocks been affected by commercial fishing? Did poor weather during the breeding season limit the birds' ability to catch fish? Unfortunately, we cannot answer these or any other relevant questions about the ecology of the terns, so we have no basis for conservation action, should this prove necessary.

Little terns face further problems. They lay their tiny, well-camouflaged eggs on open, sandy beaches on the mainland and on islands. People using the beaches cause disturbance which can, for example, disrupt the incubation of eggs or feeding of chicks. While the parents are away, the young are exposed to predation or trampling by people or livestock. The small numbers of dunlin (and other more common species like lapwing) nesting on the machair grasslands face similar dangers. It is now evident that these breeding species will need protection in the near future. Recreation, turf removal and overgrazing are likely to be taking their toll of these birds and also a range of wild flowers, including Red Data Book species.

Without information about their ecology, distribution, numbers and behaviour, little specific action can be taken to conserve the uncommon coastal fish of Connemara - sea lamprey, allis shad, twaite shad and smelt. But as Connemara's inshore waters, estuaries, rivers and lakes are generally free from pollution and obstruction, we can be reasonably certain that whatever stocks there are in the region are not in immediate danger. Arctic charr require cool, unpolluted water and most of the lakes in which they occur are free from threats except, possibly, that of fish farming. Although it is reported that arctic charr grow fat on the waste food falling from fish cages in a Scottish lake, it would be unwise to permit fish farming in any of Connemara's arctic charr lakes for fear of any as yet unknown adverse effects it might have on this rare species.

The main threats to Connemara's bats include the destruction or renovation of derelict buildings, the filling in of cracks in bridges and the use of insecticides to treat timber. Before embarking on any of these activities it is desirable to check with the National Parks and Wildlife Service that you will not be harming any bats. A survey of the bats is under way. Additional information from the general public will be welcome and should be sent to the National Parks and Wildlife Service in Galway or passed on to any of the wildlife rangers in Connemara.

Outside the blanket bogs of the Connemara National Park, nothing is known of the present status of breeding golden plovers. It is likely that their breeding habitat is coming under increasing threat of destruction from turf cutting, afforestation, overgrazing and illegal spring and summer burning. The latter is a perennial problem, involving bog burning outside the legal period which extends from 31 August to 15 April. As well as golden plover, the burning can damage other species such as red grouse, meadow pipits, skylarks, Irish hares and a variety of blanket bog plants.

The afforestation of large areas of blanket bog has reduced the feeding area available to Greenland white-fronted geese and pressure on the habitat of this important species is likely to continue unless immediate action can be taken in accordance with the new Agreement made under the 'Bonn Convention'.

Some broader conservation issues

Conservation problems in the uplands and mountains stem from the concentration on and intensification of sheep grazing in recent decades. Although statistics on the numbers of hill sheep in Connemara are not readily available, figures indicate a substantial increase in the national flock in the 1980s, which was presumably mirrored in Connemara. The growth of the sheep population has led to serious overgrazing and hill erosion in many areas. The over-stocking was encouraged by government and European Community subsidies, which favoured the production of large numbers of sheep rather than smaller numbers of better-quality animals.

Overgrazed blanket bog.

Soil washed down from the hills has been deposited in streams and rivers, threatening fish and invertebrate life. Summit peat erosion, probably initiated by overgrazing, has increased. Several rare mountain plants are now restricted mainly to the safety of ledges inaccessible to sheep.

The severe impact of overgrazing on the vegetation becomes evident when sheep are excluded from an area for several months or longer. Plant growth is vigorous and flowers, prevented by the sheep from growing, let alone flowering, reappear and bloom again.

Increased stocking has led to high levels of sheep mortality, reported to be 10 per cent overall, and very much more in some areas. This mortality has increased the carrion available to scavengers like foxes, ravens and hooded crows whose numbers may well have increased in response. Clearly the interests of farmers, sheep and the environment will best be served by a new system which encourages and pays for a considerable reduction in the Connemara sheep flock and a modest increase in cattle numbers. A change in the ratio of sheep to cattle could reduce the bracken problem as well as the overgrazing.

Environmental problems in Connemara have been complicated by the emotive issue of commonage - land held in common by several people. Should commonage be retained or should it be divided among the owners to add to their existing personal holdings? Is commonage good or bad for wildlife? What impact will commonage division have on the landscape? Will it lead to the sale of land for piecemeal afforestation? These are just a few of the environmentally related questions which arise. There are many, often contradictory, answers to these questions. But, whatever the solution, it is bound to have a long-term impact on the Connemara landscape. It is important, therefore, that conservationists be involved in any debate leading to that solution.

Afforestation on Connemara's blanket bogs has been a contentious issue for some time. It has been criticised on aesthetic, ecological and economic grounds. Now, Coillte, the state forestry company, has, for economic reasons, decided to discontinue planting on bogs. But private forestry companies continue to plant extensive bogland areas, paradoxically with support from the State and the European Community. These companies operate in different financial

A tunnel of darkness.

THE DUTCH CONNECTION

While Connemara's bogs are disappearing, Dutch conservation authorities are spending millions of guilders annually restoring and maintaining tiny remnants of bog in the Netherlands. At the same time, members of the Dutch Foundation for Conservation of Irish Bogs, founded in 1983 by Dr Matthijs G.C. Schouten, have been providing practical and financial support for the conservation of some of Ireland's remaining intact raised bogs in the Midlands and some blanket bogs in the west. This international help is very welcome and should inspire Irish conservationists to tackle what often appear to be insurmountable conservation problems.

---

circumstances from Coillte. Thus they may be more willing to plant on poor land (which has conservation value) than Coillte, which must ensure the long-term survival and profitability of its plantations. The planting of Derryvicrone Bog, to the west of Ballynahinch, in the late 1980s was particularly regrettable. This bog is part of a large complex of blanket peatland which was recognised by the state as an internationally important site for rare flora and fauna. Although the National Parks and Wildlife Service objected to grant-aid being given for the development, the Minister for Energy at the time approved the development, of which half was grand-aided.

A point often raised in argument against those who express reservations about large-scale coniferous afforestation on blanket bogs is that new plantations are 'merely replacing the forests which existed in the distant past'. In terms of structures in the landscape this may be true. But in ecological terms it is not the case. Ancient forests were composed of a diversity of tree species, were very open, had a varied age structure and supported many more plants and animals. The ancient forests formed mosaics in the landscape rather than uniform blocks like modern plantations. In short, modern forestry plantations are no compensation for natural forests. Since there is little possibility of ever

recreating the sort of forests which existed in Connemara thousands of years ago, it is important that more be done to improve the ecological, wildlife and aesthetic values of the present conifer plantations. For example, there are many areas within forestry properties unsuitable for planting. These should be allowed to develop naturally. Suitable areas should be stocked with native deciduous trees. A wide range of wildlife management techniques should be employed to enhance the fauna of the plantations; for example, nest boxes should be

Conifers planted on the bank of a stream.

used to attract breeding birds and ponds developed for wildfowl. The argument against such an approach is that it is 'uneconomic'. But this hardly bears scrutiny in the light of rapidly changing economic circumstances and the long time scale over which commercial forestry operates. Society spends a lot on 'improving' other aspects of the environment. The loss of some possible future profits would be a small price to pay for the enrichment of plantations which will cover a large proportion of the Connemara landscape for many decades to come.

The acidification of the lakes and rivers of south Connemara was discussed in Chapter 4. If, as seems to be the case, coniferous plantations contribute to the process in part or all of some catchments, it may be difficult to restore the waters permanently to a satisfactory state. Presumably, only the removal of some trees and the diversion of plantation drainage away from the natural water courses will solve the problem (and reduce siltation, which also damages freshwater life). Solutions to the problem must be worked out co-operatively by the plantation managers, the fishery owners and the scientists who are investigating the problem.

Fishery management and coastal fish farming also come into conflict with wildlife from time to time. This is inevitable because, in many cases, these new enterprises intrude into the habitats of

Clear-felling in a coniferous plantation.

many animals and often compete for resources the animals have previously had all to themselves. Clearly, rather than driving away or killing the 'offending' wildlife, environmentally aware fishery managers or fish farmers should first chose sites which impinge least on important wildlife areas and secondly do all they can to protect their enterprises by means which do not harm wildlife. There is a welcome move towards this approach in Connemara by progressive, forward-thinking fishery managers and fish farmers and it is to be hoped this will become the general approach in the near future. This is not to say that control of certain animals will not be necessary on occasions. It will. But it should be undertaken only with the permission of the National Parks and Wildlife Service as specified under the Wildlife Act. The illegal and often random killing of species such as herons, cormorants, otters and seals, which happened in the past, should no longer be tolerated.

The large-scale cultivation of Atlantic salmon in coastal cages is a contentious issue and too large a subject to be more than touched upon here. Animals such as herons, cormorants, otters and seals may suffer because some fish farmers see them as pests which need to be controlled. Fortunately, this danger is being reduced as more sophisticated systems of protection are installed. There is also serious concern about the relationship between salmon farms, the increase in sea-lice and the decline of the Connemara sea trout stocks. Establishing indisputable links is difficult; yet, circumstantial evidence does suggest a correlation between the presence of salmon cages, a high level of sea-louse infestation in sea trout and the decline in their stocks in nearby rivers. The resolution of this difficult problem will require close co-operation between all the interested parties, rather than the head-on confrontation which has been the hallmark of the relationship up to now. Furthermore, there is concern about the impact of escaped farm salmon on the native salmon and their habitat. Views are divided on the immediate and long-term genetic, behavioural and ecological effects of the mixing of foreign (farmed) and native races. Some scientists believe that the effects will be slight, others are concerned that the native stocks will be harmed. As salmon have already escaped from

FISHERY MANAGEMENT AND ITS MANIPULATION OF THE LANDSCAPE

Fish farming and the manipulation of the landscape for fisheries purposes are not new to Connemara. In his scholarly book *Ponds Passes and Parcs* , Professor Noel Wilkins of University College, Galway, presents detailed accounts of the intensive fishery management activity in Connemara in the nineteenth century. For example, the catchment area of the Doohulla or Emlaghmore Fishery, in south-west Connemara, was substantially modified in the 1850s to improve the fishery. A series of canals was excavated to link the lakes in the system, dams were built to regulate and in some cases reverse the flow of the water, and a new exit channel was cut to the sea. After 140 years many of these 'developments' look quite natural and few people realise that this remote and desolate catchment area is, at least in part, the product of human engineering.

farms in large numbers and entered Connemara rivers, an experiment has been launched, so it is now only a matter of time before the truth of the various hypotheses can be checked in the rivers and lakes of Connemara.

Tourism is an expanding industry in Ireland, and Connemara is a favoured destination for many visitors. The direct impact of tourism on wildlife has not been extensive, but there is growing potential for conflict. The promotion of golfing holidays encourages the development of golf facilities, often on environmentally sensitive areas such as machair and sand-dunes. The encouragement of walking in the hills leads to erosion in heavily used areas and to conflicts with farmers. Some farmers are already reluctant to let people cross their land either because their fences may be broken down and stock allowed to escape or for fear they may be legally liable for any injury the walkers may suffer while crossing the land. At a time when outdoor pursuits are becoming popular, it is ironic, but not unexpected, that Connemara should be 'closing down' in this manner. If the privilege to walk over other people's land is abused by excessive numbers or damage to property, that privilege will be withdrawn. In this context, some conflicts might be avoided if a mechanism could be developed for the transfer to farmers of some of the profits derived by tourism from the use of their land.

It is also ironic that the safeguarding of tourism is put forward by many politicians as the main justification for nature conservation in Ireland. Clearly, this is a dangerous premise on which to base a nation's nature conservation strategy. Several aspects of tourism can be damaging to nature. Conservation as envisaged by many involved in tourism is superficial and self-serving. It fails to address the fundamental issues of nature conservation, issues which need to be tackled soon if the natural heritage of Connemara is to be protected for the benefit of both residents and visitors. A closer working relationship between tourism and conservation bodies could greatly improve the prospects for nature conservation.

With regard to the development of golf courses, there is particular concern, not only about the physical disruption and disturbance to fragile habitats, but also about the use of herbicides and pesticides to maintain greens and fairways. However, the use of dangerous chemicals can be minimised or eliminated by modern management techniques and the employment of the latter should be encouraged. Likewise, wildlife should be attracted to golf courses by the planting of a variety of trees and shrubs and minimal management of the roughs.

Tourism brings more traffic to the region - cars, caravans and touring coaches, many of the latter too large for the Connemara roads. Traffic brings fumes and, above all, noise. To this seasonal traffic we must add the local traffic which, according to Co. Galway vehicle registration statistics, increased by about 25 per cent in the seven years from 1985 to 1991. Add to all this the growing commercial traffic, much of it in the intimidating form of speeding juggernauts, the increase in planes and helicopters flying over Connemara and the cacophony of chain saws and motor mowers and we discover an environment which is becoming noisier, less attractive and more

Top: Draining blanket bog prior to conifer afforestation. Bottom: The 'sausage machine' brings up turf from beneath the surface of the bog.

dangerous for people and wildlife by the year. The peace and quiet of Connemara, its main attraction for many residents and visitors, is being destroyed at an alarming rate. So conservation must include the control of noise. Likewise it should, without jeopardising safety, limit the use of intrusive lights in the region - and in doing so, save energy. The soft lights from a window are warm and welcoming. But blinding porch lights and glaring street lamps are an insult to the night sky - which is as much part of Connemara's heritage as the rocks, water, wind and wildlife which have been the subject of this book.

We should also be aware of the growing need to conserve geological features in Connemara. Locally, many of the glacial features, such as eskers, have been quarried almost out of existence. As the pressure for more building in the region increases, so the demand to exploit these important landscape features and open up more hard rock quarries will increase. It is, therefore, necessary to select at least a representative sample of vulnerable geological sites for permanent protection. If this is not done they will in a very short time disappear - for ever.

A long term perspective

The natural history of Connemara started many millions of years ago, somewhere else on the surface of the earth. Since that distant beginning, our planet has experienced environmental upheavals of inconceivable proportions. Continents have formed, broken apart, drifted across the earth's surface and reunited in new configurations. The evidence is in the rocks of Connemara. Plants and animals have evolved, populated the sea and the land for a while and then disappeared. Some 90-98 per cent of all the organisms which ever lived are now extinct. As recently as 12,000 years ago there was little in Connemara but snow and ice. In a few thousand years (or less) the ice may return. With such a turbulent history and bleak future, why should we want to conserve what we see around us in Connemara today?

HABITATS AND CONSERVATION

It is widely accepted that the conservation of individual species can generally best be achieved by the protection and management of their habitats. This will mean taking an integrated approach to the conservation management of the hills, blanket bogs, woodlands, plantations, lakes, rivers and coastal habitats. Such an approach will require co-operation between state and local agencies and between farmers, foresters, commercial turf cutters, fishery managers, tourism promoters and all those involved in the exploitation and management of the Connemara landscape. The integration of land-use and conservation strategies will hinge on a thorough knowledge of Connemara's landscape and natural resources and, to that end, it will be necessary to record and map these features in detail. Much of the knowledge required to do this exists, but is either not available or not in a form which can be used. For example, although large-scale maps exist for individual state plantations, a single map covering the plantations of the whole region is apparently not available. The same is true for natural habitats such as blanket bogs, machair, seabird islands, semi-natural woodlands and so on. The re-survey of Areas of Scientific Interest will go some way towards rectifying this deficiency. But to produce a thoroughly integrated conservation strategy it will be necessary to record and map all habitats, whether or not they are deemed to be of scientific or heritage interest. This is because, important as Areas of Scientific Interest (Natural Heritage Areas) may be, they do not exist in a vacuum; they interact with and are influenced by the landscape and activities around them. In the long term, it will be as important to conserve the landscape in which the Areas of Scientific Interest are embedded as to conserve the sites themselves.

If we believe nature will take its course in spite of us, we can comfortably sit back and watch life drift by, extract what we want from nature and care nothing for the future. To do nothing could save a lot of money on conservation - which, it can be argued, might not be effective anyway.

But, can we watch without remorse the extinction of the corncrake within a decade? Can we allow Connemara's bogs to disappear forever in a single human generation? Are we prepared to sacrifice more species and more habitats to commercial gain? Can we human beings, in all conscience, continue to be judge, jury and executioner to our fellow travellers in the natural world?

Whether or not the end of our world comes in 1,000, 10,000 or 10 million years, we, our children and their children must continue to live on this planet. It is in the interests of all of us to ensure that the richness and variety of the natural world we inherited is passed on to future generations.

If we let the corncrake die, destroy the bogs, drive away the geese and kill off numerous lesser creatures, not only will we be sacrificing things of great beauty, products of countless years of evolution, we will be destroying the very fabric of our future and that of our descendants. The loss of the corncrake may have little immediate practical significance for any of us, even the ardent conservationists in our ranks - we do not eat corncrakes, or make money out of them. But, in a few years' time, when the corncrake has gone, the significance of its loss will begin to dawn on us. The corncrake will have died out before its time because we killed it - not with our bare hands but with our collective drive to wring as much material wealth out of nature as we possibly can, without putting anything back.

The corncrake is a symbol of all that is wrong with our attitudes to nature. Yet it could be a symbol of hope if its loss brings us to our senses, forces us to listen to nature and let Connemara live.

Postscript

At the time of going to press it seemed likely that no corncrakes bred on the Connemara mainland or islands in 1993 . . .

TEN PROPOSALS FOR THE PROMOTION OF NATURAL HISTORY AND NATURE CONSERVATION IN CONNEMARA

If natural history and nature conservation are to be integrated into the life of Connemara there are many developments and changes which should be pursued. Here are a few suggestions, presented in no particular order of merit.

Field Research, Publishing and Education

1. Improve the knowledge and appreciation of Connemara's natural history by encouraging field research by residents and visitors to the region.
2. Draw up a list of desirable projects for those looking for guidance in their field work. Emphasis should be placed on recording invertebrates and lower plants.
3. Establish a Connemara natural history database.
4. Prepare habitat and wildlife distribution maps.
5. Establish a west of Ireland natural history journal to disseminate local information.
6. Develop and implement natural history programmes for teachers and pupils in primary and secondary schools and for adult groups, including natural resource managers such as farmers.
7. Encourage the establishment of natural history clubs in schools.

Conservation

8. Promote the integration of conservation principles and practices into agriculture, forestry, fisheries, tourism and general development programmes. Prepare an integrated management plan for the whole of Connemara involving all these interests.
9. Promote co-operation between state, local and voluntary bodies with regard to conservation and development programmes.
10. Promote the implementation of national and international conservation laws and create a public awareness of their place in the conservation of Connemara's wildlife.

SPECIES LIST

PLANTS

ENGLISH	LATIN	IRISH
Alder	*Alnus glutinosa*	Fearnóg
Alpine-clubmoss	*Diphasiastrum alpinum*	Garbhógach
Alpine meadow-rue	*Thalictrum alpinum*	Rú léana Alpach
Alpine saw-wort	*Saussurea alpina*	Sábhlus sléibhe
Alternate water-milfoil	*Myriophyllum alterniflorum*	Líonán crom
Annual sea-blite	*Sueda martima*	Blide mhara
Ash	*Fraxinus excelsior*	Fuinseog
Awlwort	*Subularia aquatica*	Briogadán uisce
Barley	*Hordeum vulgare*	Eorna
Bearberry	*Arctostaphylos uva-ursi*	Lus na stalóg
Beech	*Fagus sylvatica*	Feá
Beech fern	*Phegopteris connectilis*	Raithneach feá
Bell heather	*Erica cinerea*	Fraoch cloigíneach
Bilberry	*Vaccinium myrtillus*	Tom fraochán
Birch	*Betula* spp.	Beith
Biting stonecrop	*Sedum acre*	Grafán na gcloch
Black bog-rush	*Schoenus nigricans*	Sifín
Blackthorn	*Prunus spinosus*	Draighean
Bladder campion	*Silene vulgaris*	Coireán cuill
Bladder wrack	*Fucus vesiculosus*	Feamainn bhoilgíneach
Blue moor-grass	*Sesleria albicans*	Féar boirne
	Sesleria caerulea	
Blunt-flowered rush	*Juncus subnodulosus*	Luachair dur
Blusher	*Amanita rubescens*	-
Bog asphodel	*Narthecium ossifragum*	Sciollam na móna
Bogbean	*Menyanthes trifoliata*	Pónaire chorraigh
Bog cotton	*Eriophorum* spp.	Ceannbhán móna
Bog hair-grass	*Deschampsia setacea*	Giobfhéar móna
Bog-myrtle	*Myrica gale*	Raideog
Bog orchid	*Hammarbya paludosa*	Magairlín na móna
Bog pondweed	*Potamogeton polygonifolius*	Duileasc abhann móna
Bracken	*Pteridium aquilinum*	Raithneach mhór
Bramble	*Rubus fruticosus*	Dris
Brittle bladder-fern	*Cystopteris fragilis*	Raithneach bhriosc
Broad buckler-fern	*Dryopteris dilitata*	Raithneach leathan
Broad-leaved cottongrass	*Eriophorum latifolium*	Ceannbhán leathan

Brookweed	*Samolus valerandi*	Falcaire uisce
Broom	*Cytisus scoparius*	Giolcach shléibhe
Buckthorn	*Rhamnus catharticus*	Paide bréan
Bulbous buttercup	*Ranunculus bulbosus*	Tine talún
Butterfly-bush	*Buddleja davidii*	Búidlia chorcra
Canadian waterweed	*Elodea canadensis*	Tím uisce
Carrageen	*Chondrus crispus*	Carraigín
Carrageen	*Mastocarpus stellatus*	Carraigín
Cat's-ear	*Hypochoeris radicata*	Cluas chait
Channel wrack	*Pelvetia canaliculata*	Caisíneach
Chickweed	*Cerastium* sp.	Cluas luchoige choiteann
Clover	*Trifolium* spp.	Seamair
Cock's-foot	*Dactylis glomerata*	Garbhfhéar
Common bent	*Agrostis capillaris*	Beinteach choiteann
Common bird's-foot-trefoil	*Lotus corniculatus*	Crobh éin
Common butterwort	*Pinguicula vulgaris*	Leith uisce
Common centaury	*Centaurium erythraea*	Dréimire Mhuire
Common chickweed	*Stellaria media*	Fliodh
Common cottongrass	*Eriophorum angustifolium*	Ceannbhán caolduilleach
Common couch	*Elymus repens*	Broimfhéar
Common dog-violet	*Viola riviniana*	Sailchuach chon
Common fleabane	*Pulicaria dysenterica*	Lus bui na ndreancaidi
Common marsh-bedstraw	*Galium palustre*	Rú corraigh
Common mouse-ear	*Cerastium fontanum*	Cluas luchóige fhaireogach
Common nettle	*Urtica dioica*	Neantóg
Common polypody	*Polypodium vulgare*	Scim choiteann
Common ragwort	*Senecio jacobea*	Buachalán buí
Common reed	*Phragmites australis*	Giolcach
Common scurvygrass	*Cochlearia officinalis*	Biolar trá
Common spotted-orchid	*Dactylorhiza fuchsii*	Nuacht bhallach choiteann
Common stork's-bill	*Erodium cicutarium*	Gob coirre
Cowberry	*Vaccinium vitis-idaea*	Bódhearc
Creeping bent	*Agrostis stolonifera*	Feorainn
Creeping soft-grass	*Holcus mollis*	Mínfhéar reatha
Creeping willow	*Salix repens*	Saileach shíoda
Cross-leaved heath	*Erica tetralix*	Fraoch naoscaí
Crowberry	*Empetrum nigrum*	Lus na feannóige
Cuckoo flower (Lady's-smock)	*Cardamine pratensis*	Biolar gréagáin
Daisy	*Bellis perennis*	Nóinín
Dandelion	*Taraxacum* sp.	Caisearbhán
Deergrass	*Trichophorum cespitosum*	Cíb cheanngheal
Dense-flowered orchid	*Neotinea intacta*	Magairlín glas
Devil's-bit scabious	*Succisa pratensis*	Odhrach bhallach
Dock	*Rumex* spp.	Copóg

Dorset heath	*Erica ciliaris*	Fraoch frainseach
Downy birch	*Betula pubescens*	Beith chlúmhach
Dulse	*Palmaria palmata*	Duileasc
Dwarf willow	*Salix herbacea*	Camshaileog
Early-purple orchid	*Orchis mascula*	Magairlín meidhreach
Elm	*Ulmus* sp.	Leamhán
Enchanter's nightshade	*Circaea lutetiana*	Fuinseagach
English stonecrop	*Sedum anglicum*	Póiríní seangán
Eyebright	*Euphrasia officinalis*	Glanrosc
Fir clubmoss	*Huperzia selago*	Crúibíní sionnaigh (Aiteann Muire)
Forked spleenwort	*Asplenium septentrionale*	Fionncha ladhrach
Fragrant orchid	*Gymnadaenia conopsea*	Lus togha
Fuchsia	*Fuchsia magellanica*	Fiúise
Giant rhubarb	*Gunnera tinstoria*	Gunnaire
Gipsywort	*Lycopus europaeus*	Feorán corraigh
Glaucous sedge	*Carex flacca*	Cíb liathghorm
Gorse (furze or whin)	*Ulex europaeus*	Aiteann gallda
Great fen-sedge	*Cladium mariscus*	Sábhsheisc
Great sundew	*Drosera anglica*	Drúchtín móna mór
Great wood-rush	*Luzula sylvatica*	Ollghiúnach
Green spleenwort	*Asplenium viride*	Fionncha uaine
Green-winged orchid	*Orchis morio*	Magairlín féitheach
Hair-grass	*Deschampsia* spp.	Giobfhéar
Hairy lady's-mantle	*Alchemilla filicaulis*	Bratóg Mhuire
Hairy rock-cress	*Arabis hirsuta*	-
Hard shield-fern	*Polystichum aculeatum*	Ibheag chrua
Harebell	*Campanula rotundifolia*	Méaracán gorm
Hare's-tail cottongrass	*Eriophorum vaginatum*	Ceannbhán gaelach
Hart's-tongue fern	*Asplenium scolopendrium*	Creamh na muice fia
Hawkweed	*Hieracium* sp.	Lus na seabhac
Hawthorn	*Crataegus monogyna*	Sceach gheal
Hay-scented buckler-fern	*Dryopteris aemula*	Raithneach chumhra
Hazel	*Corylus avellana*	Coll
Heath bedstraw	*Galium saxatile*	Luibh na bhfear gonta
Heath cudweed	*Gnaphalium sylvaticum*	Gnamhlus móna
Heather	*Calluna vulgaris*	Fraoch coiteann
Heath milkwort	*Polygala serpyllifolia*	Na deirfiúiríní
Heath rush	*Juncus squarrosus*	Luachair chaoráin
Hedge mustard	*Sisymbrium officinale*	Lus óir
Herb-Robert	*Geranium robertianum*	Ruithéal rí
Holly	*Ilex aquifolium*	Cuileann
Holly fern	*Polystichum lonchitis*	Ibheag dheilgneach
Honeysuckle	*Lonicera periclymenum*	Táthfhéithleann
Horse-chestnut	*Aesculus hippocastanum*	Crann cnó capaill

Horsetail	*Equisetum* sp.	Eireaball capaill
Hydrilla	*Hydrilla verticillata*	Ilphéistín fáinneach
Intermediate bladderwort	*Utricularia intermedia*	Lus an bhorraigh gaelach
Intermediate lady's-mantle	*Alchemilla xanthochlora*	Dearna Mhuire bhuí
Irish eyebright	*Euphrasia salisburgensis*	Glanrosc gaelach
Irish heath	*Erica erigena*	Fraoch camógach
Irish lady's-tresses	*Spiranthes romanzoffiana*	Cúilín gaelach
Irish saxifrage	*Saxifraga rosacea*	Mórán gaelach
Ivy	*Hedera helix*	Eidhneán
Juniper	*Juniperus communis*	Aiteal
Kidney saxifrage	*Saxifraga hirsuta*	Mórán giobach
Kidney vetch	*Anthyllis vulneraria*	Méara Muire
Knotgrass	*Polygonum avicular*	Glúineach bheag
Lady's bedstraw	*Galium verum*	Rú Mhuire
Leafy liverwort	Class Hepaticae	Aelus duilleach
Lesser bladderwort	*Utricularia minor*	Lus an bhorraigh beag
Lesser clubmoss	*Selaginella selaginoides*	Garbhógach bheag
Lesser twayblade	*Listera cordata*	Dédhuilleog bheag
Lichen		Lícean
Lodgepole pine	*Pinus contorta latifolia*	Péine contórtach
Londonpride	*Saxifraga spathularis x umbrosa (Saxifraga x urbium)*	Mórán cathrach
Lousewort	*Pedicularis sylvatica*	Lus an ghiolla
Mackay's heath	*Erica mackiana*	Fraoch Mhic Aoidh
Maidenhair spleenwort	*Asplenium trichomanes*	Fionncha dúchosach
Many-stalked spike-rush	*Eleocharis multicaulis*	Spícíneach thortógach
Marsh cinquefoil	*Potentilla palustris*	Cnó léana
Marsh clubmoss	*Lycopodiella inundata*	Garbhógach chorraigh
Marsh hawk's-beard	*Crepis paludosa*	Lus corraigh
Marsh pennywort	*Hydrocotyle vulgaris*	Lus na pingine
Marsh St John's-wort	*Hypericum elodes*	Beathnua chorraigh
Marsh willowherb	*Epilobium palustre*	Saileachán corraigh
Mat-grass	*Nardus stricta*	Fiteog
Meadow-grass	*Poa* spp.	Cuise
Meadowsweet	*Filipendula ulmaria*	Airgead luachra
Moonwort	*Botrychium lunaria*	Lus na míosa
Mountain avens	*Dryas octopetala*	Féasóg na lao
Mountain everlasting (Cat's-foot)	*Antennaria dioica*	Catluibh
Mountain fern	*Oreopteris limbosperma*	Raithneach bhuí
Mountain sorrel	*Oxyria digyna*	Samhadh sléibhe
Navelwort	*Umbilicus rupestris*	Cornán caisil
Northern bedstraw	*Galium boreale*	Rú crua
Northern yellow-cress	*Rorippa islandica*	Biolar buí na Boirne
Nuttall's Waterweed	*Elodea nuttallii*	-

Oak	*Quercus* spp.	Dair
Oarweed	*Laminaria digitata*	Coirleach
Oblong-leaved sundew	*Drosera intermedia*	Cailís Mhuire
Opposite-leaved golden saxifrage	*Chrysosplenium oppositifolium*	Glóiris
Oxeye daisy	*Leucanthemum vulgare*	Nóinín mór
Pale butterwort	*Pinguicula lusitanica*	Leith uisce beag
Pale dog-violet	*Viola lactea*	Sailchuach liath
Parsley fern	*Cryptogramma crispa*	Raithneach chas
Peat mosses	*Sphagnum* spp.	Súsán (Fionnmhóin)
Pedunculate oak	*Quercus robur*	Dair choiteann
Pepper dulse	*Laurencia* spp.	Míobhán
Pillwort	*Pilularia globulifera*	Lus an phiollaire
Pipewort	*Eriocaulon aquaticum*	Lus phíopa
Plantain	*Plantago* spp.	Slánlus
Pondweed	*Potamogeton* spp.	Duileasc abhann
Poplar	*Populus* spp.	Poibleog
Prickly saltwort	*Salsola kali*	Lus an tsalainn
Primrose	*Primula vulgaris*	Sabhaircín
Purple-loosestrife	*Lythrum salicaria*	Créachtach
Purple moor-grass	*Molinia caerulea*	Fionnán
Purple saxifrage	*Saxifraga oppositifolia*	Mórán sléibhe
Pyramidal bugle	*Ajuga pyramidalis*	Glasair bheannach
Pyramidal orchid	*Anacamptis pyramidalis*	Magairlín stuaice
Pyrenean saxifrage	*Saxifraga umbrosa*	-
Ragged-robin	*Lychnis flos-cuculi*	Lus síoda
Raspberry	*Rubus idaeus*	Tor sútha craobh
Red fescue	*Festuca rubra*	Feisciú rua
Reedmace	*Typha latifolia*	Coigeal na mban sí
Rhododendron	*Rhododendron ponticum*	Ródaideandrón fiáin
Ribwort plantain	*Plantago lanceolata*	Slánlus
Rock samphire	*Crithmum maritimum*	Craobhraic
Roseroot	*Sedum rosea*	Lus na laoch
Rough poppy	*Papaver hybridum*	Poipín garbh
Round-leaved sundew	*Drosera rotundifolia*	Drúchtín móna
Rowan	*Sorbus aucuparia*	Caorthann
Royal fern	*Osmunda regalis*	Raithneach ríúil
St Dabeoc's heath	*Daboecia cantabrica*	Fraoch na haon choise
St Patrick's cabbage	*Saxifraga spathularis*	Cabáiste an mhadra rua
Sandhill pansy	*Viola tricolor curtisii*	Goirmín duimhche
Sand sedge	*Carex arenaria*	Cíb fhéithglas
Sanicle	*Sanicula europaea*	Bodán coille
Scots pine	*Pinus sylvestris*	Péine Albanach
Sea campion	*Silene maritima*	Coireán cuille mhara
Sea-holly	*Eryngium maritimum*	Cuileann trá

Sea-milkwort	*Glaux maritima*	Lus bainne mara
Sea plantain	*Plantago maritima*	Slánlus mara
Sea sandwort	*Honkenya peploides*	Lus an ghainimh
Sedge	*Carex* spp.	Cíb
Selfheal	*Prunella vulgaris*	Duáinín an tseanchais
Serrated wrack	*Fucus serratus*	Míoránach
Sessile oak	*Quercus petraea*	Dair neamhghasánach
Sheep's-bit	*Jasione montana*	Duán na gcaorach
Sheep's-fescue	*Festuca ovina*	Feisciú caorach
Sitka spruce	*Picea sitchensis*	Sprús Sitceach
Slender cottongrass	*Eriophorum gracile*	Ceannbhán caol
Slender naiad	*Najas flexilis*	Náiad chaol
Slender sedge	*Carex lasiocarpa*	Cíb chaol
Small cudweed	*Filago minima*	Cáithluibh bheag
Small-white orchid	*Pseudorchis albida*	Magairlín bán
Smooth lady's-mantle	*Alchemilla glabra*	Bratóg Mhuire
Soft rush	*Juncus effusus*	Luachair bhog
Sorrel	*Rumex* spp.	Samhadh
Speedwell	*Veronica* spp.	Lus cré
Sphagnum	*Sphagnum* spp.	Sfagnam
Spiral wrack	*Fucus spiralis*	Casfheamainn
Spotted rock-rose	*Tuberaria guttata*	Grianrós breac
Spreading meadow-grass	*Poa subcaerulea*	Cuise
Starry saxifrage	*Saxifraga stellaris*	Mórán réaltach
Stiff sedge	*Carex bigelowii*	Cíb shléibhe
Stonewort	*Chara* spp.	-
Sycamore	*Acer pseudoplatanus*	Seiceamar
Thrift	*Armeria maritima*	Rabhán
Toothed or serrated wrack	*Fucus serratus*	Míoránach
Tormentil	*Potentilla erecta*	Néalfartach
Tufted vetch	*Vicia cracca*	Peasair na luch
Tufted hair-grass	*Deschampsia cespitosa*	Giobfhéar dosach
Tunbridge filmy-fern	*Hymenophyllum tunbrigense*	Dallán coille
Velvet bent	*Agrostis canina*	Beinteach dhonn
Water avens	*Geum rivale*	Machall uisce
Water lobelia	*Lobelia dortmanna*	Plúr an locháin
Water mint	*Mentha aquatica*	Mismín dearg
Wavy hair-grass	*Deschampsia flexuosa*	Giobfhéar
Welsh poppy	*Meconopsis cambrica*	Poipín caimbriach
Western gorse	*Ulex gallii*	Aiteann gaelach
Wheat	*Triticum aestivum*	Cruithneacht
White beak-sedge	*Rhynchospora alba*	Gobsheisc
White clover	*Trifolium repens*	Seamair bhán
White water-lily	*Nymphaea alba*	Duilleog bháite bhán

Wild angelica	*Angelica sylvestris*	Gallfhearbhrán
Wild thyme	*Thymus praecox*	Tím chreige
Willow	*Salix* spp.	Saileach
Wilson's filmy-fern	*Hymenophyllum wilsonii*	Dallán sléibhe
Wood avens	*Geum urbanum*	Macall coille
Woodruff	*Galium odoratum*	Lus molach
Wood small-reed	*Calamagrostis epigejos*	Giolc
Wood-sorrel	*Oxalis acetosella*	Seamsóg
Woolly hair-moss	*Racomitrium lanuginosum*	Glibchaonach
Wych elm	*Ulmus glabra*	Leamhán sléibhe
Yarrow	*Achillea millefolium*	Athair thalún
Yellow iris	*Iris pseudacorus*	Feileastram
Yellow-rattle	*Rhinanthus minor*	Gliográn
Yellow water-lily	*Nuphar lutea*	Duilleog bháite bhuí
Yellow-wort	*Blackstonia perfoliata*	Dréimire buí
Yew	*Taxus baccata*	Iúr

ANIMALS

As this book was being completed a new list of English bird names was adopted by the journal *British Birds* (Volume 86, January 1993). As Irish and British ornithologists will use these names in future they have been presented in this list in parentheses. To avoid confusion only the earlier names have been used in the text.

ENGLISH	LATIN	IRISH
Acorn barnacle	*Chthamalus* spp.	-
	Semibalanus balanoides	-
Allis shad	*Alosa alosa*	Sead alósach
Arctic charr	*Salvelinus alpinus*	Ruabhreac
Arctic skua	*Stercorarius parasiticus*	Meirleach Artach
Arctic tern	*Sterna paradisea*	Geabhróg Artach
Atlantic salmon	*Salmo salar*	Bradán
Atlantic white-sided dolphin	*Lagenorhynchus acutus*	-
Auger or screw shell	*Turitella communis*	Cuach coirn
Avocet	*Recurvirostra avosetta*	Abhóiséad
Badger	*Meles meles*	Broc
Barn owl	*Tyto alba*	Scréachóg reilige
Barnacle	*Chthamalus stellatus*	Garbhán carraige
Barnacle goose	*Branta leucopsis*	Gé ghiúrainn
Bar-tailed godwit	*Limosa lapponica*	Guilbneach stríocearrach
Beadlet anemone	*Actinia equina*	Bundún leice
Beautiful demoiselle	*Calopteryx virgo*	-
Belted beauty	*Lycia zonaria brittanica*	-
Bewick's swan (Tundra swan)	*Cygnus columbianus*	Eala Bhewick

Blackbird	*Turdus merula*	Lon dubh
Black darter	*Sympetrum danae*	-
Black guillemot	*Cepphus grylle*	Foracha dhubh
Black-headed gull	*Larus ridibundus*	Faoileán ceanndubh
Black-throated diver	*Gavia arctica*	- (Lóma)
Black-winged stilt	*Himantopus himantopus*	-
Blue-tailed damselfly	*Ischnura elegans*	-
Blue tit	*Parus caeruleus*	Meantán gorm
Blyborough tick	*Argas vespertilionis*	-
Bottle-nosed dolphin	*Tursiops truncatus*	-
Breadcrumb sponge	*Halichondria panicea*	- (Spúinse)
Brent goose	*Branta bernicla hrota*	Cadhan
Brimstone	*Gonepteryx rhamni*	Buíóg ruibheach
Brook lamprey	*Lampetra planeri*	Loimpre shrutháin
Brown hairstreak	*Thecla betulae*	Stiallach donn
Brown hawker	*Aeshna grandis*	-
Brown long-eared bat	*Plecotus auritus*	Ialtóg chluasach
Brown trout	*Salmo trutta*	Breac donn
Bullfinch	*Pyrrhula pyrrhula*	Corcrán coille
Bumblebee	*Bombus spp.*	Bumbóg
Butterfish	*Pholis gunnellus*	Sleamhnóg
Buzzard (Common buzzard)	*Buteo buteo*	Clamhán
Capercaillie	*Tetrao urogallus*	Capall coille
Carpet shell	*Tapes decussatus*	-
Chaffinch	*Fringilla coelebs*	Rí rua
Chinaman's hat	*Calyptraea chinensis*	-
Chough	*Pyrrhocorax pyrrhocorax*	Cág cosdearg
Clouded yellow	*Colias croceus*	Buíóg chróch
Common blue butterfly	*Polyommatus icarus*	Gormán coiteann
Common blue damselfly	*Enallagma cyathigerum*	-
Common cockroach	*Blatta orientalis*	Ciaróg dhubh
Common darter	*Sympetrum striolatum*	-
Common dolphin	*Delphinus delphis*	Deilf
Common earwig	*Forficula auricularia*	Gailseach
Common frog	*Rana temporaria*	Frog
Common green grasshopper	*Omocestus viridulus*	Dreoilín teaspaigh
Common groundhopper	*Tetrix undulata*	-
Common gull	*Larus canus*	Faoileán bán
Common hawker	*Aeshna juncea*	-
Common hermit crab	*Pagurus bernhardus*	Faocha ghliomaigh
Common limpet	*Patella vulgata*	Bairneach
Common lobster	*Homarus gammarus*	*Gliomach*
Common mussel	*Mytilus edulis*	Diúilicín
Common prawn	*Palaemon serratus*	Cloicheán

Common rat	*Rattus norvegicus*	Francach donn
Common saddle oyster	*Anomia ephippium*	-
Common sandpiper	*Actitis hypoleucos*	Gobadán
Common seal	*Phoca vitulina*	Rón beag
Common shrimp	*Crangon crangon*	Séacla
Common starfish	*Asterias rubens*	Crosóg mhara
Common tern	*Sterna hirundo*	Geabhróg
Conger eel	*Conger conger*	Eascann choncair
Coot (Common coot)	*Fulica atra*	Cearc cheannann
Corkwing wrasse	*Crenilabrus melops*	Bochar
Cormorant (Great cormorant)	*Phalacrocorax carbo*	Broigheall
Corn bunting	*Miliaria calandra*	Gealóg bhuachair
Corncrake (Corn crake)	*Crex crex*	Traonach
Cory's shearwater	*Calonectris diomedea*	-
Cowrie	*Trivia* s p	.Fínicín
Crane (Common crane)	*Grus grus*	
Crested tit	*Parus cristatus*	Meantán cuircíneach
Crossbill (Common crossbill)	*Loxia curvirostra*	Crosghob
Cuckoo	*Cuculus canorus*	Cuach
Cuckoo bee	*Psithyrus spp.*	-
Curlew (Eurasian curlew)	*Numenius arquata*	Crotach
Cuvier's beaked whale	*Ziphius cavirostris*	Míol mór Chuvier
Dark green fritillary	*Argynnis aglaja*	Fritileán dúglas
Daubenton's bat	*Myotis daubentoni*	Ialtóg Dhaubenton
Death's head hawk-moth	*Acherontia atropos*	Conach na cealtrach
Dingy skipper	*Erynnis tages*	Donnán
Dog-whelk	*Nucella lapillus*	Cuachma chon
Domestic cat	*Felis catus*	Cat
Dotterel	*Charadrius morinellus*	Amadán móinteach
Downy emerald	*Cordulia aenea*	-
Duck mussel	*Anodonta anatina*	-
Dunlin	*Calidris alpina*	Breacóg
Dunnock (Hedge accentor)	*Prunella modularis*	Donnóg
Edible periwinkle	*Littorina littorea*	Faocha
Eider	*Somateria mollissima*	Aghdar
Emerald damselfly	*Lestes sponsa*	-
European eel	*Anguilla anguilla*	Eascann
Feral goat	*Capra hircus*	Gabhar fia
Fieldfare	*Turdus pilaris*	Sacán
Flat periwinkle	*Littorina obtusata*	Faocha leathan
Flat or purple top-shell	*Gibbula umbilicalis*	Faocha Mhuire
Flounder	*Platichthys flesus*	Leith
Four-spotted chaser	*Libellula quadrimaculata*	-
Fox	*Vulpes vulpes*	ionnach (Madra rua)

Freshwater shrimp	*Gammarus* spp.	Dreancaid uisce
Fulmar	*Fulmarus glacialis*	ulmaire
Gannet (Northern gannet)	*Sula bassana*	Gainéad
Garganey	*Anas querquedula*	-
Gatekeeper	*Pyronia tithonus*	Geatóir
German cockroach	*Blatella germanica*	-
Giant Irish deer	*Megaloceros giganteus*	Fia mór na mbeann
Glaucous gull	*Larus hyperboreus*	Faoileán glas
Goldcrest	*Regulus regulus*	Cíorbhuí
Golden eagle	*Aquila chrysaetos*	Iolar fíréan
Goldeneye	*Bucephala clangula*	Orshúileach
Golden oriole	*Oriolus oriolus*	Oiréal órga
Golden plover	*Pluvialis apricaria*	Feadóg bhuí
(European golden plover)		
Goldfinch	*Carduelis carduelis*	Lasair choille
Goose barnacle	*Lepas anatifera*	Giúrann
Goshawk	*Accipiter gentilis*	-
Grasshopper warbler	*Locustella naevia*	Ceolaire casarnaí
Grayling	*Hipparchia semele*	-
Great auk	Alca (Pinguinus) impennis	*Falcóg mhór*
Great black-backed gull	*Larus marinus*	Droimneach mór
Great northern diver	*Gavia immer*	Lóma mór
Great scallop	*Pecten maximus*	Muirín
Great shearwater	*Puffinus gravis*	Cánóg mhór
Great tit	*Parus major*	Meantán mór
Greenfinch	*Carduelis chloris*	Glasán darach
Green hairstreak	*Callophrys rubi*	Stiallach uaine
Greenland white-fronted goose	*Anser albifrons flavirostris*	Gé bhánéadanach
Greenshank	*Tringa nebularia*	Ladhrán glas
(Common greenshank)		
Green-veined white	*Pieris napi*	Bánóg uaine
Greylag goose	*Anser anser*	Gé ghlas
Grey phalarope	*Phalaropus fulicarius*	Falaróp gobmhór
Grey plover	*Pluvialis squatarola*	Feadóg ghlas
Grey partridge	*Perdix perdix*	Patraisc
Grey seal	*Halichoerus grypus*	Rón glas
Grey wagtail	*Motacilla cinerea*	Glasóg liath
Guillemot (Common guillemot)	*Uria aalge*	Foracha
Gyr falcon	*Falco rusticolus*	-
Harbour porpoise	*Phocoena phocoena*	Muc mhara
Hedgehog	*Erinaceus europaeus*	Gráinneog
Hen harrier	*Circus cyaneus*	Cromán na gcearc
Heron (Grey heron)	*Ardea cinerea*	Corr réisc
Herring	*Clupea harengus*	Scadán

Herring gull	*Larus argentatus*	Faoileán scadán
Highland darter	*Sympetrum nigriscens*	-
Holly blue	*Celastrina argiolus*	Gormán cuilinn
Hooded crow	*Corvus corone cornix*	Feannóg
Hoopoe	*Upupa epops*	Húpú
House martin	*Delichon urbica*	Gabhlán binne
House mouse	*Mus musculus*	Luch thí
Iceland gull	*Larus glaucoides*	-
Irish dipper	*Cinclus cinclus hibernicus*	Gabha dubh
Irish hare	*Lepus timidus hibernicus*	Giorria
Irish stoat	*Mustela erminea hibernica*	Easóg
Jackdaw	*Corvus monedula*	Cág
Jack sail-by-the-wind	*Velella velella*	-
Jay (Eurasian jay)	*Garrulus glandarius*	Scréachóg choille
Keeled skimmer	*Orthetrum coerulescens*	-
Kestrel (Common kestrel)	*Falco tinnunculus*	Pocaire gaoithe
Kingfisher (Common kingfisher)	*Alcedo atthis*	Cruidín
Kittiwake	*Rissa tridactyla*	Saidhbhéar
Lapwing (Northern lapwing)	*Vanellus vanellus*	Pilibín
Large heath	*Coenonympha tullia*	Fraochán mór
Large marsh grasshopper	*Stethophyma grossum*	-
Large red damselfly	*Pyrrhosoma nymphula*	-
Large white	*Pieris brassicae*	Bánóg mhór
Leisler's bat	*Nyctalus leisleri*	Ialtóg Leisler
Lesser black-backed gull	*Larus fuscus*	Droimneach beag
Lesser horseshoe bat	*Rhinolophus hipposideros*	Crú-ialtóg bheag
Linnet	*Carduelis cannabina*	Gleoiseach
Little auk	*Alle alle*	-
Little egret	*Egretta garzetta*	-
Little grebe	*Tachybaptus ruficollis*	Spágaire tonn
Little tern	*Sterna albifrons*	Geabhróg bheag
Long-eared owl	*Asio otus*	Ceann cait
Long-finned pilot whale	*Globicephala melas*	Píolótach
Lugworm	*Arenicola marina*	Lugach
Lynx	*Lynx lynx*	Lincse
Mackerel	*Scomber scombrus*	Ronnach
Magpie	*Pica pica*	Snag breac
Mallard	*Anas platyrhynchos*	Mallard
Manx shearwater	*Puffinus puffinus*	Cánóg dhubh
Marsh fritillary	*Eurodryas aurinia*	Fritileán réisc
Marsh harrier	*Circus aeruginosus*	Cromán móna
Meadow brown	*Maniola jurtina*	Donnóg fhéir
Meadow pipit	*Anthus pratensis*	Riabhóg mhóna
Merlin	*Falco columbarius*	Meirliún

Mink	*Mustela vison*	Minc Mheiriceánach
Minke whale	*Balaenoptera acutorostrata*	Droimeiteach beag
Minnow	*Phoxinus phoxinus*	Bodairlín
Mottled grasshopper	*Myrmeleotettix maculatus*	Dreoilín teaspaigh breac
Mute swan	*Cygnus olor*	Eala bhalbh
Natterer's bat	*Myotis nattererila*	ltóg Natterer
Natterjack toad	*Bufo calamita*	Cnádán
Netted dog-whelk	*Hinia reticulata*	-
Nightjar	*Caprimulgus europaeus*	Tuirne lín
Nine-spined stickleback	*Pungitius pungitius*	Garmachán deich gclipe
Northern eggar	*Lasiocampa quercus callunae*	Ubhóg thuaisceartach
Norway cockle	*Laevicardium crassum*	-
Oak eggar	*Lasiocampa quercus quercus*	-
Oleander hawk-moth	*Daphnis nerii*	-
Orange tip	*Anthocaris cardamines*	Barr buí
Otter	*Lutra lutra*	Dobharchú (Madra uisce)
Oyster	*Ostrea edulis*	Oisre
Oystercatcher	*Haematopus ostralegus*	Roilleach
Pacific oyster	*Crassostrea gigas*	Oisre and Aigéin Chiúin
Painted lady	*Cynthia cardui*	Ailleán
Peacock butterfly	*Inachis io*	Péacóg
Pearl-bordered fritillary	*Botoria euphrosyne*	Fritileán péarlach
Pearl mussel	*Margaritifera margaritifera*	-
Perch	*Perca fluviatilis*	Péirse
Peregrine (Peregrine falcon)	*Falco peregrinus*	Fabhcún gorm
Pied wagtail	*Motacilla alba*	Glasóg shráide
Pike	*Esox lucius*	Liús
Pill millipede	*Glomeris marginata*	Mílechosach ceirtlíneach
Pine marten	*Martes martes*	Cat crainn
Pipistrelle	*Pipistrellus pipistrellus*	Ialtóg fheascrach
Pochard (Common pochard)	*Aythya ferina*	Póiseard
Puffin	*Fratercula arctica*	Puifín
Purple hairstreak	*Quercusia quercus*	Stiallach corcra
Purple sandpiper	*Calidris maritima*	Gobadán cosbhuí
Pygmy shrew	*Sorex minutus*	Dallóg fhraoigh
Pygmy sperm whale	*Physeter breviceps*	Caisealóid bheag
Rabbit	*Oryctolagus cuniculus*	Coinín
Raft spider	*Dolomedes fimbriatus*	-
Raven (Common raven)	*Corvus corax*	Fiach dubh
Rayed artemis	*Dosinia exoleta*	-
Razorbill	*Alca torda*	Crosán
Razor-shell	*Ensis* sp.	Scian mhara
Red admiral	*Vanessa atlanta*	Aimiréal dearg
Red-breasted merganser	*Mergus serrator*	Síolta rua

Red deer	*Cervus elaphus*	Fia rua
Red-footed falcon	*Falco vespertinus*	Fabhcún cosdearg
Red grouse	*Lagopus lagopus*	Cearc fhraoigh
Redpoll (Common redpoll)	*Carduelis flammea*	Deargéadan coiteann
Redshank (Common redshank)	*Tringa totanus*	Cosdeargán (Ladhrán trá)
Red kite	*Milvus milvus*	-
Red squirrel	*Sciurus vulgaris*	Iora rua
Red-throated diver	*Gavia stellata*	Lóma rua
Redwing	*Turdus iliacus*	Deargán sneachta
Reed bunting	*Emberiza schoeniclus*	Gealóg ghiolcaí
Ringed plover	*Charadrius hiaticula*	Feadóg chladaigh
Ringlet	*Aphantopus hyperantus*	Fáinneog
Ring ouzel	*Turdus torquatus*	Lon creige
Risso's dolphin	*Grampus griseus*	Deilf Risso
River lamprey	*Lampetra fluviatilis*	Loimpre abhann
Roach	*Rutilus rutilus*	Róiste
Robin	*Erithacus rubecula*	Spideog
Rock dove	*Columba livia*	Colm aille
Rock pipit	*Anthus petrosus*	Riabhóg chladaigh
Rook	*Corvus frugilegus*	Rúcach
Roseate tern	*Sterna dougallii*	Geabhróg rósach
Ross's gull	*Rhodostethia rosea*	Faoileán Ross
Rough periwinkle	*Littorina saxatilis*	Faocha gharbh
Rudd	*Scardinius erythrophthalmus*	Ruán
Ruff	*Philomachus pugnax*	Rufachán
Rush moth	*Coleophora caespititiella*	-
Sabine's gull	*Larus sabini*	Faoileán Shabine
Sand eel	*Ammodytes* spp.	Corr ghainimh
Sanderling	*Calidris alba*	Luathrán
Sand-hopper	*Orchestia* spp.	Dreancaid trá
Sand martin	*Riparia riparia*	Gabhlán gainimh
Sandwich tern	*Sterna sandvicensis*	Geabhróg dhuscothach
Scaup (Greater scaup)	*Aythya marila*	Lacha iascán
Sea lamprey	*Petromyzon marinus*	Loimpre mhara
Sea slater	*Ligia oceanica*	Cláirseach thrá
Sea stickleback	*Spinachia spinachia*	Garmachán farraige
Sea trout	*Salmo trutta*	Breac geal
Sea urchin	*Paracentrotus lividus*	Cuán mara
Shag	*Phalacrocorax aristotelis*	Seaga
Shanny	*Lipophrys pholis*	Ceannruán
Sheep tick	*Ixodes ricinus*	Sceartán caorach
Shore crab	*Carcinus maenas*	Portán glas
Silver-washed fritillary	*Argynnis paphia*	Fritileán geal
Siskin	*Carduelis spinus*	Siscín

Six-spot burnet	*Zygaena filipendulae*	Buirnéad sébhallach
Skylark (Sky lark)	*Alauda arvensis*	Fuiseog
Small blue	*Cupido minimus*	Gormán beag
Small copper	*Lycaena phlaeas*	Copróg bheag
Small heath	*Coenonympha pamphilus*	Fraochán beag
Small periwinkle	*Melarbhe neritoides*	Faocha bheag
Small tortoiseshell	*Aglais urticae*	Ruán beag
Small white	*Pieris rapae*	Bánóg bheag
Smooth newt	*Triturus vulgaris*	Earc sléibhe
Snipe (Common snipe)	*Gallinago gallinago*	Naoscach
Snow bunting	*Plectrophenax nivalis*	Gealóg shneachta
Song thrush	*Turdus philomelos*	Smólach
Sooty shearwater	*Puffinus griseus*	-
Sparrowhawk	*Accipiter nisus*	Spioróg
Speckled wood	*Parage aegeria*	Breacfhéileacán coille
Sperm whale	*Physeter macrocephalus*	Caisealóid
Spoonbill	*Platalea leucorodia*	Leitheadach
Spotted crake	*Porzana porzana*	-
Sprat	*Sprattus sprattus*	Salán
Star ascidian	*Botryllus schlosseri*	Ascaid réaltach
Starling (Common starling)	*Sturnus vulgaris*	Druid
Stonechat (Common stonechat)	*Saxicola torquata*	Caislín cloch
Stone loach	*Noemacheilus barbatulus*	Cailleach rua
Storm petrel (European storm-petrel)	*Hydrobates pelagicus*	Guairdeall
Striped dolphin	*Stenella coeruleoalba*	Deilf stríocach
Striped venus	*Chamelea gallina*	Maighdeog stríocach
Swallow (Barn swallow)	*Hirundo rustica*	Fáinleog
Swan mussel	*Anodonta cygnea*	-
Swift	*Apus apus*	Gabhlán gaoithe
Teal	*Anas crecca*	Praslacha
Thick top-shell	*Monodonta lineata*	Faocha chapaill
Three-spined stickleback	*Gasterosteus aculeatus*	Garmachán
Tree sparrow	*Passer montanus*	Gealbhan crainn
Trough shell	*Spisula* sp.	-
Tufted duck	*Aythya fuligula*	Lacha bhadánach
Turnstone	*Arenaria interpres*	Piardálaí trá
Twaite shad	*Alosa fallax*	Sead fhallacsach
Twite	*Carduelis flavirostris*	Gleoiseach sléibhe
Two-spot goby	*Gobiusculus flavescens*	Mac siobháin buí
Variable damselfly	*Coenagrion pulchellum*	-
Variegated scallop	*Chlamys varia*	Cluaisín
Viviparous lizard	*Lacerta vivipara*	Earc luachra
Wall brown	*Lasiommata megera*	Donnóg an bhalla

Warty venus	*Venus verrucosa*	Maighdeog fhaithneach
Water pipit	*Anthus spinoletta*	Riabhóg uisce
Water rail	*Rallus aquaticus*	Rálóg uisce
Wentletrap	*Epitonium clathrus*	Faocha bhiorach
Wheatear (Northern wheatear)	*Oenanthe oenanthe*	Clochrán
Whimbrel	*Numenius phaeopus*	Crotach eanaigh
Whinchat	*Saxicola rubetra*	Caislín aitinn
Whiskered bat	*Myotis mystacinus*	Ialtóg ghiobach
White-beaked dolphin	*Lagenorhynchus albirostris*	-
White-tailed sea eagle (White-tailed eagle)	*Haliaeetus albicilla*	Iolar mara
Whiting	*Merlangius merlangus*	Faoitín
Whooper swan	*Cygnus cygnus*	Eala ghlórach
Wigeon	*Anas penelope*	Lacha rua
Wild boar	*Sus scrofa*	Torc
Willow warbler	*Phylloscopus trochilus*	Ceolaire sailí
Wolf	*Canis lupus*	Mac tíre
Woodcock	*Scolopax rusticola*	Creabhar
Wood mouse	*Apodemus sylvaticus*	Luch fhéir
Woodpigeon (Wood pigeon)	*Columba palumbus*	Colm coille
Wood white	*Leptodea sinapsis*	Bánóg choille
Wrasse	*Labrus* spp.	Ballach
Wren	*Troglodytes troglodytes*	Dreoilín
Yellow-browed warbler	*Phylloscopus inornatus*	-
Yellowhammer	*Emberiza citrinella*	Buíóg
Yellow horned moth	*Achlya flavicornis*	-
Yellow wagtail	*Motacilla flava*	Glasóg bhuí

APPENDIX II

CONSERVATION LEGISLATION

THE WILDLIFE ACT

The Wildlife Act, currently (August 1993) under review, is administered by the National Parks and Wildlife Service and enforced by Wildlife and Park Rangers. Its main provisions include the protection of wild birds, their nests and eggs, some mammals (including dolphins, porpoises and whales), reptiles and amphibians but currently not fish. It also protects specified rare plants. The Wildlife Act specifies the animals which can be hunted and regulates the hunting seasons. It specifies the animals which, if proved to be causing a nuisance, can be controlled under licence and also the manner in which that control can be carried out. For Connemara this is a significant element in the Act because of demands to control protected species, such as seals and various fish-eating birds at fish farms, and badgers where bovine tuberculosis in cattle is a serious problem.

The Wildlife Act provides for the establishment of state and private Nature Reserves for the protection of plants and animals, Refuges for Fauna for the protection of animal species and their natural habitats, and Wildfowl Sanctuaries within which shooting is prohibited.

INTERNATIONAL LEGISLATION

The European Community has adopted a number of directives and conventions relevant to nature conservation in Connemara. All have been signed and ratified by Ireland.

Directive on the Conservation of Wildbirds, the 'Birds Directive'

One of the requirements of this directive is that member states designate Special Protection Areas (SPAs) for birds. Ireland has designated a small number of SPAs but has been slow to comply fully with the Directive in this respect. Further designations of SPAs are currently being considered and it is likely that several significant wildlife areas in Connemara will be designated. Among these are the islands off the south and west coast which are important for breeding terns and other seabirds.

Convention on the Conservation of European Wildlife and Natural Habitats, the 'Berne Convention'

This convention obliges Ireland to protect and conserve a wide range of plants, animals and their habitats, especially those listed as endangered or vulnerable. In response to this convention Ireland has established eleven Biogenetic Reserves, none of which is in Connemara. The Convention also obliges Ireland 'to promote national policies for the conservation of wild flora, wild fauna and natural habitats'. This it has not done. Ireland has no policies for nature conservation, a fact reflecting the low priority it has been given by successive Governments. However, in 1993 the new Minister for Arts, Culture and the Gaeltacht became responsible for the formulation of policy for Ireland's natural and architectural heritage. This is a positive step in the right direction and the practical benefits of this development are awaited with interest by conservationists.

Convention on the Protection of Natural and Semi-Natural Habitats and of Wild Flora and Fauna, the 'Habitats Directive'

This convention aims to 'conserve natural and semi-natural habitats and wild flora and fauna in the European territory of the Member States to which the treaty applies, including maritime areas under the sovereignty or jurisdiction of the Member States'. Adopted in 1992, it brings hope that some of Ireland's important habitats, such as Connemara's remaining intact blanket bogs, can be conserved.

Convention on the Conservation of Migratory Species of Wild Animals, the 'Bonn Convention'

This is a worldwide convention which provides for the conservation of migratory wild animals by giving strict protection to a number of endangered species listed in its Appendix I. Importantly, it provides a framework for a series of Agreements between countries for the conservation and management of species listed in its Appendix II. One such Agreement, on the conservation management of the Greenland white-fronted goose population, has been reached between Ireland, Britain, Iceland and Greenland. This is important for Connemara, as a small proportion of this population winters in the region. In the long term, it is to be hoped that similar Agreements can be reached for other migratory species such as terns, for which Connemara is an important breeding area.

LIST OF RELEVANT ORGANISATIONS

	Telephone	Fax
An Bord Pleanala (Planning Appeals Board), Floor 3, Blocks 6 & 7, Irish Life Centre, Lower Abbey Street, Dublin 1.	(01) 8728011	(01) 8722684
An Taisce (The National Trust), Tailors Hall, Back Lane, Dublin 8.	(01) 541786	(01) 533255
Bord Fáilte Éireann (Irish Tourist Board), Baggot Street Bridge, Dublin 2.	(01) 6765871	(01) 6764764
Regional Office, Aras Failte, Victoria Place, Galway.	(091) 63081	(091) 65201
Bord Iascaigh Mhara (Irish Sea Fisheries Board), Crofton Road, Dun Laoire, Co. Dublin.	(01) 2841544	(01) 2841123
Regional Office, New Docks, Galway.	(091) 63897	
Bord na Mona (Irish Peat Board), Lower Baggot Street, Dublin 2.	(01) 6688555	(01) 6601800
Central Fisheries Board, Head Office, Balnagowan Mobhi Boreen, Dublin 9.	(01) 379206	(01) 360060
Coillte Teoranta (Irish Forestry Board), Spruce House, Leeson Lane, Dublin 2.	(01) 6615666	(01) 6789527
Regional Office, Ross House, Merchants Road, Galway.	(091) 62129	(091) 67840
Conamara Environmental Education Centre, Letterfrack N.S., Letterfrack, Co. Galway.	(095) 43443	
Connacht Organic Group, c/o New Village, Oughterard, Co. Galway.	(091) 82230	
Connemara Field Studies Centre, Cloon, Cleggan, Co. Galway.	(095) 44771	(095) 44790
Connemara National Park, Letterfrack, Co. Galway.	(095) 41054	(095) 41005
Corrib Conservation Centre, Ardnasillagh, Oughterard, Co. Galway.	(091) 82519	(091) 82519
Crann Woodland Trust, Aughavas, via Cavan, Co. Leitrim.	(078) 36020	(078) 36020
Department of Agriculture and Food, Kildare Street, Dublin 2.	(01) 6789011	(01) 6616263
Regional Office, Land Commission, Custom House, Galway.	(091) 62085	
Regional Office, Farm Development and District Veterinary Office, Hynes Buildings, St Augustine Street, Galway.	(091) 63919	(091) 66148
Department of Education, Marlborough Street, Dublin 1.	(01) 8734700	(01) 8729553
Department of the Environment, Custom House, Dublin 1.	(01) 6793377	(01) 6789527
Department of the Marine, Leeson Lane, Dublin 2.	(01) 6785444	(01) 6618214
Regional Office, Ross House, Merchants Road, Galway.	(091) 67530	(091) 68316
Department of Tourism and Transport, Kildare Street, Dublin 2.	(01) 6789522	(01) 6763350
ENFO - the Environmental Information Service, 17 St Andrew Street, Dublin 2	(01) 6793144	(01) 6795204
Environmental Research Unit, St Martin's House, Waterloo Road, Dublin 4.	(01) 6602511	(01) 6504929
Farming and Conservation Liaison Group, c/o David Hickie, An Taisce, Tailors Hall, Back Lane, Dublin 8.	(01) 541786	(01) 533255
Folding Landscapes, Nimmo House, Roundstone, Co. Galway.	(095) 35886	

Foróige (National Youth Development Organisation), Irish Farm Centre, Bluebell, Dublin 12.	(01) 501022	(01) 501166
Regional Office, Ozanam House, St Augustine Street, Galway.	(091) 61002	(091) 66643
Galway County Council, County Buildings, Prospect Hill, Galway.	(091) 63151	(091) 65817
Galway Regional Technical College, Dublin Road, Galway.	(091) 53161	(091) 51107
Geographical Society of Ireland, c/o Department of Geography, University College, Galway.	(091) 24411	(091) 25051
Geological Survey of Ireland, Beggars Bush, Haddington Road, Dublin 4.	(01) 6609511	(01) 6681782
Iar-Chonemara Teo. (Connemara West Ltd.), Tully, Renvyle, Co. Galway.	(095) 41047	(095) 41112
Irish Biogeographical Society, c/o National Museum of Ireland, Natural History Division, Kildare Street, Dublin 2.	(01) 6618811	(01) 6766116
Irish Countrywomens Association, 58 Merrion Road, Dublin 4.	(01) 6680453	(01) 6609423
Irish Farmers Association, Irish Farm Centre, Bluebell, Dublin 12.	(01) 501166	(01) 551043
Regional Office, Athenry, Co. Galway.	(091) 44268	(091) 44902
Irish Organic Farmers and Growers Association, 56 Blessington Street, Dublin 7.	(01) 307996	
Irish Peatland Conservation Council, Capel Chambers, 119 Capel Street, Dublin 1.	(01) 8722397	
Irish Wildbird Conservancy, Ruttledge House, 8 Longford Place, Monkstown, Co. Dublin.	(01) 2804322	(01) 2844407
Regional contact, Neil Sharkey, 1 Glenard Crescent, Galway.	(091) 21554	
Irish Wildlife Federation, 132A East Wall Road, Dublin 3.	(01) 366821	(01) 366821
Regional contact, Martin Byrnes, Oranmore, Co. Galway.	(091) 94435	
Macra na Feirme, Irish Farm Centre, Bluebell, Dublin 12.	(01) 501166	(01) 514908
National Botanic Gardens, Glasnevin, Dublin 9.	(01) 374388	(01) 360080
National Heritage Council, Department of An Taoiseach, Government Buildings, Upper Merrion Street, Dublin 2.	(01) 6763546	(01) 6789037
National Museum of Ireland, Kildare Street, Dublin 2.	(01) 6618811	(01) 6766116
National Parks and Wildlife Service, Office of Public Works, 51 St Stephen's Green, Dublin 2.	(01) 6613111	(01) 6610747
Regional Office, 16 Eyre Square, Galway.	(091) 63016	(091) 61809
Office of Public Works, 51 St Stephen's Green, Dublin 2.	(01) 6613111	(01) 6610747
Organic Trust, Charlotte Colchester Islands, Urlingford, Co. Kilkenny.	(056) 31411	
Royal Dublin Society, Merrion Road, Ballsbridge, Dublin 4.	(01) 6680645	(01) 6604014
Royal Irish Academy, 19 Dawson Street, Dublin 2.	(01) 6764222	(01) 6762346
Salmon Research Agency of Ireland Inc., Farran Laboratory, Newport, Co. Mayo.	(098) 41107	(098) 41107
Teagasc (Agriculture and Food Development Authority), 19 Sandymount Avenue, Ballsbridge, Dublin 4.	(01) 6688188	(01) 6688023
Regional Office, Athenry, Co. Galway.	(091) 44473	(091) 44296
Tree Council of Ireland, 33 Botanic Road, Glasnevin, Dublin 9.	(01) 306996	(01) 306948
University College, Galway.	(091) 24411	(091) 25051
Western Regional Fisheries Board, Weir House, Earl's Island, Galway.	(091) 63118	(091) 66335

BIBLIOGRApI1Y

All the documents listed in the Bibliography contain reference to natural history in Connemara, however minor that reference may be. The documents include books, magazines, scientific papers, published and unpublished reports and unpublished university theses. The Bibliography is extensive, but not exhaustive. Undoubtedly, many references from foreign journals are missing. Therefore, I intend to continue expanding it and, to that end, would welcome relevant references, old and new, particularly from foreign journals. These can be sent to me at: Corrib Conservation Centre, Ardnasillagh, Oughterard, Co. Galway, Ireland.

GENERAL

Allott, N.A. *et al.* 1990. *Acidification of surface waters in Connemara and south Mayo. Current status and Causes.* duQuesne, Dublin.

Anon. 1981. *Areas of Scientific Interest in Ireland.* An Foras Forbartha, Dublin.

Beltman, B., Rouwenhorst, G., Whilde, A. and ten Cate, M. 1993. Chemical composition of rain water in western Ireland. *Ir. Nat. J.* **24** (7): 267-273.

Bowman, J.J. 1986. *Precipitation characteristics and the chemistry and biology of poorly buffered Irish lakes; a western European baseline for 'acid rain' impact assessment.* An Foras Forbartha, Dublin.

Bowman, J. 1991. *Acid sensitive surface waters in Ireland. The impact of a major new sulphur emission on sensitive surface waters in an unacidified region.* Environmental Research Unit, Department of the Environment, Dublin.

Corcoran, K. 1993. *West of Ireland Walks.* The O'Brien Press, Dublin.

Crawford, E.M. (Ed.) 1989. *Famine: the Irish experience 900-1900.* John Donald, Edinburgh.

Crawford, R.M.M. 1984. *Studies in survival.* Blackwell, Oxford.

De Bhaldraithe, P. 1990. *Saothrú an uisce. Feirmeoireacht éisc, sliogéisc agus algaí.* An Clóchomhar Tta, Baile Atha Cliath.

Department of Education. 1978. *Ainmneacha plandaí agus ainmhithe. Flora and fauna nomenclature.* Department of Education, Dublin.

Field, E.M. and Goode, D.A. 1981. *Peatland ecology in the British Isles: a bibliography.* Institute of Terrestrial Ecology and Nature Conservancy Council, Banbury.

Fish, J.D. and Fish, S. 1989. *A Student's guide to the seashore.* Unwin Hyman,London.

Fitzpatrick, T. and Whilde, T. 1992. *Insider's guide to Connemara, Galway and the Burren.* Gill and Macmillan, Dublin.

Flanagan, P.J. and Toner, P.F. 1975. *A preliminary survey of Irish lakes.* An Foras Forbartha, Dublin.

Flower, R. (Ed.) 1992. *Palaeoecological evaluation of the acidification status of lakes in the north-west and west of Ireland.* Environmental Change Research Centre, London.

Gahan, S. 1986. *The National Park concept : A case study of Connemara.* Unpublished B.A. thesis. Trinity College Dublin.

Gaskell, T.F. 1972. *The Gulf Stream.* Cassell, London.

Gorham, E. 1957. The chemical composition of some Irish freshwaters. *Proc. R. Ir. Acad.* **58B**: 237-243.

Hickie, D. 1990. *Forestry in Ireland. Policy and practice.* An Taisce, Dublin.

Keane, T. (Ed.) 1986. *Climate, weather and Irish agriculture.* Agricultural Trust, Dublin.

Keegan, B.F. and Mercer, J.P. 1986. An oceanographical survey of Killary Harbour on the west coast of Ireland. *Proc. R. Ir. Acad.* **86B** (1): 1-70.

Kruuk, H. 1989. *The social badger.* Oxford University Press, Oxford.

Lamb, H.H. 1982. *Climate, history and the modern world.* Methuen, London.

Lennox, L.J. and Toner, P.F. 1980. *The national survey of Irish rivers, a third report on water quality.* An Foras Forbartha, Dublin.

Lynam, J. (Ed.) 1982. *Irish peaks.* Constable, London.

Lynam, J. and Robinson, T. 1988. *The mountains of Connemara.* Map and hill-walkers guide. Folding Landscapes, Roundstone.

McLachlan, A.J., Pearce, L.J. and Smith, J.A. 1979. Feeding interactions and cycling of peat in a bog lake. *J. Anim. Ecol.* **48**: 851-861.

McMahon, T.G. and Patching, J.W. 1984. Fluxes of organic carbon in a fjord on the west coast of Ireland. *Est. Coastal and Shelf Sci.* **19**: 205-215.

McWilliams, B.E. (Ed.) 1991. *Climate change. Studies on the implications for Ireland.* Stationery Office, Dublin.

Meldon, J. 1992. *Structural funds and the environment. Problems and prospects.* An Taisce, Dublin.

Mitchell, G.F. 1976. *The Irish landscape.* Collins, London.

Mitchell, G.F. 1986. *The Shell guide to reading the Irish landscape.* Country House, Dublin.

Mitchell, G.F. et al. 1987. *The book of the Irish countryside.* Town House, Dublin.

Mitchell, F. 1990. *The way that I followed. A naturalist's journey around Ireland.* Country House, Dublin.

Morton, H.V. 1938. *In search of Ireland.* Methuen, London.

Mould, D.D.C.P. 1955. *The mountains of Ireland.* Batsford, London.

Ní Scannláin, E. 1989. *Landscape change in the Connemara National Park area since the early nineteenth century.* Unpublished report to the Office of Public Works, Dublin.

O'Brien, D.P. 1989. *Salmonid farming in Ireland: environmental and legislative problems assessed.* Earthwatch Special Report 4. Earthwatch, Bantry.

O'Flaherty, R. 1846. *A chorographical description of west of H-Iar Connaught.* Irish Archaeological Society, Dublin.

Oliver, P. and Colleran, E. (Eds.) 1990. *Interactions between aquaculture and the environment.* An Taisce, Dublin.

Poucher, W.A. 1953. *Journey into Ireland.* Country Life, London.

Praeger, R.Ll. 1895. Report of the Conference and Excursion held at Galway, July 11th to 17th, 1895. *Ir. Nat.* **4** (9): 225-273.

Praeger, R.Ll. 1937. *The way that I went.* Allen Figgis, Dublin. (Reprinted by Allen Figgis & Co. Ltd, Dublin, 1980)

Praeger, R.Ll. 1950. *Natural history of Ireland.* Collins, London. (Reprinted by EP Publishing Ltd, Yorkshire, 1972)

Preece, R.C., Coxon, P. and Robinson, J.E. 1986. New biostratigraphic evidence of the post-glacial colonization of Ireland and for Mesolithic forest disturbance. *J. Biogeog.* **13**: 487-509.

Quigley, M.B. (Ed.) 1991. *A guide to the sand dunes of Ireland.* European Union for Dune Conservation and Coastal Management, Dublin.

Robinson, T. 1984. *Setting foot on the shores of Connemara*. Lilliput Pamphlets, Gigginstown.

Robinson, T. 1985. *Mapping South Connemara*. Folding Landscapes, Roundstone.

Robinson, T. 1990. *Connemara*. Map and Gazetteer. Folding Landscapes, Roundstone.

Rohan, P.K. 1986. *The climate of Ireland*. Meteorological Service, Dublin.

Stone, H.J. 1906. *Connemara and the neighbouring spots of beauty and interest*. Health Resort Publishing Company, Ltd, London.

Thompson, W. 1859-61. *The natural history of Ireland*. Four volumes. London.

Twomey, E. 1953. Fertilization of some acid or bog lakes in Ireland. *Dept. Lands Ann. Rep.* App. 27: 90-103. Department of Lands, Dublin.

Whilde, A. 1975. *A preliminary assessment of the non-agricultural biological resources of the Maam Valley*. Unpublished report to An Foras Taluntais.

Whilde, A. 1978. *Irish walk guide - West*. Gill and Macmillan, Dublin.

Whilde, A. 1982. Flora and fauna of Irish mountain ranges and guide to walks in the west of Ireland. *In* Lynam, J. (Ed.) *Irish peaks*. Constable, London.

Whilde, T. 1987. An annotated bibliography of natural history for Counties Clare, Galway and Mayo. *Ir. Nat. J.* **22**: 261.

Whilde, T. 1988. *Connemara ecotour*. Corrib Conservation Centre, Oughterard.

Whilde, A. 1992. *Irish vertebrate red data book*. Unpublished report to Department of the Environment, Northern Ireland, Belfast.

Whilde, T. and Simms, P. 1991. *New Irish walk guides - West and North*. Gill and Macmillan, Dublin.

GEOLOGY

Archer, J.B. 1977. Llanvirn stratigraphy of the Galway-Mayo border area, western Ireland. *Geol. J.* **12**(1): 77-98.

Archer, J.B. 1975. *Ordovician trough margin sedimentary rocks in western Ireland*. Unpublished Ph.D. thesis, National University of Ireland, University College, Galway.

Archer, J.B. and Herries Davies, G.L. 1983. Geological field-sheets from County Galway by Patrick Ganly (1809-1899). *J. Earth Sci. R. Dubl. Soc.* **4**: 167-179.

Archer, J.B. and Ryan, P.D. (Eds.) 1983. *A geological guide to the Caledonides of western Ireland*. Geological Survey of Ireland, Dublin.

Archer, J.B. and Skevington, D. 1973. The morphology and systematics of '*Didymograptus*' *spinosus* Ruedemann 1904, and allied species from the Lower Ordovician. *Geol. Mag.* **110**: 43-54.

Aucott, J.W. 1965. Layering in the Galway Granite. *Nature* **207**: 929-930.

Aucott, J.W. 1970. Tectonics of the Galway Granite. *In* Newall, G. and Rast, N. (Eds.) Mechanisms of igneous intrusion; *Geol. J. Spec. Issue* **2**: 49-66.

Badley, M.E. 1972. *The geology of the Maumturk and Inagh Valley, Connemara*. Unpublished Ph.D. thesis, University of Nottingham.

Badley, M.E.1976.Stratigraphy, structure and metamorphism of Dalradian rocks of the Maumturk Mountains, Connemara, Ireland.*J. Geol. Soc. Lond.* **132**: 509-520.

Barber, J.P. and Yardley, W.D. 1985. Conditions of high grade metamorphism in the Dalradian of Connemara, Ireland.*J. Geol. Soc. Lond.* **142**: 87-96.

Bradshaw, R., Plant, A.G., Burke, K.C., Leake B.E. 1969. The Oughterard Granite, Connemara, Co. Galway. *Proc. R. Ir. Acad.* **68B** (3): 39-65.

Burke, K. 1957. An outline of the structure of the Galway Granite. *Geol. Mag.* **94**: 452-464.

Burke, K. 1963. Age relations of Connemara migmatites and Galway Granite. *Geol. Mag.* **100**: 470-471.

Callaway, C.1887. On the Alleged Conversion of Crystalline Schists into Igneous Rocks in County Galway. *Quart. Journ. Geol. Soc.* **XLIII**: 517-524.

Carey, M. 1990. *The geology of Moycullen, Co. Galway*. Unpublished B.Sc. thesis, National University of Ireland, University College, Dublin.

Carruthers, R.G. and Maufe, H.B. 1907. The lower palaeozoic rocks around Killary Harbour. *Ir. Nat.* **18** (1): 7-14.

Charlesworth, J.K. 1929. The glacial retreat in Iar Connacht. *Proc. R. Ir. Acad.* **39B** (11): 95-106.

Charlesworth, J.K. 1950. Recent progress in Irish geology. *Ir. Nat. J.* **10** (3): 61-71.

Charlesworth, J.K. 1953. *The geology of Ireland: an introduction*. Oliver and Boyd, London. (Revised 1966)

Charlesworth, J.K. 1959. Recent progress in Irish geology. *Ir. Nat. J.* **13** (3): 49-65.

Charlesworth, J.K. 1963a. *The historical geology of Ireland*. Oliver and Boyd, London.

Charlesworth, J.K. 1963b. The bathymetry and origin of the larger lakes of Ireland. *Proc. R. Ir. Acad.* **63B**: 61-69.

Claxton, C.W. 1968. Mineral layering in the Galway Granite, Connemara, Eire. *Geol. Mag.* **105**: 149-159.

Claxton, C.W. 1968. The petrology of the Galway Granite in the Screebe - Invermore - Rosmuc area, Connemara, Eire. *T. Instn. Min. Metall.* **77B**: 174.

Claxton, C.W. 1969. Minor intrusives in the west Galway Granite Batholith. *Ir. Nat. J.* **16** (8): 219-226.

Claxton, C.W. 1970. Some observations on the assimilation of basic xenoliths by acid magma in the Galway Granite, Co. Galway, Eire. *Sci. Proc. R. Dubl. Soc.* **3A**: 247-255.

Claxton, C.W. 1971. The petrology, chemistry and structure of the Galway Granite in the Rosmuc area, Co. Galway. *Proc. R. Ir. Acad.* **71B**: 155-169.

Coats, J.S. and Wilson, J.R. 1971. The eastern end of the Galway Granite. *Mineralog. Mag.* **38**: 138-151.

Cobbing, J.C. 1959. *The metamorphic petrology and structures of the district NW of Clifden, Co. Galway*. Unpublished Ph.D. thesis, University of Durham.

Cobbing, E.J. 1961. A note on some olivine - dolerite dykes in Connemara. *Ir. Nat. J.* **13** (11): 249-253.

Cobbing, E.J. 1964. Folding in current bedding from the Connemara schists. *Ir. Nat. J.* **14** (12): 305-309.

Cobbing, E.J. 1969. The geology of the district north-west of Clifden, Co. Galway. *Proc. R. Ir. Acad.* **67B** (14): 303-325.

Cole, G.A. J. and Croke, T. 1910. On rock specimens dredged from the floor of the Atlantic off the coast of Ireland and their bearing on submarine geology. *Memoir Geol. Surv. Irel.*

Cruse, M.J.B. and Leake, B.E. 1968. The geology of Renvyle, Inishbofin and Inishshark, north-west Connemara, Co. Galway. *Proc. R. Ir. Acad.* **67B** (1): 1-36.

Derham, J.M. 1986. Structural control of sulphide mineralization at Mace Head, Co. Galway. *In* Andrew, C.J., Crowe, R.W.A., Finlay, S., Pennell, W.M. and Pyne, J.F. (Eds.) *Geology and genesis of mineral deposits in Ireland* : 187-194. Irish Association for Economic Geology.

Derham, J.M. and Feely, M. 1988. A K-feldspar breccia from the Mo-Cu stockwork deposit in the Galway Granite, west of Ireland. *J. Geol. Soc. Lond.* **145**: 661-667.

Dewey, J.F. 1961. A note concerning the age of the metamorphism of the Dalradian rocks of western Ireland. *Geol. Mag.* **97**: 399-405.

Dewey, J.F., McKerrow, W.S. and Moorbath, S. 1970. The relationship between isotopic ages, uplift and sedimentation during Ordovician times in western Ireland. *Scott. J. Geol.* **6**: 133-145.

Dewey, J.F. and McKerrow, W.S. 1963. An outline of the Geomorphology of Murrisk and North West Galway. *Geol. Mag.* **100**: 260-275.

Dewey, J.F., Rickards, R.B. and Skevington, D. 1970. New light on the age of Dalradian deformation and metamorphism in western Ireland. *Norsk. Geol. Tidsskr.* **50**: 19-44.

Dillon, J. 1905. *Journ. Galway Arch. and Hist. Soc.* Vol **IV**.

Doyle, E.N. 1989. *The biostratigraphy and sedimentology of the Lower Silurian (Llandovery) rocks of North Galway*. Unpublished Ph.D. thesis, National University of Ireland, University College, Galway.

Doyle, E.N., Harper, D.A.T. and Parkes, M.A. 1990. The Tonalee fauna: a deep-water shelly assemblage from the Llandovery rocks of the west of Ireland. *Ir. J. Earth Sci.* **10**: 127-143.

Edmunds, W.M. and Thomas, P.R. 1966. The stratigraphy and structure of the Dalradian rocks north of Recess, Connemara, Co. Galway. *Proc. R. Ir. Acad.* **64B** (27): 517-528.

Edwards, K.J. and Warren, W.P. (Eds.) 1985. *The Quarternary history of Ireland.* Academic Press, London.

Emeleus, C.H. and Preston, J. 1969. *Field excursion guide to the Tertiary volcanic rocks of Ireland.* Belfast.

Evans, B.W. 1959. *The geology of the Toombeola district, Connemara, Éire.* Unpublished Ph.D. thesis, University of Oxford.

Evans, B.W. 1964. Fractionation of elements in the pelitic hornfelses of the Cashel-Lough Wheelaun intrusions, Connemara, Éire. *Geochim. Cosmochim Acta* **28**: 127-156.

Evans, B.W. and Leake, B.E. 1960. The composition and origin of the striped amphibolites of Connemara, Ireland. *J. Petrol.* **1**: 337-363.

Evans, B.W. and Leake, B.E. 1970. The Geology of the Toombeola District, Connemara, Co. Galway. *Proc. R. Ir. Acad.* **70B** (5): 105-139.

Fabby, D. 1990. Caves in Connemara - an update. *Spel. Union Ir. Newsletter* **18**: 8-9.

Fairhead, J.D. and Walker, P. 1977. The geological interpretation of gravity and magnetic surveys over the exposed southern margin of the Galway Granite, Ireland. *Geol. J.* **12**: 17-24.

Farrington, A. 1964. Raised beaches in Galway Bay. *Ir. Nat. J.* **14** (9): 216-217.

Farrington, A. 1967. Early references to Granite erratics. *Ir. Nat. J.* **15** (11): 330.

Farrington, A. and Stephens, N. 1964. The Pleistocene geomorphology of Ireland. *In* Steers, J.A. (ed.) *Field studies in the British Isles* : 445-461. Nelson, London.

Feely, M. 1982. *Geological, geochemical and geophysical studies on the Galway Granite in the Costelloe/Inveran sector, western Ireland.* Unpublished Ph.D. thesis, National University of Ireland, University College, Galway.

Feely, M. 1988. Thermometric analysis of fluid inclusions in the Galway Granite, western Ireland - a preliminary study. *Ir. Ass. Econ. Geol. Ann. Rev.*: 97-100.

Feely, M. and Harney, S. 1988. A visit to Clements mine in South Connemara. *Ir. Geol. Week Field Guide* **3**.

Feely, M. and Högelsberger, H. 1991. Preliminary fluid inclusion studies of the Mace Head Mo-Cu deposit in the Galway Granite. *Ir. J. Earth Sci.* **11**: 1-10.

Feely, M. and Madden, J.S. 1986. A quantitative regional gamma-ray survey on the Galway Granite, western Ireland. *In* Andrew, C.J. et al. (Eds.) *The geology and genesis of mineral deposits in Ireland* : 195-200. Irish Association for Economic Geology.

Feely, M. and Madden, J.S. 1987. The spatial distribution of K, U, Th and surface heat production in the Galway Granite, Connemara, Ireland. *Ir. J. Earth Sci.* **8**: 155-164.

Feely, M. and Madden. J.S. 1988. Trace element variation in the leucogranites within the main Galway Granite, Connemara, Ireland. *Min. Mag.* **52**: 139-146.

Feely, M., McCabe, E. and Kunzendorf, H. 1991. The evolution of REE profiles in the Galway Granite, western Ireland. *Ir. J. Earth Sci.* **11**: 71-89.

Feely, M., McCabe, E. and Williams, C.T. 1989. U, Th and REE bearing accessory minerals in a high heat production (HHP) leucogranite within the Galway Granite, western Ireland. *Trans. Inst. Mining and Metallurgy, Appl. Earth Sci.* **98B**: 27-32.

Ffrench, G.D. 1982. *The palaeoenvironmental analysis of the South Connemara Group, Western Ireland - a possible Ordovician trench-fill sequence.* Unpublished M.Sc.thesis, National University of Ireland, University College, Galway.

Ffrench, G.D. and Williams, D.M. 1984. The sedimentology of the South Connemara Group, western Ireland - a possible Ordovician trench-fill sequence. *Geol. Mag.* **121**: 505-514.

Gallagher, V., Feely, M., Högelsberger, H., Jenkin, G.R.T. and Fallick, A.E. 1992. Geological, fluid inclusion and stable isotope studies of Mo mineralization, Galway Granite, Ireland. *Min. Dep.* **27** (4): 1-12.

Gardiner, C.I. 1910. The igneous and associated sedimentary rocks of the Glensaul district, Co. Galway. *Quart. J. Geol. Soc. Lond.* **65**: 253-270.

Gardiner, C.I. 1912. The Ordovician and Silurian rocks of the Kilbride Peninsula (Mayo). *Quart. J. Geol. Soc. Lond.* **68**: 75-102.

Gardiner, C.I. and Reynolds, S.H. 1914. The Ordovician and Silurian rocks of the Lough Nafooey area (County Galway). *Quart. J. Geol. Soc. Lond.* **70**: 104-118.

Guilcher, A. and King, C.A.M. 1960. Preliminary observations on the beaches of the west coast of Ireland. *Int. Geogr. Congr. Norden, Abstracts Papers* : 109-110.

Guilcher, A., King, A.M. and Berthois, R.1961. Spits, tombolos and tidal marshes in Connemara and west Kerry, Ireland. *Proc. R. Ir. Acad.* **61B** (17): 283-338.

Harper, D.A.T. 1988. Corrib Country Fossils. *Corrib wildlife series* **6**. Corrib Conservation Centre, Oughterard.

Harper, D.A.T. and Parkes, M.A. 1989. Palaeontological constraints on the definition and development of Irish Caledonide terranes. *Quart. J. Geol. Soc. Lond.* **146**: 413-415.

Harper, J.C. 1948. The Ordovician and Silurian rocks of Ireland. *Proc. Geol. Soc. Liverpool* **20** (1): 48-67.

Herries Davies, G.L. and Stephens, N. 1978. *The geomorphology of the British Isles: Ireland.* Methuen, London.

Högelsberger, H. and Feely, M. 1991. Fluid inclusion studies on Mo-Cu-mineralizations in the Galway Granite (Ireland). *In* Pagel and Leroy (Eds.) *Source, Transport and Deposition of Metals* : 181-184. Balkema, Rotterdam.

Holland, C.H. 1981. *A geology of Ireland*. Scottish Academic Press, Edinburgh.

Ingold, L.M. 1937. The geology of the Currywongaun-Doughruagh area, Co. Galway. *Proc. R. Ir. Acad.* **43B** (10): 135-159.

Keary, R. 1965. A note on the beach sands of the Cois Fharraige coast. *Ir. Nat. J.* **15** (2): 40-43.

Keary, R. 1965. An oyster shell deposit near Galway. *Ir. Nat. J.* **15** (4): 110-111.

Keary, R. and Dunne, J. 1973. A new shell deposit near Galway. *Ir. Nat. J.* **17** (12): 422.

Kennan, P.S., Feely, M. and Mohr, P. 1987. The age of the Oughterard Granite, Connemara, Ireland. *Geol. J.* **22**: 273-280.

Kennan, P.S., Feely, M. and Mohr, P. 1989. Reply on the age of the Oughterard Granite, Connemara, Ireland. *Geol. J.* **24**: 223-225.

Kilroe, J. 1907. The Silurian and metamorphic rocks of Mayo and North Galway. *Proc. R. Ir. Acad.* **26B**: 129-160.

Kinahan, G.H. 1869. Explanation to accompany sheet 105 with that portion of sheet 114 that lies on the north of Galway Bay. *Memoir Geol. Surv. Irel.* : 1-63.

Kinahan, G.H. 1874. Geology of West Galway and S. W. Mayo, Ireland. *Geol. Mag. New Series*, Decade II, Vol **I**: 453-462.

Kinahan, G.H. 1878. *Manual of the geology of Ireland*. C. K. Paul & Co., London.

Kinahan, G.H. 1882. Palaeozoic rocks of Galway and elsewhere in Ireland, said to be Laurentians. *Sci. Proc. R. Dubl. Soc.*, Vol.**III**: 348.

Kinahan, G.H. 1892a. Quartzites and quartz rocks. *Ir. Nat.* **1** (8): 162-166.

Kinahan, G.H. 1892b. Quartzites and quartz rocks. *Ir. Nat.* **1** (9): 184-188.

Kinahan, G.H. 1892c. Supposed tertiary basalts, N. W. Donegal. *Ir. Nat.* **1** (9): 196.

Kinahan, G.H. 1894. The recent Irish glaciers. *Ir. Nat.* **3** (11): 236-240.

Kinahan, G.H. and Close, M.H. 1872. *The general glaciation of Iar-Connaught and its neighbourhood in the Counties Galway and Mayo*. Eight Volumes. Hodges, Foster & Co., Dublin.

Kinahan, G.H., Fymes, R.H., Wilkinson, S.B., Nolan, J. and Leonard, H. 1876. Explanatory memoir to accompany Sheets 73 and 74 (in part), 83 and 84 of the maps of the Geological Survey of Ireland, 33. *Memoir Geol. Surv. Irel.*

Kinahan, G.H., Leonard, H. and Cruise, R.J. 1871. Explanatory memoirs to accompany sheets 104, 113 with the adjoining portions of sheets 103 and 112 of the maps of the Geological Survey of Ireland. *Memoir Geol.Surv. Irel.*

Kinahan, G.H., Nolan, J. and Leonard, H. 1878. Geological structure of the district around Clifden, Connemara. *Expl. Memoir Geol. Surv. Irel.* **39**.

Kirwan, R.E. 1895. Geological notes from W. Galway. *Ir. Nat.* **4** (6): 151.

Laird, M.G. 1968. Rotational slumps and slump scars in Silurian rocks, western Ireland. *Sedimentology* **10**: 111-120.

Laird, M.G. 1969. *Sedimentation studies in the Silurian rocks of North West Galway, Éire*. Unpublished Ph.D. thesis, University of Oxford.

Laird, M.G. and McKerrow, W.S. 1970. The Wenlock sediments of northeast Galway, Ireland. *Geol. Mag.* **107**: 297-317.

Lawrence, G. 1968. *The geochemistry of the Galway Granite of Lettermullen, Co. Galway, Eire*. Unpublished Ph.D. thesis, University of Bristol.

Lawrence, G. 1975. The use of Rb/Sr ratios as a guide to mineralisation in the Galway Granite, Ireland. *In* Elliot, I.L. and Fletcher, W.K. (Eds.) *Geochemical Exploration* : 353-370. Elsevier.

Leake, B.E. 1958. The Cashel - Lough Wheelaun Intrusion, Co. Galway. *Proc. R. Ir. Acad.* **59B** (9): 155-203.

Leake, B.E. 1958. Composition of Pelites from Connemara. *Geol. Mag.* **95**: 281-296.

Leake, B.E. 1963. A possible fossil in a graphitic marble in the Connemara Schist, Connemara, Co. Galway. *Geol. Mag.* **100**: 44-66.

Leake, B.E. 1967. Zoned garnets from the Galway Granite and its aplites. *Earth and Planetary Sci. Lett.* **3**: 311-316.

Leake, B.E. 1970a. The fragmentation of the Connemara basic and ultrabasic intrusions. *In* Newall, G. and Rast, N. (Eds.). Mechanisms of Igneous Intrusion; *Geol. J. Spec. Issue* **2**: 103-122.

Leake, B.E. 1970b. The origin of the Connemara Migmatites of the Cashel district, Connemara, Ireland. *Quart. J. Geol. Soc. Lond.* **125**: 219-276.

Leake, B.E. 1972. Garnetiferous striped amphibolites from Connemara, Western Ireland. *Min. Mag.* **38**: 646-665.

Leake, B.E. 1974. The crystallisation history and mechanism of emplacement of the western part of the Galway Granite, Connemara, western Ireland. *Min. Mag.* **39**: 498-513.

Leake, B.E. 1986. The Geology of SW Connemara, Ireland: a fold and thrust Dalradian and metagabbroic-gneiss complex. *Quart. J. Geol. Soc. Lond.* **143**.

Leake, B.E. 1989. The metagabbros, orthogneisses and paragneisses in the Connemara complex, western Ireland. *Quart. J. Geol. Soc. Lond.* **146**: 575-596.

Leake, B.E. and Evans, B.W. 1960. The composition and origin of the striped amphibolites of Connemara. *J. Petr.* **1**: 337-361.

Leake, B.E. and Leggo, P.J. 1963. On the age relations of the Connemara migmatites and the Galway Granite, west of Ireland. *Geol. Mag.* **100**: 193-204.

Leake, B.E., MacIntyre, R.M. and Elias, E. 1984. Tectonic position of the Dalradian rocks of Connemara and its bearing on the evolution of the Midland Valley of Scotland. *Trans. R. Soc. Edin., Earth Sci.* **75**: 165-171.

Leake, B.E. and Skirrow, G. 1960. The pelitic hornfelses of the Cashel - Lough Wheelaun intrusion, Co. Galway, Éire. *J. Geol.* **68**: 23-40.

Leake, B.E., Tanner, P.W.G. and Senior, A. 1975. The composition and origin of the Connemara dolomite marbles and ophicalcites, Ireland. *J. Petrol.* **16**: 237-277.

Leake, B.E., Tanner, P.W.G. and Senior, A. 1981. *The geology of Connemara*, 1:63,360 Geological Map, University of Glasgow.

Leake, B.E., Tanner, D.W.G., Singh, D. and Halliday, A.N. 1983. Major southward overthrusting of the Dalradian rocks of Connemara, western Ireland. *Nature* **305**: 210-213.

Lees, A., Buller, A.T. and Scott, J. 1969. Marine carbonate sedimentation processes, Connemara, Ireland: an interim report. Reading University (Geology Department) *Geological Report* No. **2**: 1-119.

Leggo, P.J. 1963. *The geology and mineralogy of the Maam Cross - Screebe district, Connemara, Éire*. Unpublished Ph.D. thesis, University of Bristol.

Leggo, P.J. 1966. A study of the Potash Felspar Gneisses of Connemara and Felspar comparisons with the Galway Granite. *Geol. Mag.* **103**: 522-533.

Leggo, P.J., Compston, W. and Leake, B.E. 1966. The geochronology of the Connemara granites and its bearing on the antiquity of the Dalradian series. *Quart. J. Geol. Soc. Lond.* **122**: 91-188.

McCabe, A.M. and Dardis, G.F. 1989. Sedimentology and depositional setting of late Pleistocene drumlins, Galway Bay, western Ireland. *J. Sed. Petrology* **59** (6): 944-959.

McHenry A. 1903. Report on the Ox Mountain rocks and their probable continuation from Galway and Mayo into Donegal, Tyrone and Londonderry. *Proc. R. Ir. Acad.* **24B**: 371-378.

MacIntyre, R.M., McMenamin, T. and Preston, J. 1975. K-Ar results from Western Ireland and their bearing on the timing and siting of Thulean magmatism. *Scott. J. Geol.* **11**: 227-249.

McKerrow, W.S. and Campbell, C.J. 1960. The stratigraphy and structure of the lower Palaeozoic rocks of North-West Galway. *Sci. Proc. R. Dubl. Soc.* **IA**: 27-52.

McKie, D. and Burke, K. 1955. The geology of the islands of south Connemara. *Geol. Mag.* **92**: 487-498.

McLaren, D.J. and Miller, T.G. 1948. Notes on the geology of Killary Harbour. *Geol. Mag.* **85**: 217-221.

McManus, J. 1967. Sedimentology of the Partry Series in the Partry Mountains, Co. Mayo, Eire. *Geol. Mag.* **104**: 585-607.

Madden, J.S. 1987. *Gamma-ray spectrometric studies of the main Galway Granite, Connemara, west of Ireland.* Unpublished Ph.D. thesis, National University of Ireland, University College, Galway.

Max, M.D. 1970. Some metadolerites in Connemara. *Geol. Surv. Ir.* B **I**: 23-30.

Max, M.D., Long, C.B. and Geoghegan, M. 1978. The Galway Granite and its setting. *Geol. Surv. Ir. Bull.* **2**: 223-233.

Max, M.D., Long, C.B., Keary, R., Ryan, P.D., Geoghegan, M., O'Grady, M., Inamdar, D.D., McIntyre, T. and Williams, C.E. 1975. *Preliminary report on the geology of the north-western approaches to Galway Bay and part of its landward area.* Geological Survey of Ireland RS75/3.

Max, M.D. and Ryan, P.D. 1975. The Southern Upland Fault and its relation to the metamorphic rocks of Connemara. *Geol. Mag.* **112**: 610-612.

Mitchell, J.G. and Mohr, P. 1986. K-Ar systematics in Tertiary dolerites from West Connacht, Ireland. *Scott. J. Geol.* **22**: 225-420.

Mitchell, J.G. and Mohr, P. 1987. Carboniferous dykes of West Connacht, Ireland. *Trans. R. Soc. Edin., Earth Sciences* **78**: 133-151.

Mohr, P. 1986. Possible late Pleistocene faulting in Iar (West) Connacht, Ireland. *Geol. Mag.* **123**: 545-552.

Mohr, P. 1992. A Palaeocene dolerite intrusion newly discovered from Loch Ana, Clifden, Connemara. *Ir. Nat. J.* **24** (1): 21-23.

Mohr, P. and Feely, M. 1990. Report on a Discussion Meeting on the Geology of Connemara, Western Ireland. *Terra Nova* **1990**: 516-518.

Moorbath, S. 1968. Geochronological studies in Connemara and Murrisk, Western Ireland. *In* Hamilton, E.J. and Farquhar, R.M. (Eds.) *Radiometric dating for Geologists* : 259-298.

Morris, P. 1973. Density, magnetic and resistivity measurements on Irish rocks. *Dubl. Inst. Adv. Stud. Geophys. Bull.* **31**: 1-48.

Morris, W.A. and Tanner, P.W.G. 1977. The use of palaeomagnetic data to delineate the history of the development of the Connemara Antiform. *Can. J. Earth Sci.* **14**: 2601-2613.

Nawaz R. 1977. Pyrometamorphic rocks at the contact of a Dolerite plug near Bunowen, Co. Galway, Ireland. *Ir. Nat. J.* **19** (4): 101-104.

Nealon, T.M. 1988. *The sedimentology of the Silurian (Wenlock) deposits of North Galway, Ireland.* Unpublished Ph.D. thesis, National University of Ireland, University College, Galway.

Nealon, T.M. 1989. Deep basinal turbidites reinterpreted as distal tempestites: the Silurian Glencraff Formation of North Galway. *Ir. J. Earth Sci.* **10**: 55-65.

Nealon, T.M. and Williams, D.M. 1988. Storm influenced shelf deposits from the Silurian of western Ireland: a reinterpretation of deep basin sediments. *Geol. J.* **23**: 311-320.

O'Connell, M. and Warren, W.P. (Eds.) 1988. *Connemara.* I.Q.U.A. Field Guide 11.

Orme, A.R. 1967. Drumlins and the Weichsel glaciation of Connemara. *Ir. Geogr.* **5**: 262-274.

Phillips, W.E.A., Kennedy, M.J. and Dunlop, G.M. 1969. Geological comparison of western Ireland and north-eastern Newfoundland. *In* Kay, M. (Ed.) North Atlantic - geology and continental drift, a symposium. *Mem. Am. Ass. Petrol. G.* **12**: 194-211.

Pidgeon, R.T. 1969. Zircon U-Pb ages from the Galway granite and the Dalradian, Connemara, Ireland. *Scott. J. Geol.* **5**: 375-392.

Piper, D.J.W. 1967. A new interpretation of the Llandovery sequence of North Connemara, Éire. *Geol. Mag.* **104**: 253-267.

Piper, D.J.W. 1969. *Silurian sediments in western Ireland.* Unpublished Ph.D. thesis, University of Cambridge.

Piper, D.J.W. 1970a. Geosyncline - Margin sedimentary rocks in the Silurian of West Connacht, Ireland. *Am. Assoc. Petrol. Geol. Mem.* **12**: 289-297.

Piper, D.J.W. 1970b. A Silurian deep sea deposit in western Ireland and its bearing on the nature of turbidity currents. *J. Geol.* **78**: 509-522.

Piper, D.J.W. 1972. Sedimentary environments and palaeogeography of the late Llandovery and earliest Wenlock of N. Connemara, Ireland. *J. Geol. Soc.* **128**: 33-51.

Plant, A.G. 1968. *Geology of the Leam-Shannawona district, Connemara, Ireland*. Unpublished Ph.D. thesis, University of Bristol.

Purton, L. 1993. *The evolution of Dog's Bay/Gorteen Bay tombolo.* Unpublished M.Sc. thesis, Trinity College, Dublin.

Reed, F.R.C. 1945. Revision of certain Lower Ordovician faunas from Ireland. 1 Trilobites. *Geol. Mag.* **82**: 55-66.

Rickards, R.B. and Smyth, W.R. 1968. The Silurian graptolites of Mayo and Galway. *Sci. Proc. R. Dubl. Soc.* **3A**: 129-134.

Rothenstein, A.T.V. 1957. The Dawros peridotite, Connemara, Éire. *Quart. J. Geol. Soc. Lond.* **113**: 1-29.

Rothenstein, A.T.V. 1961. A synorganic peridotite at Dawros, Connemara. *Acta Geologica* **7**: 221-232.

Rothenstein, A.T.V. 1961. Phase relations in the peridotites of Dawros (Éire) and Belhevie (Scotland). *Izvest. Akad. Nauk. SSSR. Ser. Geol.* **3**: 69-86.

Rothenstein, A.T.V. 1964. New light on the Dawros peridotite. *Geol. Mag.* **101**: 283-285.

Ryan, P.D. and Feely, M. 1983. The main Galway Granite. *In* Archer, J.B. and Ryan, P.D. (Eds.) *Geological guide to the Caledonides of western Ireland* : 15-18. Geological Survey of Ireland GS **4**.

Ryan, P.D., Floyd, P.D. and Archer, J.B. 1980. The stratigraphy and petrochemistry of the Lough Nafooey Group (Tremadocian), western Ireland. *Quart. J. Geol. Soc. Lond.* **137**: 443-458.

Ryan, P.D. Sawal, V.K. and Rowlands, A.S. 1983. Ophiolitic melange separates ortho- and para-tectonic Caledonides in western Ireland. *Nature* **301**: 50-51.

Senior, A. 1973. *The geology of the Shannavara district, Connemara, Eire*. Unpublished Ph.D. thesis, University of Bristol.

Skevington, D. 1971. The age and correlation of the Rosroe Grits, North West, Co. Galway. *Proc. R. Ir. Acad.* **71B**: 75-83.

Skevington, D.G. and Archer, J.B. 1971. A review of the Ordovician graptolite faunas of western Ireland. *Ir. Nat. J.* **17** (3): 70-78.

Sollas, W.J. and M'Henry, A. 1896. On a volcanic neck of tertiary age, in the county of Galway. *Trans. Roy. Ir. Acad.*, Vol. **XXX**: 729-742.

Starkey, J. 1960. *Studies on the geology and mineralogy of the Maumturk area of Connemara, Eire*. Unpublished Ph.D. thesis, University of Liverpool.

Synge, F.M. 1963. Geomorphology of Murrisk and North West Galway. *Geol. Mag.* **100**: 574.

Tanner, P.W.G. 1967. The Dalradian of Connemara, Eire. *Ins. African Geol. Univ. Leeds 11th Ann. Rept.*: 26-28.

Tanner, P.W.G. and Shackleton, R.M. 1979. Structure and stratigraphy of the Dalradian rocks of the Bennabeola area, Connemara, Eire. *In* Harris, A.L., Holland, C.H. and Leake, B.E. (eds.). *The Caledonides of the British Isles - reviewed*. 243-256. Spec. Publ. geol. Soc. London, 8.

Theokritoff, G. 1951. Ordovician rocks, near Leenane, Ireland. *Proc. R. Ir. Acad.* **54B** (3): 25-49.

Townend, R. 1966. The geology of some granite plutons form western Connemara, Co. Galway. *Proc. R. Ir. Acad.* **65B** (4): 157-202.

Wager, L.R. 1932. The geology of the Roundstone district, County Galway. *Proc. R. Ir. Acad.* **41B** (5): 46-72.

Wager, L.R. 1939. Outline of the geology of Connemara. *Proc. Geol. Assoc.* **50**: 346.

Wager, L.R. and Andrew, G. 1930. The age of the Connemara Schists and their metamorphism. *Geol. Mag.* **67**: 271-275.

Whittow, J.B. 1975. *Geology and scenery in Ireland*.Penguin, Middlesex.

Whitworth, M.P. and Feely, M. 1989. The geochemistry of selected pegmatites and their host granites from the Galway Granite, western Ireland. *Ir. J. Earth Sci.* **10**: 89-97.

Williams, A. 1972. An Ordovician whiterock fauna in western Ireland. *Proc. R. Ir. Acad.* **72B** (12): 209-219.

Williams, A. and Curry, G.B. 1985. Lower Ordovician Brachiopoda from the Tourmakeady Limestone, Co. Mayo, Ireland. *Bull. Brit. Mus. (Nat. Hist.) Geology* **38**: 183-269.

Williams, D.M. 1980. Evidence for glaciation in the Ordovician rocks of western Ireland. *Geol. Mag.* **117**: 81-86.

Williams, D.M. 1984a. The geology around Killary Harbour, Co. Galway. *Ir. Geol. Ass., Field Guide Series* **3**.

Williams, D.M. 1984b. The stratigraphy and sedimentology of the Ordovician Partry Group, south-eastern Murrisk, Ireland. *Geol. J.* **19**: 173-186.

Williams, D.M., Armstrong, H.A. and Harper, D.A.T. 1988. The age of the South Connemara Group, Ireland and its relationship to the Southern Upland Zone of Scotland and Ireland. *Scott. J. Geol.* **24** (3): 279-287.

Williams, D.M. and Harper, D.A.T. 1988. A basin model for the Silurian of the Midland Valley of Scotland and Ireland. *Quart. J. Geol. Soc. Lond.* **145**: 741-748.

Williams, D.M. and Harper, D.A.T. 1991. End-Silurian modifications of Ordovician terranes in western Ireland. *Quart. J. Geol. Soc. Lond.* **148**: 165-171.

Williams, D.M. and Nealon, T. 1987. The significance of large-scale sedimentary structures in the Silurian of western Ireland. *Geol. Mag.* **124**: 361-366.

Williams, D.M. and O'Connor, P. 1987. Environment of deposition of conglomerates from the Silurian of north Galway, Ireland. *Trans. R. Soc. Edin. Earth Sciences* **78**: 129-132.

Williams, D.M. and Rice, A.H.N. 1989. Low-angle extensional faulting and the emplacement of the Connemara Dalradian, Ireland. *Tectonics* **8**: 417-428.

Wright, P.C. 1961. *The petrology and geochemistry of the Galway Granite, of the Carna district, Connemara, Éire.* Unpublished Ph.D. thesis, University of Bristol.

Wright, P.C. 1964. The petrology, chemistry and structure of the Galway Granite of the Carna area, Co. Galway. *Proc. R. Ir. Acad.* **63B** (14): 239-264.

Yardley, B.W.D. 1974. *The deformation, metamorphism and metasomatism of the rocks of the Cur area, Connemara, Eire.* Unpublished Ph.D. thesis, University of Bristol.

Yardley, B.W.D. 1976. Deformation and metamorphism of Dalradian rocks and the evolution of the Connemara cordillera. *Quart. J. Geol. Soc. Lond.* **132**: 521-542.

Yardley, B.W.D. and Senior, A. 1982. Basic magmatism in Connemara, Ireland: evidence for a volcanic arc? *J. Geo. Soc. Lond.* **139**: 67-70.

FLORA

FLOWERS AND VEGETATION

Akeroyd, J.R. and Curtis, T.G.F. 1980. Some observations on the occurence of machair in western Ireland. *Bull. Ir. Biogeog. Soc.* **4**: 1-12.

Babington, C.C. 1836. Observations made during a visit to Connemara and Joyce's Country in August, 1835. *Magazine of Natural History* **9**: 119-130.

Balfour, I.B. 1902. Forms of *Erica tetralix* in Connemara. *Ir. Nat.* **11** (11): 287.

Balfour, J.H. 1876. Notes of an excursion to Connemara in September, 1874. *Trans. Bot. Soc. Edin.* **12**: 371-377.

Bannister, P. 1965. Biological flora of the British Isles: *Erica cinerea* L. *J. Ecol.* **53**: 527-542.

Bannister, P. 1966. Biological flora of the British Isles: *Erica tetralix* L. *J. Ecol.* **54** (3): 795-814.

Bannister, P. 1978. Flowering and shoot extension in heath plants of different geographical origin. *J. Ecol.* **66**: 117-131.

Barrington, R.M. 1915. Plants of Ben Lettery. *Ir. Nat.* **24** (9):169.

Bassett, J.A. and Curtis, T.G.F. 1985. The nature and occurence of sand-dune machair in Ireland. *Proc. R. Ir. Acad.* **85B** (1): 1-20.

Bell, J.N. and Tallis, J.H. 1973. Biological flora of the British Isles: *Empetrum nigrum* L. *J. Ecol.* **61** (1): 289-306.

Bellamy, D. 1986. *The wild boglands.* Country House, Dublin.

Bellamy, D. and Bellamy, R. 1966. An ecological approach to the classification of the lowland mires of Ireland. *Proc. R. Ir. Acad.* **65B** (6): 237-251.

Bleasdale, A. and Sheehy Skeffington, M. 1992. The influence of agricultural practices on plant communities in Connemara. *In* Feehan, J. (Ed.) 1992. *Environment and Development in Ireland* : 331-336. The Environment Institute, University College, Dublin.

Boatman, D.J. 1957. An ecological study of two areas of blanket bog on the Galway-Mayo peninsula, Ireland. *Proc. R. Ir. Acad.* **59B** (3): 29-42.

Boatman, D.J. 1960. The relationships of some bog communities in western Galway. *Proc. R. Ir. Acad.* **61B** (8): 141-168.

Booth, E.M. 1974. A second station in West Galway for *Carex punctata* Gaud. *Ir. Nat. J.* **18** (1): 23.

Booth, E.M. and Scannell, M.J P. 1975. *Koeleria cristata* Pers. as a constituent of ant-hill flora. *Ir. Nat. J.* **18** (7): 221.

Bowler, M. 1986. *A vegetation history of Connemara National Park, Co. Galway.* Unpublished M.Sc. thesis, National University of Ireland, University College, Galway.

Boyle, P.J. 1968. Preliminary account of *Spartina pectinata* Link. new to Ireland. *Ir. Nat. J.* **16** (3): 74-75.

Brenan, S.A. 1896. Irish hawkweeds etc. *Ir. Nat.* **5** (1): 27.

Britten, J. 1892. *Cuscuta epilinum* (Renvyle). *J. Bot.* **30**: 14.

Brodie, J. and Sheehy Skeffington, M. 1990. Inishbofin: A re-survey of the flora. *Ir. Nat. J.* **23** (8): 293-298.

Caffrey, J.M. and Rorslett, B. 1989. The macrophytic vegetation in Rusheenduff (Renvyle) Lough, Co. Galway. *Ir. Nat. J.* **23** (4): 125-128.

Cain, S.A. 1950. Some impressions of Irish vegetation. *Ir. Nat. J.* **10**: 11-14.

Chadwick, M.J. 1960. Biological flora of the British Isles: *Nardus stricta* L. *J. Ecol.* **48** (1): 255-267.

Charlesworth, J.K. 1932. The distribution of the Irish peats. *Ir. Nat. J.* **4** (2): 37-39.

Chase, C.D. 1927. *Bartsia viscosa* in Connemara. *Ir. Nat. J.* **1**: 277.

Clapham, A.R., Tutin, T.G. and Moore, D.M. 1987. *Flora of the British Isles.* Cambridge University Press, Cambridge.

Colgan, N. 1900. Botanical notes on the Galway and Mayo highlands. *Ir. Nat.* **9** (5): 111-118.

Conaghan, J.P. 1989. *A study of the phytosociology and ecology of* Daboeciacantabrica *in Connemara.* Unpublished B.Sc. thesis, National University of Ireland, University College, Galway.

Connemara National Park. 1981. *List of ferns and flowering plants.* National Parks and Monuments Service, Dublin.

Connolly, G. 1930. The vegetation of southern Connemara. *Proc. R. Ir. Acad.* **39B** (12): 203-231.

Cross, J.R. 1975. Biological flora of the British Isles: *Rhododendron ponticum* L. *J. Ecol.* **63** (1): 345-364.

Cross, J.R. 1982. The invasion and impact of *Rhododendron ponticum* in native Irish vegetation. *In* White, J. (Ed.) 1982. *Studies on Irish Vegetation* : 209-220. Royal Dublin Society, Dublin.

Crowder, A.A., Pearson, M.C., Grubbs, P.J. and Langlois, P.H. 1990. Biological flora of the British Isles, *Drosera* L. *J. Ecol.* **78**: 233-267.

Curran, P.L., O'Toole, M.A. and Kelly, F.G. 1983. Vegetation of terraced hill grazings in north Galway / south Mayo. *J. Life Sci. R. Dubl. Soc.* **4**: 195-201.

Curtis, T.G.F. and McGough, H.N. 1983. An unusual habitat for *Dryas octopetala* L. *Bull. Ir. Biogeog. Soc.* **7**:11-13.

Dony, J.G., Jury, S.L. and Perring, F.H. 1986. *English names of wild flowers.* The Botanical Society of the British Isles, Reading.

Doorslaer, L. van. 1990. *The ecology of* Erica mackaiana *Bab. with reference to its conservation in Connemara (Ireland).* Unpublished Ph.D. thesis, National University of Ireland, University College, Galway.

Doyle, G.J. 1982. The vegetation, ecology and productivity of Atlantic blanket bog in Mayo and Galway, Western Ireland. *In* White, J. (Ed.) *Studies on Irish Vegetation* : 147-164. Royal Dublin Society, Dublin. *J. Life. Sci. R. Dubl. Soc.* **3**.

Doyle, G. (Ed.) 1990. *Ecology and conservation of Irish peatlands.* Royal Irish Academy, Dublin.

Doyle, G.J. and Kirby E.N. 1987. *Listera cordata* (L.) R. BR. (Lesser Twayblade) growing in the Twelve Bens Range, Connemara. *Ir. Nat. J.* **22** (6): 246-248.

Druce, C.C. 1929. New or rare plants of Ireland. *Ir. Nat. J.* **2** (8): 163-165.

Dublin Microscopical Club. 1895. July 18th - meeting and exhibits. *Ir. Nat.* **4** (10): 292.

Dyos, H., Proctor, J. and Sheehy Skeffington, M. 1991. Notes on the vegetation of the Dawros and other ultrabasic rock outcrops in Connemara. *Ir. Nat. J.* **23** (10):415-419.

Eager, A.R., Nelson, E.C. and Scannell M.J.P. 1978. *Erica ciliaris* L. in Connemara, 1846-1853. *Ir. Nat. J.* **19** (7): 244-245.

Eber, W. 1982. The ecology of bogs and bog plants. *In* White J. (Ed.) *Studies on Irish Vegetation* : 243-254. Royal Dublin Society, Dublin. *J. Life. Sci. R. Dubl. Soc.* **3**.

Farmer, A.M. 1989. Biological flora of the British Isles, *Lobelia dortmanna* L. *J. Ecol.* **77**: 1161-1173.

Ferguson, D. and Westhoff, V. 1987. An account of the flora and vegetation of Derryclare Wood, Connemara (Co. Galway), Western Ireland. *Proc. R. Dutch Acad. Sci.* **C 90** (2): 139-172.

Fitter, A. 1978. *An atlas of the wild flowers of Britain and Northern Europe.* Collins, London.

Fitter, R. and Fitter, A. 1984. *Collins guide to the grasses, sedges, rushes and ferns of Britain and Northern Europe.* Collins, London.

Foss, P.J. 1986. *The distribution, phytosociology, autecology and post-glacial history of* Erica erigena *R. Ross in Ireland.* Unpublished Ph.D. thesis, National University of Ireland, University College, Dublin.

Foss, P.J. and Doyle, G.J. 1988. Why has *Erica erigena* (the Irish heather) such a markedly disjunct European distribution? *Plants Today* **9/10 1988**: 161-168.

Gibbons, M. and Higgins, J. 1988. Connemara's emerging prehistory. *Archaeol. Irel.* **2**: 63-66.

Gimmingham, C.H. 1960. Biological flora of the British Isles: *Calluna vulgaris* L. Hull. *J. Ecol.* **48** (2): 455-484.

Godwin, Sir H. 1984. *The history of the British flora.* Cambridge University Press, Cambridge.

Goodwillie, R. 1980a. *Peatland sites of scientific interest in Ireland.* Report to the Nature Reserves Committee of the Wildlife Advisory Council, Dublin.

Goodwillie, R. 1980b. *European peatlands.* Nature and Environment Series 19. Council of Europe, Strasbourg.

Graham, R. 1840. An account of an excursion to the west of Ireland. *Ann. Rept. Bot. Soc. Edin.* **3**: 54-57.

Grimes, M. 1940. Phenological report for 1939. *Ir. Nat. J.* **7**(9): 259-266.

Groenendael, J.M. van, Hochstenbach, S.M.H., Mansfeld, M.J.M. van and Roozen, A.J.M. 1979. *The influence of the sea and of parent material on wetlands and blanket bog in West Connemara, Ireland.* Department of Geobotany, Catholic University, Nijmegen.

Groenendael, J.M. van, Hochstenbach, S.M.H., Mansfeld, M.J.M. van and Roozen, A.J.M. 1983a. Plant communities of lakes, wetlands and blanket bog in western Connemara, Ireland. *J. Life Sci. R. Dubl. Soc.* **4**: 103-128.

Groenendael, J.M. van, Hochstenbach, S.M.H., Mansfeld, M.J.M. van and Roozen, A.J.M. 1983b. Soligenous influences on wetlands and blanket bog in western Connemara, Ireland. *J.Life Sci. R. Dubl. Soc.* **4**: 129-137.

Groenendael, J.M. van, Hochstenbach, S.M.H., Mansfeld, M.J.M. van, Roozen, A.J.M. and Westhoff, V. 1982. The influence of the sea on the vegetation of lakes in southwest Connemara. *In* White, J. (Ed.). 1982. *Studies on Irish Vegetation* : 221-242. Royal Dublin Society, Dublin. *J. Life. Sci. R. Dubl. Soc.* **3**.

Halliday G., Argent, G.C. and Hawksworth, D.L. 1967. Some Irish plant records. *Ir. Nat. J.* **15** (11): 313-316.

Hannon, G.E. and Bradshaw, R.H.W. 1989. Recent vegetation dynamics on two Connemara lake islands, western Ireland. *J. Biogeog.* **16**: 75-81.

Hart, H.C. 1883. Report on the flora of the Mayo, Galway mountains. *Proc. R. Ir. Acad.* **3B**: 694-768.

Heijnis, H. 1987. *Vegetational development of the Owengarve River valley during the Holocene. Connemara National Park, Co. Galway.* Drs. thesis, Institute of Earth Sciences, Amsterdam.

Hewet, D.G. 1964. Biological flora of the British Isles: *Menyanthes trifoliata* L. *J. Ecol.* **52** (3): 723-736.

Higgins, U.C. 1985. *Corrib Country reedswamps.* Corrib wildlife series **2**. Corrib Conservation Centre, Oughterard.

Holland, P.G. 1972. The pattern of species density of old stone walls in western Ireland. *J. Ecol.* **60** (3): 799-805.

Huang, C.C. and O'Connell, M. 1992. Recent land-use history in eastern Connemara: a palaeoecological case study at Ballydoo Lough, Connemara, Co. Galway. *In* Feehan, J. (Ed.) 1992. *Environment and Development in Ireland* : 318-330. The Environment Institute, University College, Dublin.

Hurst, C.P. 1902. Notes on Connemara botany. *Ir. Nat.* **11** (2): 45.

Irish Peatland Conservation Council. 1989. *Save our boglands.* Irish Peatland Conservation Council, Dublin.

Jessen, K. 1949. Studies in late quaternary deposits and flora-history of Ireland. *Proc R. Ir. Acad.* **52B** (6): 85-290.

Joyce, D.J. 1976. *A pollen analytical investigation of coastal peat at Carna, Co. Galway.* Unpublished B.Sc. thesis, National University of Ireland, University College Galway.

Keane, S. 1988. *Palaeoecological studies at Lough Sheeauns, Cleggan, Co. Galway.* Unpublished B.Sc. thesis, National University of Ireland, University College, Galway.

Kelly, D.L. 1985. Plant records from about Ireland 1965-1983. *Ir. Nat. J.* **21** (9): 416-419.

Kelly, D.L. and Kirby, E.N. 1987. Irish native woodlands on limestone. *In* White, J. (Ed.) *Studies in Irish Vegetation* : 181-198. Royal Dublin Society, Dublin.

Kirby, E.N. and O'Connell, M. 1982. Shannawoneen Wood, County Galway, Ireland: the woodland and saxicolous communities and the epiphytic flora. *J. Life Sci. R. Dubl. Soc.* **4**: 73-96.

Lambert, D. 1969. Double forms of *Potentilla procumbens* in Connemara. *Ir. Nat. J.* **16** (5): 142.

Leighton Hare, C. 1945. The study of *Eriocaulon septangulare* With. *J. Linn. Soc. Bot.* **53**: 422-449.

Levinge, H.C. 1893. *Limosella aquatica* in Ireland. *J. Bot.* **Oct 1893**. Note on it in *Ir. Nat.* **2** (11): 300-301.

Linton, E.F. 1888. *Carex trinervis* in Ireland. *J. Bot.* **26**: 56.

Linton, E.F. and Linton, W.R. 1886. Notes of a botanical tour in west Ireland. *J. Bot.* **24**: 18-21.

Lockhart, N.D., O'Connell, M., Sheehy Skeffington, M. and van Doorslaer. 1989. Scraw (Schwingmoor) plant communities at Loch an Chorcail, Carna, Co. Galway. *Ir. Nat. J.* **23**(4):128-134.

Lüdi, W. 1950. Impressions of a Swiss botanist in Ireland. *Ir. Nat. J.* **10**; 9-11.

Mackay, J.T. 1830. Notice of a new indigenous heath, found in Cunnamara. *Trans. Roy. Ir. Acad.* **16**: 127-128.

Mackie, G.N. 1970. Plant records from west Galway and Westmeath. *Ir. Nat. J.* **16** (10): 319.

McCalla, W. 1834. Botany - The wild mountains of Roundstone, Connemara. *Dublin Penny Journal* **2** (80): 217.

McClintock, D. 1968. Further notes on *Erica ciliaris* in Ireland. *Proc. bot. Soc. Br. Isl.***7**: 177.

McClintock, D. 1969. Some notes on *Erica "mediterranea"*. *Ir. Nat. J.* **16** (6): 154-158.

McClintock, D. 1970. White flowered *Daboecia cantabrica*. *Ir. Nat. J.* **16** (12): 391-392.

McClintock, D. 1971. *Daboecia cantabrica* "praegerae". *Ir. Nat. J.* **17** (1): 24.

McClintock, D. 1979. *Acaena* in Ireland. *Ir. Nat. J.* **19** (10): 365-367.

McClintock, D. 1980. The typification of *Erica ciliaris* L., of *E. tetralix* and of their hybrid *E.* x *watsonii* Bentham. *Bot. J. Linn. Soc.* **80**: 207-211.

McClintock, D. 1983. The Carna colony of *Erica mackaiana*, a new variety. *Ir. Nat. J.* **21** (2): 85-86.

McCracken, E. 1971. *The Irish woods since Tudor times*. David & Charles, Newton Abbot.

McDonnell, K. 1988. *Studies towards the Post-Glacial history of Lough Corcal, Carna, Co. Galway*. Unpublished B.Sc. thesis, National University of Ireland, University College Galway.

Mills, J.N. 1955. A puzzling *Galium* from Connemara. *Proc. Bot. Soc. Brit. and Irel.* **1954**: 263.

Mitchell, G.F. and Watts, W.A. 1970. The history of the Ericaceae in Ireland during the quaternary epoch. *In* Walker, D. and West, R.G. (Eds.). *Studies in the vegetational history of the British Isles* : 13-21. Cambridge University Press, Cambridge.

Molloy, K. 1989. *Palaeoecological investigations towards the reconstruction of prehistoric human impact in north-west Connemara, western Ireland*. Unpublished Ph.D. thesis, National University of Ireland, University College, Galway.

Molloy, K. and O'Connell, M. 1987. The nature of the vegetational changes at about 5,000B.P. with particular reference to the elm decline: fresh evidence from Connemara, western Ireland. *New Phytol.* **106**: 203-220.

Molloy, K. and O'Connell, M. 1988. Neolithic agriculture - fresh evidence from Cleggan, Connemara. *Archaeol. Irel.* **2**: 67-70.

Molloy, K. and O'Connell, M. 1991. Palaeoecological investigations towards the reconstruction of woodland and land-use history at Lough Sheeauns, Connemara, western Ireland. *Rev. Palaeobot. Palynol.* **67**: 75-113.

Molloy, K. and O'Connell, M. 1993. Early land-use and vegetation history at Derryinver Hill, Renvyle Peninsula, Co. Galway, Ireland. *In* Chambers, F.M. (Ed.) 1993. *Climatic change and impact on the landscape*. Chapman and Hall, London.

Moon, J. Mck. 1955. *Epilobium linnaeoides* Hook, f. in Ireland. *Ir. Nat. J.* **11**: 292.

More, A.G. 1869. Discovery of *Aira uliginosa* at Roundstone, Co. Galway. *J. Bot.* **7**: 265-266.

More, A.G. 1876. Report on the flora of Inishbofin, Co. Galway. *Proc. R. Ir. Acad.* **2**: 553- 578.

Morley, B. and Scannell, M.J.P. 1972. *Erica erigena* R. Ross - the Mediterranean Heath in Ireland. *Ir. Nat. J.* **17** (6): 203-204.

Nelson, E.C. 1978. Craiggamore - the earliest record. *Ir. Nat. J.* **19** (7): 250.

Nelson, E.C. 1979. Historical records of Irish Ericaceae with particular reference to the discovery of and naming of *Erica mackaiana*. *J. Soc. Biblphy. Nat. Hist.* **9**: 289-299.

Nelson, E.C. 1981a. Studies in *Erica mackaiana* Bab. 1 : Distribution in Connemara, Ireland. *Ir. Nat. J.* **20** (5): 199-202.

Nelson, E.C. 1982. Historical records of the Irish Ericaceae - Additional notes on *Arbutus unedo*, *Daboecia cantabrica*, *Erica erigena*, *E. mackaiana* and *Ledum palustre*. *Ir. Nat. J.* **20** (9): 364-369.

Newman, E. 1846. Occurrence of *Erica ciliaris* in the county Galway, west of Ireland. *Phytologist* **2**: 683.

Newman, E. 1852, *Najas flexilis* at Roundstone. *Phytologist* **4**: 724.

O'Connell, C. (Ed.) 1987. *The IPCC guide to Irish peatlands*. Irish Peatland Conservation Council, Dublin.

O'Connell, M. 1982. *Ranunculus scleratus* L. and *Rorippa sylvestris* (L.), Bess, near Spiddal, West Galway, H.16. *Ir. Nat. J.* **20** (11): 506.

O'Connell, M. and Huang, C.C. 1992. Palaeoecological evidence of erosion rates in Connemara during the 19th and 20th centuries. *In* Feehan, J. (Ed.) 1992. *Environment and development in Ireland*. The Environment Institute, University College, Dublin.

O'Connell, M., Molloy, K. and Bowler, M. 1988. Post-glacial landscape evolution in Connemara, Western Ireland with particular reference to woodland history. *In* Birks, H.H., Birks, H.J.B., Kaland, P.E. and Moe, D. *The cultural landscape- past, present and future* : 267-287. Cambridge University Press, Cambridge.

O'Connell, M. Ryan, J.B. and MacGowran, B.A. 1984. Wetland communities in Ireland: a phytosociological review. *In* P.D. Moore (ed.) *European mires*. Academic Press, London.

Ogilby, L. 1845. Notes of a botanical ramble in Connemara and Aran. *Phytologist* **2**: 345-351.

Parnell, J. and Webb, D.A. 1991. The *Flora Hibernica* herbarium of J.T. Mackay. *Ir. Nat. J.* **23** (9): 359-364.

Pearsall, W.H. 1936. *Hydrilla verticillata* Presl, a plant new to Ireland. *Ir. Nat. J.* **6** (1): 20-21.

Pearsall, W.H. 1950. *Mountains and moorlands*. Collins, London.

Pearsall, W.H. and Lind, E.M. 1941. A note on a Connemara bog type. *J. Ecol.* **29**: 62-68.

Pearsall, W.H. and Lind, E.M. 1942. The distribution of phytoplankton in some northwest Irish loughs. *Proc. R. Ir. Acad.* **48B**: 1-24.

Perring, F.H. and Walters, S.M. (Eds.) 1990. *Atlas of the British flora.* Botanical Society of the British Isles, Reading.

Praeger, R.Ll. 1896. The island flora of the Connemara lakes. *Ir. Nat.* **5** (11): 292-293.

Praeger, R.Ll. 1901a. Irish hawkweeds. *Ir. Nat.* **10** (3): 74.

Praeger, R.Ll. 1901b. Irish topographical botany. *Proc. Roy. Ir. Acad.* **7** (3): 1-410.

Praeger, R.Ll. 1905. *Pilularia* in Connemara. *Ir. Nat.* **14**: 165.

Praeger, R.Ll. 1906. Notes of a western ramble. *Ir. Nat.* **15** (12): 257-266.

Praeger, R.Ll. 1907. On the recent extentions of the range of some rare western plants. *Ir. Nat.* **16** (8): 241-243.

Praeger, R.Ll. 1909a. *Erica mackaii* on Urrisbeg. *Ir. Nat.* **18** (2): 53.

Praeger, R.Ll. 1909b. *Bartsia viscosa* in Connemara. *Ir. Nat.* **18**: 253.

Praeger, R.Ll. 1911. Flora of Inishbofin. *Ir. Nat.* **20**: 165-172.

Praeger, R.Ll. 1912. Plants from western Ireland. *Ir. Nat.* **21** (1): 26.

Praeger, R.Ll. 1913. Irish water plants. *Ir. Nat.* **22** (1): 18.

Praeger, R.Ll. 1934. *The botanist in Ireland.* Hodges Figgis, Dublin. (Reprinted by EP Publishing Ltd,Yorkshire, 1974)

Praeger, R.Ll. 1934a. *Caltha radicans* in Ireland. *Ir. Nat. J.* **5** (4): 98-102.

Praeger, R.Ll. 1934b. The *Sorbus aria* group in Ireland. *Ir. Nat. J.* **5** (3): 50-52.

Praeger, R.Ll. 1950. Our changing flora. *Ir. Nat. J.* **10** (4): 89-93.

Praeger, R.Ll. et al. 1895. Report of the Conference and Excursion held at Galway, July 11th to 17th 1895. *Ir. Nat.* **4** (9): 225-273.

Preston, C.D., Stewart, N.F. and Webster, S.D. 1991. Records of aquatic plants from Connemara and the Burren. *Ir. Nat. J.* **23** (11): 464-467.

Proctor, M.C.F. 1960. Biological flora of the British Isles: *Tuberaria guttata* (L.) Fourreau. *J. Ecol.* **48** (1): 243-254.

Robinson, T. 1984. Plant records from west Galway. *Ir. Nat. J.* **21** (8): 345-347.

Roden, C. 1979. A note on the flora of the Lough Corrib region including some new records for west Galway (H16), north-east Galway (H17) and south Mayo (H26). *Bull. Ir. Biogeog. Soc.* **3**: 34-36.

Roden, C. 1986. A survey of the flora of some mountain ranges in the west of Ireland. *Ir. Nat. J.* **22** (2): 52-59.

Roden, C.M. 1993. *Orchis morio* L. in the west of Ireland. *Ir. Nat. J.* **24** (5): 220-222.

Rose, F. 1967. *Eriophorum gracile* Roth, new to Ireland. *Ir. Nat. J.* **15** (12): 361-362.

Scannell, M.J.P. 1973. *Rorippa islandica* (oeder Ex Murray) Berbás in Ireland. *Ir. Nat. J.* **17** (10): 348-351.

Scannell, M.J.P. 1975a. *Ruppia cirrhosa* (Petagne) Grande, an addition to the flora of west Galway. *Ir. Nat. J.* **18** (7): 220-221.

Scannell, M.J.P. 1975b. Craiggamore and Craiggabeg in west Galway. *Ir. Nat. J.* **18** (7): 224-225.

Scannell, M.J.P. 1976. *Hydrilla verticillata* in flower in the wild. *Ir. Nat. J.* **18** (12): 350.

Scannell, M.J.P. 1976. *Erica erigena* R. Ross: The second station in West Galway. *Ir. Nat. J.* **18** (9): 270-271.

Scannell, M.J.P. 1977. *Juncus planifolius* R. Br. - An extension in range. *Ir. Nat. J.* **19** (1): 26.

Scannell, M.J.P. 1977. *Trifolium medium* L., mainland stations in West Galway. *Ir. Nat. J.* **19** (1): 25-26.

Scannell, M.J.P. 1983. *Erica erigena* R. Ross and *Daboecia cantabrica* (Huds) C. Koch - some further notes on the historical records. *Ir. Nat. J.* **21** (1): 29-30.

Scannell, M.J.P. 1985. *Erica mackaii* - Unpublished notes by M.C. Knowles written about 1910. *Ir. Nat. J.* **21** (10): 425-430.

Scannell, M.J.P. and McClintock, D. 1974. *Erica mackaiana* Bab. in Irish localities and other plants of interest. *Ir. Nat. J.* **18** (3): 81-85.

Scannell, M.J.P. and Synnott, D.M. 1987. *Census catalogue of the flora of Ireland*. Stationery Office, Dublin.

Scannell, M.J.P. and Webb, D.A. 1976. The identity of the Renvyle *Hydrilla*. *Ir. Nat. J.* **18** (11): 327-331.

Scott, N.E. and Sheehy-Skeffington, M.J. 1987. A new record for *Oenanthe pimpinelloides*, L. in Ireland. *Ir. Nat. J.* **22** (8): 351-353.

Scully, C.A. 1989. *Ecological studies of the aquatic species* Eriocaulon aquaticum (Hill) Druce *and* Lobelia dortmanna L. Unpublished M.Sc. thesis, National University of Ireland, University College, Galway.

Sparling, J.H. 1962. Occurrence of *Schoenus nigricans* L. in blanket bogs of western Ireland and N.W. Scotland. *Nature* **195**: 723-724.

Sparling, J.H. 1967. The occurence of *Schoenus nigricans* L. in blanket bogs. 1. Environmental conditions affecting the growth of *S. nigricans* in blanket bog. *J. Ecol.* **55** (1): 1-13.

Sparling, J.H. 1968. Biological flora of the British Isles - *Schoenus nigricans* L. (*Chaetospora nigricans* Kunth). *J. Ecol.* **56** (3): 883-900.

Speight, M.C.D. 1985. The extinction of indigenous *Pinus sylvestris* in Ireland: relevant faunal data. *Ir. Nat. J.* **21**: 449-453.

Stace, C. 1991. *New flora of the British Isles*. Cambridge University Press, Cambridge.

Stelfox, A.W. 1945. On the forms of the purple saxifrage occurring in Ireland. *Ir. Nat. J.* **8** (8): 315-316.

Stelfox, A.W. 1946. An erroneous record for *Saxifraga geum*. *Ir. Nat. J.* **8**: 437.

Stelfox, A.W. 1947. C. C. Babingtons's record for *Saxifraga geum* in Connemara. *Ir. Nat. J.* **9** (1): 29.

Stelfox, A.W. 1948. The Irish mossy saxifrages. *Ir. Nat. J.* **9** (6): 155-156.

Stelfox, A.W. 1970. A possible early record for *Eriophorum gracile* from west Galway by C.C. Babington in 1836. *Ir. Nat. J.* **16** (9): 282.

Stelfox, A.W. and Wood, P.W. 1960. What is the origin of the heath *Daboecia cantabrica* var. *praegerae* ? *Ir. Nat. J.* **13** (5): 121-122.

Summerfield, R.J. 1974. Biological flora of the British Isles: *Narthecium ossifragum* (L.) Huds. *J. Ecol.* **62** (1): 325-340.

Tansley, A.G. 1908. The British Vegetation Committee's visit to the west of Ireland. *New Phytol.* **7**: 253-260.

Tansley, A.G. 1949. *The British islands and their vegetation* I and II. Cambridge University Press, London.

Teunissen, D. and Teunissen-van Oorschot, H.G.C.M. 1980. The history of the vegetation in SW Connemara (Ireland). *Acta Bot. Neerl.* **29** (4): 285-306.

Tomlinson, W.J.C. 1909. *Habenaria intacta* in west Galway. *Ir. Nat.* **18**: 156.

Waddell, C.H. 1909. On some Irish hawkweeds. *Ir. Nat.* **18** (7): 149-150.

Webb, D.A. 1947. Two new western plant records. *Ir. Nat. J.* **9** (4): 100.

Webb, D.A. 1948. The Robertsonian saxifrages of Galway and Mayo. *Ir. Nat. J.* **9** (5):105-107.

Webb, D.A. 1954a. Notes on four Irish heaths: part I. *Ir. Nat. J.* **11** (7): 187-195.

Webb, D.A. 1954b. Notes on four Irish heaths: part II. *Ir. Nat. J.* **11** (8): 215-219.

Webb, D.A. 1954c. A western subspecies of *Pedicularis sylvatica*. *Ir. Nat. J.* **11** (8):235.

Webb, D.A. 1955. Biological flora of the British Isles - *Erica mackaiana* Bab. (*E. mackayi* Hook., ined). *J. Ecol.* **43**: 319-330.

Webb, D.A. 1956. *Spergularia rubra* in Connemara. *Ir. Nat. J.* **12** (4): 111.

Webb, D.A. 1957a. *Hypericum canadense* L. a new American plant in western Ireland. *Ir. Nat. J.* **12**: 113-116.

Webb, D.A. 1957b. An unusual habitat for *Orchis morio* (Lough Naweelaun). *Ir. Nat. J.* **12**: 198-199.

Webb, D.A. 1957c. *Hypericum canadense* L. in western Ireland. *Watsonia* **4**: 140-145.

Webb, D.A. 1959. New records for *Spiranthes romanzoffiana, Stachys officinalis* and *Eriophorum latifolium*. *Ir. Nat. J.* **13** (1): 20-21.

Webb, D.A. 1965. *Spiranthes romanzoffiana* on Lough Corrib. *Ir. Nat. J.* **15** (1): 21.

Webb, D.A. 1966. *Erica ciliaris* in Ireland. *Proc. Bot. Soc. Brit. Isles* **6**: 221-225.

Webb, D.A. 1977. *An Irish Flora*. Dundalgan Press, Dundalk.

Webb, D.A. 1982. Plant records from Connemara and the Burren. *Ir. Nat. J.* **20**(11): 467-471.

Webb, D.A. and Akeroyd, J.R. 1991. Inconstancy of sea-shore plants. *Ir. Nat. J.* **23** (9): 384-385.

Webb, D.A. and Glanville, E.V. 1961. The vegetation and flora of some islands in the Connemara lakes. *Proc. R. Ir. Acad.* **62B**: 31-55.

Webb, D.A. and Halliday, G. 1973. The distribution, habitat and status of *Hypericum canadense* L. in Ireland. *Watsonia* **9**: 333-356.

Webb, D.A. and Hodgson, J. 1968. The flora of Inishbofin and Inishshark. *Proc. bot. Soc. Br. Isl.* **7** (3): 345-363.

Webb, D.A. and Scannell, M.J.P. 1983. *Flora of Connemara and the Burren*. Royal Dublin Society, University Press, Cambridge.

Webb, D.A. and Scannell, M.J.P. 1984. Flora of Connemara and the Burren, some corrections and additions. *Ir. Nat. J.* **21**: 286-288.

Webster, S.D. 1991. *Ranunculus penicillatus* (Damort) Bab. in Ireland. *Ir. Nat. J.* **23** (9):346-354.

Wein, R.W. 1973. Biological flora of the British Isles: *Eriophorum vaginatum* L. *J. Ecol.* **61** (2): 601-615.

Welch, D. 1966. Biological flora of the British Isles: *Juncus squarrosus* L. *J. Ecol.* **54** (2): 535-548.

White, J. (Ed.) 1982. *Studies on Irish vegetation*. Royal Dublin Society, Dublin.

White, J. and Doyle, G.J. 1981. The vegetation of Ireland. A catalogue raisonné. *In* White, J. (Ed.) 1982. *Studies on Irish vegetation* : 289-368. Royal Dublin Society, Dublin.

Wilson, G.W. and Bourke, K. 1934. Phenological report for 1933. *Ir. Nat. J.* **5** (1): 2-8 and **5** (2): 26-30.

Woodell, S.R.J. 1957. The island flora of a Connemara lake. *Ir. Nat. J.* **12**: 133-137.

Woodell, S.R.J. 1958. Biological flora of the British Isles. *Daboecia cantabrica* K. Koch. *J. Ecol.* **46**: 205-216.

FERNS

Bannister, P. and McAllister, H.A. 1966. *Asplenium septentrionale* (L.) Hoffm. in West Galway. *Ir. Nat. J.* **15** (5): 149.

Barrington, R.M. 1899. Records of Connemara ferns. *Ir. Nat.* **8** (6): 142.

Jahns, H.M. 1983. *Collins guide to the ferns, mosses and lichens of Britain and Northern and Central Europe*. Collins, London.

Jermey, A.C., Arnold, H.R., Farrell, C. and Perring, F.H. 1978. *Atlas of ferns of the British Isles*. Botanical Society of the British Isles and British Pteridological Society, London.

Praeger, R.Ll. 1902. Maidenhair fern in north east Galway. *Ir. Nat.* **11** (12): 321.

Richards, P.W. and Evans, G.B. 1972. Biological flora of the British Isles: *Hymenophyllum tunbrigense* (L.) Sm. and *Hymenophyllum wilsonii* Hooker. *J. Ecol.* **60** (1): 245-268.

Scannell, M.J.P. 1978. *Asplenium cuneifolium* viv. in W. Galway, Ireland. *Ir. Nat. J.* **19** (7): 245.

Scannell, M.J.P. and White, J. 1976. *Cryptogramma crispa* in west Ireland. *Ir. Nat. J.* 18 (11): 336.

Seebohm, H. 1851. List of ferns found in Connemara. *Naturalist* **1**: 220-222.

Stirling, A.McG. and Beckett, K.A. 1966. Plant records: *Asplenium septentrionale*. *Proc. Bot. Soc. Brit. Isles* **6**: 236.

MOSSES

Caffrey, J.M. and Synnott, D.M. 1987. The aquatic vegetation of Derrylea Lake, West Galway, Ireland, with special reference to the mosses, *Fissidens polyphyllus* Wil. ex Br. Eur. and *Calliergon trifarium* (Web. and Mohr) Kindb. *Bull. Ir. biogeog. Soc.* **10**: 94-98.

Daniels, R.E. and Eddy, A. 1985. *Handbook of European sphagna*. Institute of Terrestrial Ecology, Abbots Ripton.

Douglas, C. 1987. The distribution and ecology of *Sphagnum pulchrum* (Braithw.) Warnst. in Ireland. *Glasra* **10**: 75-81.

Hill, M.O., Preston, C.D. and Smith, A.J.E. 1992. *Atlas of the bryophytes of Britain and Ireland. Vol. 2 Mosses (except Diplolepideae)* . Harley Books, Colchester.

Kooijman, A.M. and Whilde, J. (In press) Variation in growth rates between local populations of *Scorpidium scorpioides* with different habitats. *J. Bryol.*

Lett, H.W. 1915. Census report on the mosses of Ireland. *Proc. R. Ir. Acad.* **32B**: 65-166.

Lobey, E.M. 1958. The meeting of the British Bryological Society in Co. Galway, 1957. *Ir. Nat. J.* **12** (11): 285-290.

Lobey, E.M. 1964. Some records for bryophytes. *Ir. Nat. J.* **14** (2): 43-44.

Megaw, W.R. 1935. Irish moss records. *Ir. Nat. J.* **5** (7): 173.

Ratcliffe, D.A. 1962. The habitat of *Adelanthus unciformis* (Tayl.) Mitt., and *Jamesoniella carringtonii* (Balf.) Spr. in Ireland. *Ir. Nat. J.* **14** (2): 38-40.

LIVERWORTS

Hill, M.O., Preston, C.D. and Smith, A.J.E. 1991. *Atlas of the bryophytes of Britain and Ireland*. Harley Books, Colchester.

McArdle, D. 1904. A list of Irish Hepaticae. *Proc. R. Ir. Acad.* **24B**: 387-502.

Paton, J.A. 1969. Four hepatics new to Ireland. *Ir. Nat. J.* **16** (6): 171-173.

LICHENS

Adams, M.A. 1909. The distribution of lichens in Ireland. *Proc. R. Ir. Acad.* **27B** (10): 193-234.

Bailey, R.H. 1973. Some Irish lichen records. *Ir. Nat. J.* **17** (11): 392-394.

Boyle, A.P., McCarthy, P.M. and Stewart, D. 1987. Geochemical control of saxicolous lichen communities on the Creggaun Gabbro, Letterfrack, Co. Galway, western Ireland. *Lichenologist* **19**: 307-317.

Folan, A. 1965. New station for *Cetraria islandica* (L.). *Ir. Nat. J.* **15** (1): 21.

Folan, A.C.M. and Mitchell, M.F. 1970. The lichens and lichen parasites of Derryclare Wood, Connemara. *Proc. R. Ir. Acad.* **70B** (7): 163-170.

Knowles, M.C. 1912. Notes on west Galway lichens. *Ir. Nat.* **21** (2): 29-36.

Knowles, M.C. 1929. The lichens of Ireland. *Proc. R. Ir. Acad.* **38B** (12): 179-434.

McCarthy, P.M. 1989. The lichens of Inishbofin, Co. Galway. *Ir. Nat. J.* **22** (9): 403-407.

McCarthy, P.M. and Mitchell, M.E. 1992. Bibliography of Irish lichenology: 1971-1989. *Glasra* **1**: 117-133.

McCarthy, P.M., Mitchell, M.E. and Schouten, M.G.C. 1985. Lichens epiphytic on *Calluna vulgaris* (L.) Hull in Ireland. *Nova Hedwigia* **42**: 91-98.

Mitchell, M.E. 1959. On some interesting lichens from Gorumna (Western Ireland). *Ir. Nat. J.* **13** (1): 13-16.

Porter, L. and Fitzgerald, J.W. 1951. Additions to Irish lichen records and some Irish liverwort records. *Ir. Nat. J.* **10** (8): 213-214.

Scannell, M.J.P. 1983. *Vezdaea leprosa* (P. James) vezda, a lichen new to Ireland. *Ir. Nat. J.* **21** (4): 178-179.

Seaward, M.R.D. and Hitch, C.J.B. (eds.) 1982. *Atlas of the lichens of the British Isles. Volume 1.* Natural Environment Research Council, Institute of Terrestrial Ecology, Cambridge.

FUNGI

Adams, J. and Pethybridge, G.H. 1910. A census catalogue of Irish fungi. *Proc. R. Ir. Acad.* **28B** (4): 120-166.

Cate, R.S. ten and Ligtenberg, F.K. (In litt.) Macrofungi in west Galway. *Ir. Nat. J.*

Cate, R.S. ten and Noordeloos, M.E. (In prep.) *Entoloma jennyi* SP.N. Noordeloos and ten Cate - an addition to the fungus flora of Ireland. *Ir. Nat. J.*

Dickinson, C.H. and Dooley, M. 1969. Fungi associated with Irish peat bogs. *Proc. R. Ir. Acad.* **68B**: 109-136.

Muskett, A.F. 1943. A contribution to the known fungus flora of Co. Galway. *Ir. Nat. J.* **8** (3): 60.

Noordeloos, M.E. 1993. *Studies in Entoloma* **14**. New species and new records. Rijksherbarium, Leiden.

Reid, D.A. 1953. Fungi from the Galway Bay area. *Ir. Nat.J.* **11** (3): 64-65.

Scannell, M.J.P. 1979. A contribution to the fungus flora of west Galway (H16). *Ir. Nat. J.* **19** (11): 395-397.

ALGAE

Brook, A.J. 1958. Desmids from the plankton of some Irish loughs.*Proc. R. Ir. Acad.* **59B** (6): 71-79.

Burrows, E.M. and Dixon, P.S. 1959. List of marine algae from the west coast of Ireland collected by the members of the Third International Seaweed Symposium. *Phycol. Bull.* **1** (7): 47-60.

Casley, B. 1975. *Acrothrix gracilis* Kylin on the Galway and Clare coasts.*Ir. Nat. J.* **18** (1): 20.

Cullinane, J.P. and Whelan, P.M. 1977. Marine algal records from the south coast of Ireland. *Ir. Nat. J.* **21** (7): 302-304.

Cullinane, J.P. and Whelan, P.M. 1981. The ecology and distribution of *Stenogramme interrupta* (C. Agardh) Montague ex Harvey on the coast of Ireland. *Proc. R. Ir. Acad.* **81B**: 111-116.

De Valéra, M. 1942. A red algae new to Ireland *Asparagopis armata* Harv on the west coast. *Ir. Nat. J.* **8** (2): 30-33.

De Valéra, M. 1958. *A topographical guide to the seaweeds of Galway Bay with some brief notes on other districts on the west coast of Ireland.* Institute for Industrial Research and Standards, Dublin.

De Valéra, M. and O'Ceidigh, P. 1964. West of Ireland. *In* Crisp, D.J. (Ed.) The effects of the severe winter of 1962-63 on marine life in Britain: 198-199. *J. Anim. Ecol.* **33**: 165-210.

Dooley, M. 1973. On the occurrence of *Halosphaera parkeae* Boalch and Mommaerts in Atlantic waters of Ireland. *Ir. Nat. J.* **17** (9): 316-317.

Eager, A.R. and Scannell, M.J.P. 1981. William McCalla (c1814-1849), phycologist; his published papers of 1846. *J. Life Sci., R. Dub. Soc.* **2**: 109-136.

Foslie, M. 1899. A visit to Roundstone in April. *Ir. Nat.* **8** (8): 175-180.

Guiry, M.D. 1978. *A consensus and bibliography of Irish seaweeds.* Cramer, Vaduz.

Herdman, W.A. 1891. Biological results of Argo Cruise. *Trans. Liverpool Biol. Soc.* **5**: 181-212.

Johnson, T. 1892. Sea weeds from the west coast of Ireland. *Ir. Nat.* **1** (1): 4-6.

Keyes-McDonnell, J. and Fahy, E. 1978. An annotated list of the algae comprising a lotic community in western Ireland. *Ir. Nat. J.* **19** (6): 184-187.

Kinahan, G.H. 1869. The seaweeds of Yar-Connaught, and their uses. *Quart. J. Sci.* **6**: 331-341.

Lind, E.M. and Pearsall, W.H. 1945. Plankton algae from north-western Ireland. *Proc. R. Ir. Acad.* **50B**: 311-320.

Lynn, M.J. 1935. Rare algae from Strangford Lough: Part 1.*Ir. Nat. J.* **5** (8): 201-208 and (11); 275-283.

Minchin, A. 1991. Further distribution records of the adventive marine brown alga *Colpomenia peregrina* (Phaeophyta) in Ireland. *Ir. Nat. J.* **23** (9): 380-381.

Nelson, E.C. 1981b. William McCalla - a second 'panegyric' for an Irish phycologist. *Ir. Nat. J.* **20** (7): 275-283.

Norton, T.A. (Ed.) 1985. *Provisional atlas of the marine algae of Britain and Ireland.* Institute of Terrestrial Ecology, Abbots Ripton.

Ottway, B. 1979a. *Red tides in Killary Harbour and coastal waters of north Connemara.* Fisheries Research Centre, Castleknock.

Ottway, B. 1979b. *Gracilaria foliifera* an alga new to Ireland. *Ir. Nat J.* **19** (9): 327.

Ottway, B. and Mc Donnacha, C. 1980. *Gracilaria bursa-pastoris* in Connemara. *Ir. Nat. J.* **20** (2): 74.

Pearsall, W.H. and Lind, E.M. 1948. The distribution of phytoplankton in some north-west Irish loughs. *Proc. R. Ir. Acad.* **48B** (1): 1-24.

Phillips, I.N. 1900. *Chara canescens* Loisel., in Galway. *Ir. Nat.* **9**: 243.

Pybus, C. 1977. The ecology of *Chondrus crispus* and *Gigartina stellata* (Rhodophyta) in Galway Bay. *J. mar. biol. Ass. U.K.* **57**: 609-628.

Roden, C., Rodhouse, P.G., Hensey, M.P., McMahon, T., Ryan, T.H. and Mercer, J.P. 1987. Hydrography and the distribution of phytoplankton in Killary Harbour: a fjord in western Ireland. *J. Mar. Biol. Ass. U.K.* **67**: 359-371.

Round, F.E. 1959. A comparative study of the epipelic diatom flora of some Irish loughs. *Proc. R. Ir. Acad.* **60B** (5): 193-215.

Round, F.E. and Brook, A.J. 1959. The phytoplankton of some Irish loughs and an assessment of their trophic status. *Proc. R. Ir. Acad.* **60B** (4): 167-191.

Stewart, N.F. and Church, J.M. 1992. *Red Data Books of Britain and Ireland: Stoneworts.* Joint Nature Conservancy Council, Peterborough.

Webster, A. 1972. A note on *Corallina squamata* Ellis as it occurs in the eulittoral zone in counties Clare and Galway. *Ir. Nat. J.* **17** (8): 267-268.

West, W. 1892. A contribution to the freshwater algae of the west of Ireland. *Journ. Linn. Soc., Botany* **29**.

West, W. and West, G.S. 1906. A comparative study of the plankton of some Irish lakes. *Proc. R. Ir. Acad.* **33B** (2): 77-116.

FAUNA

GENERAL

Ní Lamhna, E. (Ed.) 1979. *Provisional distribution atlas of amphibians, reptiles and mammals in Ireland.* An Foras Forbartha, Dublin.

O'Rourke, F.J. 1960. More passengers on the Gulf Stream. *Ir. Nat. J.* **13** (5): 122.

Ryland, J.S. and Nelson-Smith, A. 1975. Littoral and benthic investigations on the west coast of Ireland - IV. (Section A : Faunistic and ecological studies.) Some shores in Counties Clare and Galway. *Proc. R. Ir. Acad.* **75B** (11): 245-266.

Southward, A.J. and Crisp, D.J. 1954. The distribution of certain intertidal animals around the Irish coast. *Proc. R. Ir. Acad.* **57B** (1): 1-29.

MAMMALS

Andersen, R.J. 1904. Irish cetaceans. *Proc. Int. Zool. Conf.* , Berne: 703-711.

Andersen, R.J. 1914. Some notes on a specimen of *Tursiops tursio* killed in Galway Bay. *Int. Congr. Zool.* (Monaco 1931) **9**: 557-558.

Anon. 1915. Cetacea stranded on the coasts of the British Islands. *Ir. Nat.* **24** (6): 108.

Arnold, H.R. 1978. *Provisional atlas of the mammals of the British Isles.* Institute of Terrestrial Ecology, Abbots Ripton.

Barrett-Hamilton, G.E.H. 1890. Sperm whale in Mayo. *Zool.* **14** (3).

Barrett-Hamilton, G.E.H. 1898a. Notes on the introduction of the brown hare into Ireland. *Ir. Nat.* **7** (3): 69-76.

Barrett-Hamilton, G.E.H. 1898b. Introduction of Scotch hares in Ireland and south Scotland. *Ir. Nat.* **7** (3): 76.

Barton, D. 1938. Bone of a whale built into a house. *Ir. Nat. J.* **7** (4): 123.

Berrow, S. and Stark, D. 1990. White-sided dolphin *Lagenorhynchus acutus* (Gray). *Ir. Nat. J.* **23** (8): 334.

Cabot, D. 1966. A further example of Cuvier's whale *Ziphius cavirostris* from the west coast of Ireland. *Ir. Nat. J.* **15** (7): 212.

Casburn, P.J., Fairley, J.S. and MacLoughlin, E. 1990a. Pilot whale *Globiocephala melaena* (Traill). *Ir. Nat. J.* **23** (8): 331.

Casburn, P.J., Fairley, J.S. and MacLoughlin, E. 1990b. White-sided dolphin *Lagenorhynchus acutus* (Gray). *Ir. Nat. J.* **23** (8): 333.

Chapman, P.J. and Chapman, L.L. 1982. *Otter survey of Ireland*. The Vincent Wildlife Trust, London.

Corbet, G.B. and Harris S. (Eds.) 1991. *The handbook of British mammals*. Blackwell, Oxford.

Cotton, D.C.F. 1978. Observations of the vertebrates recorded in the Cong district of Co. Mayo between the 8th and 11th April 1977. *Bull. Ir. biogeog. Soc.* **2**: 55-57.

Evans, P.G.H. (Ed.) 1980. *Whale and seabird cruise N.E. Atlantic, Summer 1980*. Cetacean Group, Oxford.

Fairley, J.S. 1964. The fieldmouse on some Irish islands. *Ir. Nat. J.* **14** (12): 309-311.

Fairley, J.S. 1972a. *Irish wild mammals: a guide to the literature*. The Author, Galway.

Fairley, J.S. 1972b. Food of otters (*Lutra lutra*) from Co. Galway, Ireland, and notes on other aspects of their biology. *J. Zool. Lond.* **166**: 469-474.

Fairley, J.S. 1976. Natterer's bat in Co. Galway. *Ir. Nat. J.* **18** (9): 285.

Fairley, J.S. 1979. Pilot whale ashore at Barna, Co. Galway. *Ir. Nat. J.* **19** (11): 405.

Fairley, J.S. 1981. *Irish whales and whaling*. Blackstaff Press, Belfast.

Fairley, J.S. 1983a. Common dolphin *Delphinus delphis* L. *Ir. Nat. J.* **21** (4): 186.

Fairley, J.S. 1983b. Pilot whale *Globiocephala melaena* (Triall). *Ir. Nat. J.* **21** (4): 185-186.

Fairley, J.S. 1984a. *An Irish beast book*. Blackstaff Press, Belfast.

Fairley, J.S. 1984b. Otters feeding on breeding frogs. *Ir. Nat. J.* **21** (8): 372.

Fairley, J.S. 1989a. Cuvier's whale *Ziphius cavirostris* (Cuvier). *Ir. Nat. J.* **23** (4): 155.

Fairley, J.S. 1989b. Pilot whale *Globiocephala melaena* (Triall). *Ir. Nat. J.* **23** (4): 157.

Fairley, J.S. 1989c. Common dolphin *Delphinus delphis* L.; *Ir. Nat. J.* **23** (4): 159.

Fairley, J.S. 1990. Euphrosyne dolphin *Stenella coeruleoalbe* (Meyen). *Ir. Nat. J.* **23** (8): 336.

Fairley, J.S. 1991. Common dolphin *Delphinus delphis* L. at Renvyle, Co. Galway. *Ir. Nat. J.* **23** (12): 502.

Fairley, J.S. 1992. *Irish wild mammals: a guide to the literature*. 2nd Ed. The Author, Galway.

Fairley, J.S. and Clarke, F.L. 1971. A pilot whale *Globiocephala melaena* (Triall) stranded at Leagaun, Claddaghduff, Co. Galway. *Ir. Nat. J.* **17** (3): 103.

Fairley, J.S. and Dawson, B. 1981. White-sided dolphin stranded at Galway. *Ir. Nat. J.* **20** (8): 350.

Fairley, J.S. and Dawson, B. 1987. Pilot whale *Globiocephala melaena* (Traill) at Ballynahown, Co. Galway. *Ir. Nat J.* **22** (8): 360.

Fairley, J.S. and de Griffith, D. 1982. Remains of minke whale near Salruck, Co. Galway. *Ir. Nat. J.* **20** (10): 450.

Fairley, J.S. and MacLoughlin, E. 1990a. White-sided dolphin *Lagenorrhynchus acutus* (Gray). *Ir. Nat. J.* **23** (8): 333.

Fairley, J.S. and MacLoughlin, E. 1990b. Euphrosyne dolphin *Stenella coeruleoalba* (Meyen). *Ir. Nat. J.* **23** (8): 336.

Fairley, J.S., MacLoughlin, E. and Sullivan, C.M. 1990. Pilot whale *Globiocephala melaena* (Traill). *Ir. Nat. J.* **23** (8): 331.

Fairley, J.S. and O'Riordan, C.E. 1976. Remains of a sperm whale on Inishnee Island, Co. Galway. *Ir. Nat. J.* **18** (9): 285.

Fairley, J.S. and Smal, C.M. 1987. Feral house mice in Ireland. *Ir. Nat. J.* **22** (7): 284-290.

Grainger, J.P. and Fairley, J.S. 1978. Studies on the biology of the pygmy shrew *Sorex minutus* in the west of Ireland. *J. Zool., Lond.* **186**: 109-141.

Humphreys, G. 1910. Marten in Co. Galway. *Ir. Nat.* **19** (7): 140.

Hynes, J.A. and Fairley, J.S. 1978. A population study of fieldmice in dry-stone walls. *Ir. Nat. J.* **19** (6): 180-184.

Kelly, P.A. and Fairley, J.S. 1981. Fieldmice and other mammals on islands off Galway and Mayo. *Ir. Nat. J.* **20** (8): 352-353.

Kelly, P.A., Mahon, G.A.T. and Fairley, J.S. 1982. An analysis of morphological variation in the fieldmouse *Apodemus sylvaticus* (L.) on some Irish islands. *Proc. R. Ir. Acad.* **82B** (3): 39-51.

Kennedy, B. and Jacques, P. 1990. Pilot whale *Globiocephala melaena* (Triall). *Ir. Nat. J.* **23** (4): 157.

Kyne, M.J., Kyne, M.J. and Fairley, J.S. 1990. A summer survey of otter sign on Roundstone Bog, South Connemara. *Ir. Nat. J.* **23** (7): 273-276.

Lockley, R.M. 1966. The distribution of grey and common seals on the coasts of Ireland. *Ir. Nat. J.* **15** (5): 136-143.

Lunnon, R.M. and Reynolds, J.D. 1991. Distribution of the otter *Lutra lutra* in Ireland, and its value as an indicator of habitat quality. *In* Jeffrey, D.W. and Madden (Eds.) *Bioindicators and environmental management* : 435-443. Academic Press, London.

McCarthy, D.T. 1985. *Interaction between seals and salmon drift net fisheries in the west of Ireland.* Fishery Leaflet 126. Fisheries Research Centre, Dublin.

McCarthy, T.K. and Hassett, D.J. 1993. *Cryptocotyle lingua* (Creplin) (Digenea: Heterophydae) and other parasites of a coastal otter *Lutra lutra* (L.). *Ir. Nat. J.* **24** (7): 280-282.

McMillan, N.F. 1960. Ancient Irish "greyhound" pig. *Ir. Nat. J.* **13** (7): 170-171.

Maguire, S.J. 1954. Some notes on the natural history of Iar-Connacht in the seventeenth century. *Galway Reader* **4** (2/3): 102-106.

Moffat, C.B. 1938. The mammals of Ireland. *Proc. R. Ir. Acad.* **44B**: 61-128.

Nairn, R.G.W. and Curry, M.G. 1979. Further records of Risso's dolphins in Co. Mayo and Co. Galway. *Ir. Nat. J.* **19** (11): 404.

O'Donnell, G. 1992. Stoat carrying a fish. *Ir. Nat. J.* **24**(4): 174-175.

O'Riordan, C.E. 1972. Provisional list of Cetacea and turtles stranded or captured on the Irish coast. *Proc. R. Ir. Acad.* **72B** (15): 253-274.

O'Riordan, C.E. 1976. Marine fauna notes from the National Museum of Ireland, III. *Ir. Nat. J.* **18** (12): 349-350.

O'Riordan, C.E. 1981. A review of the provisional list of Cetacea stranded or captured on the Irish coast. *Ir. Nat. J.* **20** (5): 203-204.

O'Sullivan, P.J. 1983. The distribution of the pine marten (*Martes martes*) in the Republic of Ireland. *Mammal Rev.* **13** (1): 39-44.

O'Sullivan, P.J. (In press) Bat survey of the Republic of Ireland 1985-1989. *Ir. Nat. J.*

Santulli, A. 1991. Minke whale *Balaenoptera acutorostrata* Lacépèd at Doonloughan Bay, Co. Galway. *Ir. Nat. J.* **23** (12): 495.

Scharff, R.F. 1900. A list of the Irish Cetacea: whales, dolphins and porpoises. *Ir. Nat.* **9** (4): 83-91.

Scharff, R.F. 1919. A new Irish whale. *Ir. Nat.* **28** (11/12): 130-131.

Sherlock, M. 1992. *A study of the food of red deer* Cervus elaphus *L. in the Connemara National Park.* Unpublished B.Sc. thesis, National University of Ireland, University College, Galway.

Sherlock, M.G. and Fairley, J.S. 1993. Seasonal changes in the diet of red deer *Cervus elaphus* in the Connemara National Park. *Proc. Roy. Ir. Acad.* **93B** (2): 85-90.

Smal, C., Feore, S. and Montgomery, I. 1992. *The Irish badger survey: 1989-1992.* Unpublished interim report. National Parks and Wildlife Service, Dublin and Queen's University, Belfast.

Stark, D., Fairley, J.S. and MacLoughlin, E. 1990. White-sided dolphin *Lagenorhynchus acutus* (Gray). *Ir. Nat. J.* **23** (8): 334.

Summers, C.F., Warner, P.J., Nairn, R.G.W., Curry, M.G. and Flynn, J. 1980. An assessment of the status of the common seal *Phoca vitulina vitulina* in Ireland. *Biol. Conserv.* **17**: 115-123.

Warner, P. 1983. An assessment of the breeding populations of common seals (*Phoca vitulina vitulina* L.) in the Republic of Ireland during 1979. *Ir. Nat. J.* **21** (1): 24-26.

Whilde, A. 1977. A lesser horseshoe bat in west Galway. *Ir. Nat. J.* **19** (3): 99.

Whilde, A. 1992. The prey of two rural domestic cats. *Ir. Nat. J.* **24** (4): 173-174.

BIRDS

Berrow, S.D., Mackie, K.L., O'Sullivan, O., Shepherd, K.B., Mellon, C. and Coveney, J.A. 1992. *The 2nd international chough survey: Ireland.* (In litt.) Report to the Royal Society for the Protection of Birds, Sandy.

Bignal, E. and Curtis, D.J. 1988. *Choughs and land-use in Europe.* Scottish Chough Study Group, Tarbert.

Bowler, J. and Einarsson, O. 1990. *Irish whooper swan survey: 10-23 January 1990.* Unpublished report, Wetlands and Wildfowl Trust, Slimbridge.

Bullock, I.D., Drewett, D.R. and Mickleburgh, S.P. 1983. The chough in Ireland. *Ir. Birds* **2** (3): 257-271.

Cabot, D. 1965. The status and distribution of the chough *Pyrrhocorax pyrrhocorax* (L) in Ireland, 1960-65. *Ir. Nat. J.* **15** (4): 95-100.

Cott, H.B. 1921. *Brit. Birds* **1921**: 188.

Cramp, S., Bourne, W.R.P. and Saunders, D. 1974. *The seabirds of Britain and Ireland.* Collins, London.

Davenport, D.L. 1981. The spring passage of pomarine and long-tailed skuas off the south and west coasts of Britain and Ireland. *Ir. Birds* **2** (1): 73-79.

Davenport, D.L. 1984. Large passage of skuas off Scotland and Ireland in May 1982 and 1983. *Ir. Birds* **2** (4): 515-520.

Forsyth, I. 1980. A breeding census of mute swans in Ireland in 1978. *Ir. Birds* **1** (4): 492-501.

Forsyth, I. 1992. Irish ringing report for 1991. *Ir. Birds* **4** (4): 611-634.

Gibbons, D., Reid, J. and Chapman, B. (In press) *The new atlas of breeding birds in Britain and Ireland: 1988-91.* Academic Press, London.

Green, M., Knight, A., Cartmel, S. and Thomas, D. 1990. The status of wintering waders on the non-estuarine west coast of Ireland. *Ir. Birds* **3** (4): 569-574.

Harrison, C. 1982. *An atlas of the birds of the western palaearctic.* Collins, London.

Haworth, P.F. 1987. *Survey of west Galway.* Unpublished report to World Wildlife Fund, U.K.

Hibbert, R.F. 1896. Stock dove in Co. Galway. *Ir. Nat.* **5** (7): 192.

Hogan, D. and Gibbons, M. 1991. *Inis Bó Finne. A Guide to the natural history and archaeology.* Connemara Field Studies Centre, Cleggan.

Humphreys, G.R. 1912. Unusual nesting site of the tree-creeper. *Ir. Nat.* **21** (2): 46-47.

Humphreys, G.R. 1920. *Brit. Birds* **1920**: 275.

Hutchinson, C.D. 1979. *Ireland's wetlands and their birds.* Irish Wildbird Conservancy, Dublin.

Hutchinson, C.D. 1989. *Birds in Ireland.* Poyser, Calton.

Hutchinson, C.D. and Ruttledge, R.F. 1978. The birds of Inishbofin and Inishshark, Co. Galway. *Ir. Birds* **1** (2): 211-224.

Kennedy, P.G., Ruttledge, R.F., Scroope, C.F. and Humphreys, G.R. 1954. *Birds of Ireland.* Oliver and Boyd, Edinburgh and London.

Kirby, J.S., Rees, E.C., Merne, O.J. and Gardarsson, A. (In press) International census of whooper swans in Britain, Ireland and Iceland: January 1991. *Wildfowl* **43**.

Lack, P. (Ed.) 1986. *The atlas of wintering birds in Britain and Ireland.* Poyser, Calton.

Lloyd, C.S., Bibby, C.J. and Everett, M.J. 1975. Breeding terns in Britain and Ireland in 1969-74. *Brit. Birds* **68** (11): 507-513.

Lloyd, C.S., Tasker, M.L. and Partridge, K. 1991. *The status of seabirds in Britain and Ireland.* Poyser, London.

Love, J.A. 1983. *The return of the sea eagle.* Cambridge University Press, Cambridge.

Lysaght, L.S. 1991. *The birds at Murlach, Ballyconneely, County Galway.* Unpublished report to the National Parks and Wildlife Service, Galway.

Lysaght, L.S. 1993. *The birds of the Park -Connemara National Park.* Office of Public Works, Dublin.

Macdonald, R.A. 1987. The breeding population and distribution of the cormorant in Ireland. *Ir. Birds* **3** (3): 405-416.

Mayes, E. and Stowe, T. 1989. The status and distribution of the corncrake in Ireland, 1988. *Ir. Birds* **4** (1): 1-12.

Merne, O. and Murphy, C.W. 1986. Whooper swans in Ireland, January 1986. *Ir. Birds* **3** (2): 199-206.

Nairn, R.G.W. and Sheppard, J.R. 1985. Breeding waders of sand-dune machair in north-west Ireland. *Ir. Birds* **3**: 53-70.

Norriss, D. and Wilson, H.J. 1986. *Greenland white-fronted geese in Ireland 1985/86. A progress report.* Department of Tourism, Fisheries and Forestry. Forest and Wildlife Service.

Norriss, D. and Wilson, H.J. 1987. *Greenland white-fronted geese in Ireland 1986/87. A progress report.* Office of Public Works. Wildlife Service.

Ogilvie, M.A. 1983. *The population of the Greenland barnacle goose. Report on an aerial survey, March - April 1983.* Report to the Wildfowl Trust, Slimbridge.

O'Meara, M. 1979. Distribution and numbers of corncrakes in Ireland in 1978. *Ir. Birds* **1** (3): 381-405.

O'Meara, M. 1986. Corncrake declines in seven areas, 1978-1985. *Ir. Birds* **3** (2): 237-244.

Palmer, J.E. 1896. Birds of Connemara. *Ir. Nat.* **5** (3): 88.

Partridge, J.K. 1984. Survey of heronries in Connemara, 1974-1977. *Ir. Birds* **2** (4): 457-465.

Partridge, J.K. 1986. Results of ringing herons in Connemara. *Ir. Birds* **3** (2): 267-272.

Patten, C.J. 1901. The natural history of the grey phalarope (*Phalaropus fulicarius*). *Ir. Nat.* **10** (3): 53-67.

Patten, C.J. 1920a. Sora rail at Slyne Head, Co. Galway, a bird new to Ireland. *Ir. Nat.* **29** (6): 59.

Patten, C.J. 1920b. Sanderlings obtained on migration from Slyne Head light house. *Ir. Nat.* **29** (8): 79.

Payne-Gallwey, Sir R. 1882. *The Fowler in Ireland.* Ashford Press, Southhampton.

Pettitt, R.G. 1972. A comparison of auk movements in spring in north-west Spain and western Ireland. *Seabird Report* **1970**: 9-15.

Prater, A.J. 1981. *Estuary birds of Britain and Ireland.* Poyser, Calton.

Ratcliffe, D. 1980. *The peregrine falcon.* Poyser, Calton.

Ruttledge, R.F. 1920. Little stint and fork-tailed petrel obtained on migration. *Ir. Nat.* **29** (12): 134.

Ruttledge, R.F. 1932. Fulmar petrels breeding on Inishshark, Co. Galway. *Brit. Birds* **26**.

Ruttledge, R.F. 1933a. Notes on the status of the wheatear in western Connaught. *Ir. Nat. J.* **4** (7): 135-136.

Ruttledge, R.F. 1933b. Ornithological notes for Mayo and Galway. *Brit. Birds* **27** (6): 158-160.

Ruttledge, R.F. 1938a. Is the yellow hammer decreasing? *Ir. Nat. J.* **7** (3): 86.

Ruttledge, R.F. 1938b. Bird-migration by the overland route between Killala Bay and Galway Bay. *Brit. Birds* **27** (5): 130-135.

Ruttledge, R.F. 1944. Report on observations of birds at Irish light stations, 1943. *Ir. Nat. J.* **8** (5): 154-158.

Ruttledge, R.F. 1945. Results of exploration in search of Leach's fork-tailed petrel, *Oceandroma L. leuchorrhoa* (Vieill.). *Ir. Nat. J.* **8** (7): 264-265.

Ruttledge, R.F. 1947. Report on observations of birds at Irish light stations, 1946. *Ir. Nat. J.* **9** (3): 57-61.

Ruttledge, R.F. 1949. Report on observations of birds at Irish light stations, 1948. *Ir. Nat. J.* **9** (10): 256-261.

Ruttledge, R.F. 1950. A list of the birds of the counties Galway and Mayo showing their status and distribution. *Proc. R. Ir. Acad.* **52B** (8): 315-381.

Ruttledge, R.F. 1952a. Red-breasted flycatcher in Co. Galway. *Ir. Nat. J.* **10** (11): 302-303.

Ruttledge, R.F. 1952b. Report on observations of birds at Irish light stations, 1951. *Ir. Nat. J.* **10** (12): 314-318.

Ruttledge, R.F. 1957. The birds of Inishbofin, Co. Galway with some notes on those of Inishshark. *Bird Study* **4** (2): 71-80.

Ruttledge, R.F. 1960. The breeding-range and status of the redshank in western Ireland. *Bird Study* **8** (1): 2-5.

Ruttledge, R.F. 1966. *Ireland's birds.* Witherby, London.

Ruttledge, R.F. 1969. Winter distribution and numbers of scaup, long-tailed duck and common scoter in Ireland. *Bird Study* **17** (3): 241-246.

Ruttledge, R.F. 1974. Winter distribution of whooper and Bewick's swans in Ireland. *Bird Study* **21** (2): 141-145.

Ruttledge, R.F. 1975. *A list of the birds of Ireland.* Stationery Office, Dublin.

Ruttledge, R.F. 1989. *Birds in Counties Galway and Mayo.* Irish Wildbird Conservancy, Monkstown.

Ruttledge, R.F. and Hall Watt, R. 1957. The distribution and status of wild geese in Ireland. *Bird Study* **5** (1): 22-33.

Ruttledge, R.F. and Williamson, K. 1952. Early arrival of white-fronted geese in Ireland. *Ir. Nat. J.* **10** (10): 263-264.

Sharrock, J.T.R. 1976. *The atlas of breeding birds in Britain and Ireland.* British Trust for Ornithology / Irish Wildbird Conservancy, Berkhamsted.

Sheldon, J. and Bradshaw, D. 1971. Shearwaters and other seabirds at Slyne Head, Co. Galway in the autumn of 1969. *Seabird Report* **1970**: 25-26.

Sheppard, J.R. (In press) *Ireland's wetland wealth - the birdlife of the estuaries, lakes, coasts, rivers, bogs and turloughs of Ireland.* Report of the winter wetlands survey, 1984/85 to 1986/87. Irish Wildbird Conservancy, Monkstown.

Stroud, D.A. and Fox, A.D. 1985. *A conspectus of information relevant to the conservation of the Greenland white-fronted Goose (*Anser albifrons flavirostris*) in the British Isles.* Greenland White-fronted Goose Study Group, Aberystwyth.

Thomas, G.J. 1982. Breeding terns in Britain and Ireland, 1975-79. *Seabird Report* **6**: 59-69.

Ussher, R.J. 1890. On the coast of Connaught. *Zoologist* **14** (3): 361.

Ussher, R.J. 1896. Birds of Connemara. *Ir. Nat.* **5** (12): 319.

Ussher, R.J. and Warren, R. 1900. *Birds of Ireland.* London.

Walsh, A. and Merne, O. 1988. Barnacle geese in Ireland, spring 1988. *Ir. Birds* **3** (4): 539-550.

West, B., Cabot, D. and Greer Walker, M. 1975. The food of the cormorant *Phalacrocorax carbo* at some breeding colonies in Ireland. *Proc. R. Ir. Acad.* **75B**: 285-304.

Whilde, A. 1977a. *Birds of Galway and Mayo.* Irish Wildbird Conservancy, Galway.

Whilde, A. 1977b. The autumn and winter food of mallard, *Anas p. platyrhynchos* L., and some other Irish wildfowl. *Ir. Nat. J.* **19** (1): 18-21.

Whilde, A. 1977c. Aspects of the biology of the storm petrel and the corncrake. *Ir. Univ. Rev.* **7** (1):70-72.

Whilde, A. 1978a. A survey of gulls breeding inland in the west of Ireland in 1977 and 1978 and a review of the inland breeding habit in Ireland and Britain. *Ir. Birds* **1** (2): 134-160.

Whilde, A. 1978b. Further observations on the autumn and winter food of some Irish wildfowl. *Ir. Nat. J.* **19** (5): 149-152.

Whilde, A. 1979. Auks trapped in salmon drift-nets. *Ir. Birds* **1** (3): 370-376.

Whilde, A. 1982. *Irish wetlands survey. I and II.* Federation of Hunting Associations of the E.E.C. / National Association of Regional Game Councils, Brussels.

Whilde, A. 1983. A re-survey of gulls breeding in the west of Ireland. *Ir. Birds* **2** (3): 344-345.

Whilde, A. 1985a. *The all Ireland tern survey 1984.* Unpublished report to theRoyal Society for the Protection of Birds / Irish Wildbird Conservancy.

Whilde, A. 1985b. The 1984 all Ireland tern survey. *Ir. Birds* **3** (1): 1-32.

Whilde, A. 1986a. *An ecological evaluation of potential areas in the west of Ireland for the re-introduction of white-tailed (sea) eagles (*Haliaeetus albicilla L.*).* Unpublished report to the Irish Wildbird Conservancy, Monkstown.

Whilde, A. 1986b. *Computerisation, analysis and application of Irish wetland habitat data.* Corrib Conservation Centre, Oughterard.

Whilde, A. 1987. A County Galway winter waterbird inventory. *Ir. Nat. J.* **22** ( ): 185-188.

Whilde, A. 1989. The chough in Ireland: numbers and distribution. *In* Bignal, E.M. and Curtis, D.J. (eds.) *The chough and land-use in Europe.* Proceedings of an international workshop on the conservation of the chough, *Pyrrhocorax pyrrhocorax*, in the E.C. Scottish Chough Study Group, Islay.

Whilde, A. 1990a. An assessment of the breeding heron (*Ardea cinerea*) population of Connemara, Co. Galway in 1989. *Brit. Ecol. Soc. Bull.* **1** (1): 40-42.

Whilde, A. 1990b. *Birds of Galway. A review of recent records and Field studies.* Irish Wildbird Conservancy, Galway.

Whilde, A., Cotton, D.C.F. and Sheppard, J.R. (in press) Changes in the numbers of gulls breeding inland in the west of Ireland between 1977-8 and 1992-3. *Irish Birds.*

Whilde, A. and Lansdown, R. 1984. Some results from an intensive winter atlas survey in the west of Ireland. *Ir. Birds* **2** (4): 521-525.

Williams, E. 1892. Golden eagle (*Aquila chrysaetus*) in Co. Galway. *Ir. Nat.* **1** (4): 83.

Wilson, H.J. and Norriss, D.W. 1986. Results of the Greenland white-fronted goose survey in Ireland, 1982/83 to 1984/85. *Shooting News* **5** (1): 31-36.

Witherby, H.F. 1896a. A fortnight with the birds of Connemara. *Ir. Nat.* **5** (1): 1-5.

Witherby, H.F. 1896b. Birds of Connemara. *Ir. Nat.* **5** (11): 299.

REPTILES

Went, A.E.J. 1944. A note on the habits of the common lizard, *Lacerta vivipara* Jacq. *Ir. Nat. J.* **8** (5): 181.

FISH

Anon. 1987. *Report of the salmon review group. Framework for the development of Ireland's salmon fishery.* Stationery Office, Dublin.

Anon. 1989. The Sea Trout Action Group Interim Report. *Sea Trout News* **1**.

Anon. 1991. The Sea Trout Action Group Report. An investigation in the 1989/90 collapse of sea trout stocks in Galway and South Mayo. *Sea Trout News* **2**.

Anon. 1992. The Sea Trout Action Group 1991 Report. *Sea Trout News* **3**.

Browne, J. and Gallagher, P. 1980. *Population estimates of juvenile salmonids in the Corrib system 1980.* Fisheries Research Centre, Dublin.

Browne, J. and Gallagher, P. 1987. *Population estimates of juvenile salmon in the Corrib system from 1982 to 1984.* Fisheries Research Centre, Dublin.

Cheetham, J M. and Fives, J.M. 1990. The biology and parasites of the butterfish *Pholis gunnellus* (Linnaeus,1758) in the Galway Bay area. *Proc. R. Ir. Acad.* **90B**: 127-149.

Cross, T. and Ottway, B. (Eds.) 1990. *Proceedings of the Institute of Fisheries Management 2 0th annual study course, 1989.* Galway.

Dunne, J. 1973. A further record of *Ciliata septentrionalis* Collett. *Ir. Nat. J.* **17** (11): 394-395.

Dunne, J. 1981. A contribution to the biology of Montagu's sea snail *Liparis montagui* Donovan, (Pisces). *Ir. Nat. J.* **20** (6): 217-222.

Dunne, J. 1983. Gobiesocidae occurring in the coastal waters of Connemara. *Ir. Fish. Invest. Ser. A* **23**: 32-36.

Dunne, J. and Byrne, P. 1979. Notes on the biology of the tompot blenny, *Blennius gattorugine* Brunnich. *Ir. Nat. J.* **19** (12): 414-418.

Dunne, J. and Cooper, T. 1980. The occurrence of Yarrell's blenny in Galway Bay. *Ir. Nat. J.* **20** (4): 156-160.

Dunne, J. and Konnecker, G. 1976. Some inshore fishes from the Connemara coast. *Ir. Nat. J.* **18** (9): 267-270.

Dunne, J. and Milcendeau, B. 1980. Further records of the northern rockling *Ciliata septentrionalis. Ir. Nat. J.* **20** (2): 79.

Fahy, E. 1977. Characteristics of the freshwater occurrence of sea trout *Salmo trutta* in Ireland. *J. Fish Biol.* **11**: 635-646.

Fahy, E. 1978. Performance of a group of sea trout rod fisheries, Connemara, Ireland. *Fish. Man.* **9** (1): 22-31.

Fahy, E. 1979. Performance of the Crumlin sea trout fishery, Co. Galway. *Fishery Leaflet* **101**.

Fahy, E. 1985. *Child of the tides. A sea trout handbook.* Glendale Press, Dun Laoghaire.

Fahy, E. 1986. *Capture of sea-trout by illegal means in the Western Fisheries Region. Some observations for discussion.* Fishery Leaflet 130. Fisheries Research Centre, Dublin.

Fahy, E. , Murphy, M. and Dempster, S. 1984. Salmonid carrying capacity of streams in the Connemara region, a resource appraisal. *Fish. Bull.* **9**.

Fahy, E. and Nixon, J.J. 1982. Spawning trout in Eastern Connemara. *Fish. Bull.* **6**.

Fahy, E. and Rudd, R. 1990. When Finnock failed..... *The Salmon and Trout Magazine* **Autumn 1990**: 66-70.

Kennedy, M. and Fitzmaurice, P. 1971. Growth and food of brown trout *Salmo trutta* (L.) in Irish waters. *Proc. R. Ir. Acad.* **71B** (18): 269-352.

King, P.A. 1989. Littoral and benthic investigations on the west coast of Ireland - XXII. The biology of a population of shore clingfish *Lepadogaster lepadogaster* (Bonnaterre, 1788) at Inishbofin, Co. Galway. *Proc. R. Ir. Acad.* **89B**: 47-58.

King, P.A. and Fives, J.M. 1990. Littoral and benthic investigations on the west coast of Ireland - XXIII. A contribution to the biology of the thickback sole *Microchirus variegatus* (Donovan 1808) in the Galway Bay area. *Proc. R. Ir. Acad.* **90B**: 23-31.

McFadden, Y.M.T. and Fairley, J.S. 1984. Fish predation as a possible influence on the sizes of crayfish eaten by otters. *Ir. Nat. J.* **21** (8): 364.

Maitland, P.S. 1972. *Key to British freshwater fishes.* Freshwater Biological Association, Ambleside.

Maitland, P.S. 1979. The status and conservation of rare freshwater fishes in the British Isles. *Proc. Inst. Br. Freshwat. Conf.* : 237-248.

Maitland, P.S. and Campbell, R.N. 1992. *Freshwater fishes*. Harper Collins, London.

Mills, C.P.R. and Piggins, D.J. (Eds.) 1988. *Sea trout workshop March 1988, Galway*. Irish National Branch of the Institute of Fisheries Management, Dublin.

Moriarty, C. 1972. Studies of the eel *Anguilla anguilla* in Ireland. 1. In the lakes of the Corrib System. *Ir. Fish. Invest. Ser. A.* **10**: 1-39.

Moriarty, C. 1978. *Eels. A natural and unnatural history*. David and Charles, Newton Abbot.

Moriarty, C. 1980. *Eel research 1978-1979*. Department of Fisheries and Forestry, Dublin.

Moriarty, C. 1988. *The eel in Ireland. Went Memorial Lecture 1987.* Royal Dublin Society, Dublin.

Nall, G.H. 1931. Irish sea trout. Notes on collections of scales from the west coast of Ireland. *Proc. R. Ir. Acad.* **40B** (1): 1-36.

O'Ceidigh, P. 1959. The blennies, Genus *Blennius* L., of Kilkieran Bay, Connemara. *Ir. Nat. J.* **13** (3): 72-74.

O'Farrell, M.M. and Whelan, K.F. (in press). Management of migratory trout (*Salmo trutta* L.) in the Erriff and other catchments in western Ireland. *Proc. Symp. Irish Rivers: Biology and Management.* Royal Irish Academy, Dublin.

O'Reilly, P. 1987. *Trout and salmon loughs of Ireland*. Unwin Hyman, London.

O'Riordan, C.E. 1979. Marine fauna notes from the National Museum of Ireland - VI. *Ir. Nat. J.* **19** (10): 356-358.

Quigley, D.T.G. and Nolan, F. 1984. First record of char *Salvelinus alpinus* (L.) from Shannakeela Lake, Maam Cross, Galway. *Ir. Nat. J.* **21** (5): 235.

Regan, C.T. 1909. The char of Ireland. *Ir. Nat.* **18** (1): 3-6.

Ryland, J.S. 1969. Some shore fishes from Galway Bay. *Ir. Nat. J.* **16**: 127-131.

Warner, R., Linnane, K. and Browne, P.R. 1980. *Fishing in Ireland, the complete guide*. Appletree Press, Belfast.

Went, A.E.J. 1943. Salmon of the River Corrib, together with notes on the growth of brown trout in the Corrib system.*Proc. R. Ir. Acad.* **48B** (12): 269-298.

Went, A.E.J. 1945. The distribution of Irish char (*Salvelinus* spp.). *Proc. R. Ir. Acad.* **50 B** (8): 167-189.

Went, A.E.J. 1955a. Notes on Irish char. *Salvelinus colii* Gunther: V. *Ir. Nat. J.* **11** (9): 246-248.

Went, A.E.J. 1955b. Captures of specimens of char, *Salvelinus* spp. *Ir. Nat. J.* **11** (10): 291.

Went, A.E.J. 1956. Sea trout of the Cashla River, with notes on the salmon. *Salm. and Trout Mag.* **146**: 63-76.

Went, A.E.J. 1962. Irish sea trout, a review of investigations to date. *Sci. Proc. R. Dub. Soc.* **1** (10): 265-296.

Went, A.E.J. 1964. The pursuit of salmon in Ireland. *Proc. R. Ir. Acad.* **63C** (6): 191-244.

Went, A.E.J. 1971. The distribution of Irish char (*Salvelinus alpinus*). *Ir. Fish. Invest. Ser. A* **6**: 5-11.

Went, A.E.J. and Kennedy, M. 1976. *List of Irish fishes*. Stationery Office, Dublin.

Went, A.E.J. and Twomey, E. 1957. Notes on Irish char, *Salvelinus colii* Gunther: VI. *Ir. Nat. J.* **12** (8): 205-206.

Wheeler, A. 1968. Notes on some Irish fishes. *Ir. Nat. J.* **16** (3): 62-66.

Whelan, K. 1989. *The angler in Ireland. Game, coarse and sea*. Country House, Dublin.

Whelan, K.F. 1992. Salmon Research Agency of Ireland management of salmon and sea trout stocks. *In* Feehan, J. (Ed.) 1992. *Environment and development in Ireland*. The Environment Institute, University College, Dublin: 457-466.

Wilkins, N.P. 1989. *Ponds, passes and parcs. Aquaculture in Victorian Ireland*. Glendale Press, Dublin.

INSECTS

Anderson, R. 1984. Staphylinidae (Coleoptera) in Ireland - 3: Steninae. *Ir. Nat. J.* **21** (6): 242-251.

Anon. 1980. *Atlas of the bumblebees of the British Isles*. Institute of Terrestrial Ecology, Cambridge.

Ashe, P., O'Connor, J.P. and Casey, R.J. 1991. Irish mosquitoes (Diptera : Culicidae): A checklist of species and their known distribution. *Proc. R. Ir. Acad.* **91B** (2): 21-36.

Baynes, E.S.A. 1954. Report on migrant insects in Ireland for 1953. *Ir. Nat. J.* **11** (7):195-197.

Baynes, E.S.A. 1963. Report on migrant insects in Ireland for 1962. *Ir. Nat. J.* **14** (5): 86-89.

Baynes, E.S.A. 1965. Irish Lepidoptera: some recent discoveries. *Ir. Nat. J.* **15** (1): 13-16.

Beirne, B.P. 1941. A list of the microlepidoptera of Ireland. *Proc. R. Ir. Acad.* **47B** (4): 53-147.

Chalmers-Hunt, J.M. 1982. On some interesting Irish Lepidoptera in the National Museum of Ireland. *Ir. Nat. J.* **20** (12): 531-537.

Chaster, G.W. 1902. Two beetles from Roundstone, new to the Irish list. *Ir. Nat.* **12**: 167.

Claassens, J.M. and O'Rourke, F.J. 1966. The distribution and general ecology of the Irish Siphonaptera. *Proc. R. Ir. Acad.* **64B** (23): 413-463.

Collingwood, C.A. 1958. A survey of Irish Formicidae. *Proc. R. Ir. Acad.* **59B** (11): 213-219.

Cornwell, P.B. 1968. The incidence of German and Oriental cockroaches in Ireland. *Ir. Nat. J.* **16** (4): 97-100.

Costello, M.J. 1988a. A review of the distribution of stoneflies (Insecta, Plecoptera) in Ireland. *Proc. R. Ir. Acad.* **88B** (1): 1-22.

Costello, M.J. 1988b. Preliminary observations on wing-length polymorphism in stoneflies (Plecoptera: Insecta) in Ireland. *Ir. Nat. J.* **22** (11): 461-504.

Costello, M.J., McCarthy, T.K. and O'Farrell, M.M. 1984. The stoneflies (Plecoptera) of the Corrib catchment area, Ireland. *Annls. Limnol.* **20** (1-2): 25-34.

Cotton, D.C.F. 1980. Distribution records of Orthoptera (Insecta) from Ireland. *Bull. Ir. biogeog. Soc.* **4**: 13-22.

Crawford, W.M. 1934. Irish Coleoptera records. *Ir. Nat. J.* **5** (5): 121.

Crawford, W.M. 1936a. Records of Irish Coleoptera. *Ir. Nat. J.* **6** (1): 25.

Crawford, W.M. 1936b. Irish Coleoptera records. *Ir. Nat. J.* **6** (4): 102.

Crichton, M. and Ní Lamhna, E. 1975. *Provisional atlas of butterflies of Ireland* . An Foras Forbartha, Dublin.

Crisp, D.T. 1959. Hydracarines and Nematodes parasitizing *Corixa scotti* (D. and S.) (Hemiptera) in western Ireland. *Ir. Nat. J.* **13** (4): 88-92.

Crisp, D.T. and Heal, O.W. 1958a. The Corixidae (O. Hemiptera), Gyrinidae (O. Coleoptera) and Cladocera (Subphylum Crustacea) of a bog in western Ireland.*Ir. Nat. J.* **12** (11): 297-304.

Crisp, D.T. and Heal, O.W. 1958b. The Corixidae (O. Hemiptera), Gyrinidae (O. Coleoptera) and Cladocera (Subphylum Crustacea) of a bog in western Ireland.*Ir. Nat. J.* **12** (12): 318-324.

Cruttwell, C.T. 1900. Abundance of *Colias edusa* in Connemara. *Ent. Mo. Mag.* **26**: 1.

Disney, R.H.I. 1977. Scuttle Flies (Diptera: Phoridae) from Inishbofin, Co. Galway. *Ir. Nat. J.* 19 (3): 57-61.

Ellerton, J. 1967. A fortnight in Connemara, 12th - 29th August 1966. *Ent. Rec.* **79**: 125-127.

Emmet, A.M. 1968. Lepidoptera in West Galway. *Ent. Gaz.* **19**: 45-48.

Emmet, A.M. 1971. More Lepidoptera in West Galway. *Ent. Gaz.* **22**: 3-18.

Emmet, A.M. 1975. A preliminary list of the Nepticulidae of Ireland.*Proc. Trans. Br. Ent. Nat. Hist. Soc.* **8**: 31-38.

Fahy, E. 1970. The distribution of the Irish Psocoptera. *Proc. R. Ir. Acad.* **69B** (6): 139-164.

Fahy, E. 1974. Distribution data on the Ephemeroptera and Plecoptera in Ireland. *Ent. Gaz.* **25**: 141-146.

Fahy, E. 1976. An explanation for the distribution in Ireland of *Aphelocheirus aestivalis* (Fabricius) (Hemiptera: Aphelocheiridae). *Ent. Gaz.* **27**: 275-276.

Faris, R.C. and O'Rourke, F.J. 1946. *Orthetrum cancellatum* L. A dragonfly new to Ireland, and other dragonfly notes from Connaught. *Ir. Nat. J.* **8** (11): 387-390.

Haes, E.C.M. (Ed.) 1990a. Orthoptera Recording Scheme. *Biol. Rec. Centre Newsletter* **15**.

Haes, E.C.M. (Ed.) 1990b. Orthoptera Recording Scheme. *Biol. Rec. Centre Newsletter* **16**.

Halbert, J.N. 1935. A list of the Irish Hemiptera (Heteroptera and Cicadina). *Proc. R. Ir. Acad.* **42B** (8): 211-318.

Hammond, C.O. 1977. *The dragonflies of Great Britain and Ireland.* Curwen Press, London.

Haynes, R.F. 1953. Collecting moths and butterflies in Connemara and N. Mayo, June 1952. *Ir. Nat. J.* **11** (2): 33-34.

Haynes, R.F. 1963. Notes on Lepidoptera in the west of Ireland. *Ir. Nat. J.* **14** (8): 174-177.

Haynes, R.F. and Lavery, T.A. 1990. Report on migrant insects in Ireland for 1989. *Ir. Nat. J.* **23** (7): 277-279.

Heath, J. and Skelton, M.J. (Eds.) 1973. *Provisional atlas of the insects of the British Isles*, II. Biological Records Centre, Abbots Ripton.

Heneghan, L. 1986. *The Chironomidae of Connemara National Park*. National Parks and Wildlife Service, Office of Public Works, Dublin.

Hickin, N. 1992. *The butterflies of Ireland. A field guide*. Roberts Rinehart, Schull.

Higgins, L. 1947. Lepidoptera collected at Oughterard, Co. Galway in May 1946. *Ir. Nat. J.* **9** (4): 99-100.

Higgins, L.G. and Riley, N.D. 1980. *A field guide to the butterflies of Britain and Europe*. Collins, London.

Hillis, J.P. 1973. August butterflies in the Carna district, Connemara. *Ent. Gaz.* **24**: 313-314.

Hillis, J.P. 1976. Report on migrant insects in Ireland for 1975. *Ir. Nat. J.* **18** (12): 356-359.

Kane, W.F. de V. 1893. A catalogue of the Lepidoptera of Ireland. *Ent.* **26**: 212.

Kane, W.F. de V. 1897. *Asteroscopus sphinx* numerous in Co. Galway. *Ent. Rec.* **9**: 63.

Lavery, T. 1993. A review of the distribution, ecology and status of the marsh fritillary *Euhydras aurinia* Rottenburg, 1775 (Lepidoptera: Nymphalidae) in Ireland. *Ir. Nat. J.* **24** (5): 192-199.

Lott, D.A. and Bilton, D.T. 1991. Records of Coleoptera from Irish wetland sites in 1989. *Bull. Ir. biogeog. Soc.* **14** (1): 60-72.

MacNeill, N. 1960. Odonata - Irish distribution. *Ir. Nat. J.* **13** (8): 190.

MacNeill, N. 1968. Odonata - Irish distribution. *Ir. Nat. J.* **16** (1): 25.

MacNeill, N. 1973. A revised and tabulated list of the Irish Hemiptera-Heteroptera: Part 1 Geocorisae. *Proc. R. Ir. Acad.* **73B** (3): 57-60.

Marcon, J.N. 1953. A holiday in western Ireland. *Ent. Rec.* **65**: 105-107.

Mendel, H. 1988. *Provisional atlas of the click beetles (Coleoptera : Elateroidea)*. Institute of Terrestrial Ecology, Grange-over-Sands.

Morris, M.G. 1971. New vice county records of Irish weevils (Coleoptera : Curculionoidea). *Ir. Nat. J.* **17** (4): 136.

Morris, M.G. 1987. New vice county records of weevils (Coleoptera : Curculionoidea) from Ireland. *Bull. Ir. biogeog. Soc.* **10**: 124-144.

Morris, M.G. 1993. A critical review of the weevils (Coleoptera, Curculionoidea) of Ireland and their distribution. *Proc. Roy. Ir. Acad.* **93B** (2): 69-84.

Murray, D.A. 1972. A list of the Chironomidae (Diptera) known to occur in Ireland, with notes on their distribution. *Proc. R. Ir. Acad.* **72B** (16): 275-293.

Murray, J.W. 1973. *Distribution and ecology of living benthic Foraminiferids*. Heineman, London.

Nash, R. 1975. The butterflies of Ireland. *Proc. Brit. Ent. Nat. Hist. Soc.* **7**: 69-73.

O'Connor, J.P. and Murphy, D. 1988. Some records of Irish Odonata (Insecta). *Bull. Ir. biogeog. Soc.* **11**: 35-40.

O'Rourke, F.J. 1946. The occurrence of three Mermithogynes at Roundstone, Connemara, with notes on the ants of the area. *Ent. Rec.* **58**: 65-70.

O'Rourke, F.J. 1952. A preliminary ecological classification of ant communities in Ireland. *Ent. Gaz.* **3**: 69-72.

Pack-Beresford, D.R. 1903. Two beetles from Roundstone, new to the Irish list. *Ir. Nat.* **12** (6): 167.

Pont, A. 1987. *Provisional atlas of the Sepsidae (Diptera) of the British Isles*. Institute of Terrestrial Ecology, Grange-over-Sands.

Speight, M.C.D. 1975. *Conops vesicularis, Epistrophe nitidicollis* and *Ctenophora atrata* : insects new to Ireland. *Ir. Nat. J.* **18** (6): 191-192.

Speight, M.C.D. 1983. Irish Otitidae and Platystomatidae (Diptera) including a key to the genera known in Ireland and /or Great Britain. *Ir. Nat. J.* **21** (3): 130-136.

Speight, M.C.D., Chandler, P.J. and Nash, R. 1975. Irish Syrphidae (Diptera): notes on the species and an account of their known distribution. *Proc. R. Ir. Acad.* **75B** (1): 1-80.

Stelfox, A.W. 1936. The Irish Ichneumon-flies of the genus *Banchus*. *Ir. Nat. J.* **6** (3): 63-64.

Torlesse, A.D. 1964. Western Ireland 1963. *Ent. Rec.* **76**: 40-44.

Tully, O., McCarthy, T.K. and O'Donnell, D. 1991. The ecology of the Corixidae (Hemiptera: Heteroptera) in the Corrib catchment, Ireland. *Hydrobiologia* **210**: 161-169.

Varian, S. 1991. *The Polladirk River: Macroinvertebrate species assemblages and variation in community structure.* Unpublished B.Sc. thesis, National University of Ireland, University College, Galway.

Walton, G.A. 1967. A site of particular zoological interest - Doughruagh Mountain, Kylemore, Co. Galway. *Ir. Nat. J.* **15** (11): 309-312.

Walton, G.A. 1986. *Saldula connemarae* SP. N. (Hemiptera: Saldidae), a new species of shore bug from Co. Galway, Ireland. *Ir. Nat. J.* **22** (2): 51-52.

Worms, C.G.M. de. 1966. *Sirex gigas* L. in Connemara. *Ent. Rec.* **78**: 26.

MOLLUSCS

Alcock, T. 1864. Notes on natural history specimens lately received from Connemara. *Proc. Lit. and Phil. Soc. Manchr* **4**: 192-199.

Alcock, T. 1865. Notes on natural history specimens lately received from Connemara. *Proc. Lit. and Phil. Soc. Manchr.* **4**: 200-208.

Bloomer, H.H. 1927. *Margaritifera margaritifera.* Notes on the variation of the British and Irish forms. *Proc. Malac. Soc. Lond.* **17**: 208-216.

Buckland, F.T. 1864. A run through Connemara and Galway. Chapter X, *Field* **24**: 400.

Buckland, F.T. 1878. *Curiosities of Natural History* . Richard Bentley, London: 334-338.

Chaster, G.W. 1895. *Adeorbis imperspicuus*, Monterosato off Roundstone. *J.Malacology* **Sept**. and *Ir. Nat.* **4** (12): 348.

Chaster, G.W. and Tomlin, B. 1903. The rediscovery of *Vertigo lilljeborgi* in Ireland. *Ir. Nat.* **12** (1): 13-14.

Croome, R.J. 1972a. *Growth of the American hard-shelled clam,* Venus mercenaria *L. in the west of Ireland.* Unpublished M.Sc. thesis, National University of Ireland, University College, Galway.

Croome, R.J. 1972b. *Population dynamics of* T. decussatus *L. on the west coast of Ireland.* Unpublished Ph.D. thesis. National University Ireland, University College Galway.

Darbishire, R.D. 1885. Land shells at Dog's Bay, Connemara. *J.Conch.* **4**: 317.

Farran, C. 1845. Upon the rare species and peculiar habits of the shells of the western coast and of the characteristic features of Roundstone and Birterbuy Bays, Connemara. *Ann. Rep. Dubl. Nat. Hist. Soc.* **7**: 14-16.

Gibson, F.A. 1959. Notes on the escallop (*Pecten maximus* L.) in three closely associated bays in the west of Ireland. *J. cons. perm. int. Explor. Mer.* **24** (2):366-371.

Gibson, F.A. 1970. Further introductions of American hand-shelled clam, *Mercenaria mercenaria*, into Irish waters. *Ir. Nat. J.* **16** (12): 396.

Hensman, R.1895. Some causes of the disintegration of shells. *Ir. Nat.* **4** (6): 137-141.

Holmes, J.M.C., McGrath, D., Picton, B.E. and Mulligan, N. 1983. Records of some interesting crabs from the coast of Ireland. *Ir. Nat. J.* **21** (2): 79-81.

Jackson, J.S. 1958. On two occurrences of living *Jarthina brittanica* Forbes and Harley from the west coast of Ireland. *Ir. Nat. J.* **12** (12): 330-331.

Jackson, J.W. 1925. The distribution of *Margaritifera margaritifera* in the British Isles. *J. Conch.* **17**: 195-211.

Just, H. and Edmunds, M. 1985. North Atlantic Nudibranchs (Mollusca) seen by Henning Lemche. *Ophelia* suppl. **2**: 138-140.

Keegan, B.F. 1966. *A survey of the seasonal variations of the Palagic Copepoda of Killeany Bay.* Unpublished M.Sc. thesis, National University of Ireland, University College, Galway.

Keegan, B.F. 1972. *Benthic studies in Kilkieran Bay and in Galway Bay with particular reference to the class Bivalvia.* Unpublished Ph.D. thesis, National University of Ireland, University College, Galway.

Keegan, B.F. 1974. Littoral and benthic investigations on the west coast of Ireland - III (Section A: faunistic and ecological studies) The bivalves of Galway Bay and Kilkieran Bay. *Proc. R. Ir. Acad.* **74B** (8): 85-123.

Kerney, M.P. 1973. Mapping non-marine Mollusca in north-west Ireland, summer 1972. *Ir. Nat. J.* **17** (9): 310-316.

King, P.A., McGrath, D. and Gosling, E.M. 1989. Reproduction and settlement of *Mytilus edulis* on an exposed rocky shore in Galway Bay, west coast of Ireland. *J. mar. biol. Ass. U.K.* **69**: 355-365.

Macan, T.T. and Lund, J.W.G. 1954. Records from some Irish lakes: Part 1. Mollusca, *Gammarus, Asellus*, Ephemeroptera and Heteroptera; Part 2. Phytoplankton. *Proc. R. Ir. Acad.* **56B** (4): 135-158.

McCalla, W. 1836. A list of species of shells found near Roundstone. *Nat. Mag. Hist.* **9**: 130.

McGrath, D. 1981. *Danilia tinei* (Calcara), a gastropod new to the Irish fauna, from the west coast of Ireland. *Ir. Nat. J.* **20** (5): 202.

Marshall, J.T. 1890. Dredging off Connemara. *J. Conch., Lond.* **6**: 250.

Minchin, D., McGrath, D. and Duggan, C.B. 1987. *Calyptraea chinensis* (Mollusca, Gastropoda) on the west coast of Ireland: a case of accidental introduction? *J. Conch.* **32**: 297-301.

Nunn, J. 1993. *Aeolidiella alderi* (Cocks, 1852) (Mollusca: Opisthobranchia) in Ireland. *Ir. Nat. J.* **25** (6): 258-260.

Nunn, J. and McGrath, D. 1989. *Rissoella globularis* (Jeffries) (Mollusca: Gastropoda) in Ireland. *Ir. Nat. J.* **23** (4): 161.

O'Loughlin, E.F.M. 1989. Notes on the distribution of *Calliostoma zizyphinum* (L.) (Mollusca) on the shores and shallow waters of the Irish coast. *Bull. Ir. biogeog. Soc.* **12**: 22-30.

Partridge, J.K. 1977a. *Studies on* Tapes decussatus *L. in Ireland. Natural populations, artificial propagation and mariculture potential with an inventory of the major European fisheries and a fully annotated bibliography.* Unpublished Ph.D. thesis. National University of Ireland, University College, Galway.

Partridge, J.K. 1977b. Littoral and benthic investigations on the west coast of Ireland - VI. Annotated bibliographies of the genus Tapes (Bivalvia; Veneridae): Part 1 - *Tapes decussatus* (L.); Part II - *Tapes semidecussatus* (Reeve). *Proc. R. Ir. Acad.* **77B** (1): 1-64.

Phillips, R.A. and Stelfox, A.W. 1918. Recent extensions of the range of *Pisidium hibernicum. Ir. Nat.* **27** (3): 33-50.

Rodhouse, P.G., Roden, C.M., Burnell, G.M., Hensey, M.P., McMahon, T., Ottway, B. and Ryan, T.H. 1984. Food resource, gametogenesis and growth of *Mytilus edulis* on the shore and in suspended culture: Killary Harbour, Ireland. *J. mar. biol. Ass. U.K.* **64**: 513-529.

Rodhouse, P.G., Roden, C.M., Hensey, M.P. and Ryan, T.H. 1984. Resource allocation in *Mytilus edulis* on the shore and in suspended culture. *Marine Biology* **84**: 27-34.

Rodhouse, P.G., Roden, C.M., Hensey, M.P. and Ryan, T.H. 1985. Production of mussels, *Mytilus edulis*, in suspended culture and estimates of carbon and nitrogen flow: Killary Harbour, Ireland. *J. mar. biol. Ass. U.K.* **65**: 55-68.

Ross, E.D. 1984. *Studies on the biology of freshwater mussels (Lamellibranchia; Unionacea) in Ireland.* Unpublished M.Sc. thesis, National University of Ireland, University College, Galway.

Rostron, D. 1982. *Hancockia uncinata* - A nudibranch mollusc new to Ireland with notes on its distribution and ecology. *Ir. Nat. J.* **20** (11): 491-493.

Scharff, R.F. 1892. The Irish land and freshwater mollusca. *Ir. Nat.* **1** (4): 65-67, **1** (5): 87-90, **1** (6): 105-111, **1** (7): 135-138, **1** (8): 149-153 and **1** (9): 177-181.

Scharff, R.F. 1906. *Helix tormensis* in Ireland. *Ir. Nat.* **15** (8): 190.

Schmitz, H. 1938. On the Irish species of the Dipterous family Phoridae. *Proc. R. Ir. Acad.* **44B** (9): 173-204.

Seaward, D.R. (Ed.) 1982. *Sea area atlas of the marine molluscs of Britain and Ireland.* Nature Conservancy Council, Shrewsbury.

Stelfox, A.W. 1907. Some notes on the land and freshwater mollusca of Galway and district. *Ir. Nat.* **16** (12): 353-364.

Stelfox, A.W. 1911. A list of the land and freshwater molluscs of Ireland. *Proc. R. Ir. Acad.* **29B** (3): 65-164.

Sykes, B.A. 1905. The Molluscs and Brachiopods of Ballynakill and Bofin Harbours, Co. Galway and of the deep water off the west and south-west coasts of Ireland. *Ann. Rep. Fish. Ireland* (1902-1903). H.M.S.O., Dublin.

Welch, R. 1896a. Marine Mollusca of Co. Galway. *Ir. Nat.* **5** (10): 274.

Welch, R. 1896b. Land and freshwater Mollusca from Great Killary and Westport. *Ir. Nat.* **6** (11): 304-305.

Went, A.E.J. 1947. Notes on Irish pearls. *Ir. Nat. J.* **9** (2): 41-45.

Went, A.E.J. 1962a. Historical notes on the oyster fisheries of Ireland. *Proc. R. Ir. Acad.* **62**: 195-223.

Went, A.E.J. 1962b. Fan Mussels *Pinna fragilis* Penn from the Irish coasts. *Ir. Nat. J.* **14** (4): 82.

Whilde, A. 1969. *Observations on Kilkieran Bay Oyster Beds*. Unpublished Report to the Irish Sea Fisheries Board (Bord Iascuagh Mhara).

Whilde, A. 1972a. *An investigation into the management and development of the oyster fisheries in Galway Bay, Ireland*. Unpublished Ph.D. thesis. University of Edinburgh.

Whilde, A. 1972b. *The oyster beds of Galway Bay*. Unpublished Report to the Irish Sea Fisheries Board (Bord Iascuagh Mhara).

Whilde, A. 1973. *Evaluation survey of oyster beds in Galway Bay and along the Galway coast*. B. I. M. Resource Record Paper 24. Dublin.

Wilson, A.G. 1896. *Littorina obtusa* at Bunowen, Connemara. *Ir. Nat.* **5** (9): 248.

CRUSTACEANS

Brady, G.S. and Robertson, D. 1869. Notes of a week's dredging in the west of Ireland. *Ann. Mag. Nat. Hist.* **3**: 353-374.

Chilton, C. 1899. Some land isopods from County Galway. *Ir. Nat.* **8** (5): 115.

De Bhaldraithe, P. 1972. Notes on the occurence of the isopod parasite *Bopyrus squillarum* hatreille. *Ir. Nat. J.* **17** (8): 276-279.

Doogue, D. and Harding, P.T. 1982. *Distribution atlas of woodlice in Ireland*. An Foras Forbartha, Dublin.

Doogue, D. Reardon, N.M. and Harding, P.T. 1979. Further records of uncommon Irish woodlice (Crustacea : Isopoda). *Ir. Nat. J.* **19** (10): 343-347.

Duignan, C.A. 1990. A historical review of research on Irish Chydoridae (Branchiopoda : Anompoda) with a checklist of taxa recorded in Ireland. *Ir. Nat. J.* **23** (7): 239-246.

Gotto, R.V., Holmes, J.M.C. and Lowther, R.P. 1984. Description of the adult male *Mychophilus roseus* Hesse (Copepoda : Cyclopoida): a copepod with remarkable sensory equipment. *Ir. Nat. J.* **21** (7): 305-313.

Gotto, R.V. and McGrath, D. 1980. Choniostomatid copepods from Irish coastal waters. *Ir. Nat. J.* **20** (3): 113-114.

Harding, P.T. and Sutton, S.L. 1988. The spread of the terrestrial amphipod *Arcitalitrus dorrieni* in Britain and Ireland: watch this niche! *Isopoda* **2**: 7-10.

Heal, O.W. 1962. Note on a swarm of zooplankton. *Ir. Nat. J.* **14** (2): 42-43.

Holmes, J.C. and Gotto, R.V. 1992. A list of the Poecilostomatoida (Crustacea : Copepoda) of Ireland. *Bull. Ir. biogeog. Soc.* **15**: 2-33.

McCalla, W. 1845. Observations on the productions of Roundstone and Binterbie Bay, Connemara, chiefly Crustacea, sponges, and zoophytes. *Saunder's News Letter* **1845**.

McGrath, D. 1978. *Stenula latipes* (Chevreux and Fage) (Crustacea: Amphipoda), associated with the hermit crab *Pagurus bernhardus* (L.), new to the Irish fauna. *Ir. Nat. J.* **19** (6): 196-197.

McGrath, D. and Atkins, P. 1979. Some parasitic Isopoda (Epicaridea) from the Galway Bay area, west coast of Ireland. *Ir. Nat. J.* **19** (12): 437-439.

McPadden, C.A. 1976. *Exploratory and experimental fishing for* Palaemon serratus *(Pennant) on the west coast of Ireland*. Unpublished M.Sc. thesis, National University Ireland, University College, Galway.

Minchin, D. and Holmes, J.M.C. 1993. A skeleton shrimp *Capella andreaae* Mayer (Crustacea: Amphipoda) new to Ireland, and other strandings in September 1991. *Ir. Nat. J.* **24** (7): 285-286.

Norman, A.M. 1905. Irish Crustacea, Ostracoda. *Ir. Nat.* **14** (6): 137-155.

Oakes, N.M. 1978. *A palaeolimnological survey of Lough Bofin, Co. Galway*. Unpublished B.Sc. thesis, National University of Ireland, University College, Dublin.

O'Ceidigh, P. 1963. *A list of Irish marine decapod crustacea*. Stationery Office, Dublin.

O'Connor, J.P., O'Connor, M.A. and Holmes, J.M.C. 1991. Ornamental plants and the distribution of exotic amphipods (Crustacea) in Ireland. *Ir. Nat. J.* **23** (12): 490-492.

Popple, E. 1912. Some Irish Entomostraca. *Ir. Nat.* **21** (11): 220-221.

OTHER INVERTEBRATES

Barber, A.D. and Keay, A.N. 1988. *Provisional atlas of the centipedes of the British Isles.* Institute of Terrestrial Ecology, Grange-over-Sands.

British Myriapod Group. 1988. *Preliminary atlas of the millipedes of the British Isles.* Natural Environment Research Council, Huntingdon.

Kemp, S.W. 1905a. The marine fauna of the west coast of Ireland III. Echinoderms from Ballynakill and Bofin Harbours, Co. Galway and of the deep water off the west coast of Ireland. *Ann. rep. Fish., Ireland* (1902-1903): 1-31.

Kemp, S.W. 1905b. The marine fauna of the west coast of Ireland III. Echinoderms of Ballynakill and Bofin Harbours. *Sci. Invest. Fish. Br. Ireland*, (1902-03) **6**: 176-206.

McCarthy, T.K. 1975. Observations on the distribution of the freshwater leeches (Hirudinea) of Ireland. *Proc. R. Ir. Acad.* **75B** (21): 401-451.

McCarthy, T.K. 1993. The exotic land planarian *Geoplana sanguinea* (Moseley) naturalized in the Galway area (Turbellaria, Tricladida, Terricola). *Ir. Nat. J.* **25** (6): 257-258.

McGrath, D. 1985. The by-the-wind sailor *Velella velella* (L.) (Coelenterata: Hydrozoa) in Irish waters 1976-1984. *Ir. Nat. J.* **21** (11): 469-508.

Martyn, K.P. 1988. *Provisional atlas of the ticks (Ixodoidea) of the British Isles.* Institute of Terrestrial Ecology, Grange-over-Sands.

Munday, B.W. and Keegan, B.F. 1992. Population dynamics of *Amphiura chiajei* (Echinodermata, Ophiuroidea) in Killary Harbour, on the west coast of Ireland. *Mar. Biol. (Berl.)* **114** (4): 595-606.

O'Connor, B. 1984. *Hipponoa gaudichaudi* Audovin and Milne Edwards (Polychaeta: Amphinomidae), an interesting new stranding on Irish shores. *Ir. Nat. J.* **21** (6): 262-264.

Pocock, R.I. 1893. Notes upon some Irish Myriopoda. *Ir. Nat.* **2** (12): 309-312.

Ryland, J.S. and Stebbing, A.R.D. 1971. Two little known bryozoans from the west of Ireland. *Ir. Nat. J.* **17** (3): 65-69.

Sankey, J.H.P. 1988. *Provisional atlas of the harvest-spiders (Arachnida : Opiliones) of the British Isles.* Institute of Terrestrial Ecology, Grange-over-Sands.

Scharff, R.F. 1900. The Irish species of land planarians. *Ir. Nat.* **9** (9): 215-218.

Selbie, C.M. 1913. New records of Irish myriapods. *Ir. Nat.* **22** (7): 131-135.

Shin, P.K.S. 1981. The development of sessile epifaunal communities in Kylsalia, Kilkieran Bay (West Coast of Ireland). *J. exp. Mar. Biol. Ecol.* **54**: 97-111.

Stephens, J. 1905. Irish fresh water sponges. *Ir. Nat.* **14** (11): 247.

Wright, J. 1900. The Foraminifera of Dog's Bay, Connemara. *Ir. Nat.* **9** (3): 51-55.

Wyse Jackson, P.N. 1991. Distribution of Irish marine Bryozoa, together with biographical notes relating to the chief researchers in the group. *Bull. Ir. biogeog. Soc.* **14**: 129-184.

SPECIES, SUBJECT AND PLACENAME INDEXES

Plants and animals mentioned in the text for which there is an English name. The Latin and Irish names of these species are presented in Appendix I.

PLANTS

Plants and animals mentioned in the text for which there is only a Latin name.

PLANTS

ANIMALS